PEPTIDES

PEPTIDES

Proceedings of the Fifth European Symposium

Oxford, September 1962

Edited by

G. T. YOUNG

A Pergamon Press Book

THE MACMILLAN COMPANY

NEW YORK

1963

THE MACMILLAN COMPANY
60 Fifth Avenue
New York 11, N.Y.

This book is distributed by
THE MACMILLAN COMPANY · NEW YORK
pursuant to a special arrangement with
PERGAMON PRESS LIMITED
Oxford, England

Library of Congress Card Number 63–18735

Printed in Great Britain by
The Whitefriars Press Ltd., London and Tonbridge

PREFACE

IN September 1958 a small group from various European centres met in Prague at the invitation of the Czechoslovak Academy of Science, to discuss methods of peptide synthesis. In subsequent years, meetings have been held in Munich (1959), Basle (1960), Moscow (1961), and Oxford (1962), each country acting in turn as host. The *Proceedings* (including recorded discussion) of the Prague meeting were published in the *Collection of Czechoslovak Chemical Communications* as a Special Issue in Volume 24 (1959). Abstracts of the Munich meeting (the " 2nd European Peptide Symposium ") appeared in *Angewandte Chemie*, **71**, 741 (1959); of the Basle meeting in *Chimia*, **14**, 366 (1960); and of the Moscow meeting in *Zhurnal Mendeleyevskovo Obshchestva* **7**, 353, 468 (1962) (in Russian) and in the *Collection of Czechoslovak Chemical Communications*, **27**, 2229 (1962) (in English, German and French)

The Organizing Committee of the Oxford meeting felt it would be helpful to those not present at the Symposium if the papers given there were published in full, provided that publication was rapid; I am grateful to the authors, and to the Pergamon Press, for enabling this to be achieved. The discussion was not recorded, but contributions which were put in writing before the end of the meeting have been included.

G. T. YOUNG

v

CONTENTS

SECTION I

SYNTHESIS: METHODS OF PROTECTION

SECTION II

SYNTHESIS: METHODS OF COUPLING

SECTION IV

CHEMICAL AND PHYSICAL PROPERTIES OF PEPTIDES

SECTION V

NOMENCLATURE

LIST OF PARTICIPANTS

Dr. S. BAJUSZ, Research Institute for Pharmaceutical Industry, Budapest.

Dr. G. C. BARRETT, The Washington Singer Laboratories, Exeter University.

Dr. H. C. BEYERMAN, Organic Chemistry Department, Technical University of Delft.

Dr. K. BLÁHA, Institute of Organic Chemistry and Biochemistry, Czechoslovak Academy of Science, Prague.

Dr. H. BLOCK, Courtaulds Research Laboratory, Maidenhead.

Dr. M. BODANSZKY, Squibb Institute for Medical Research, New Brunswick, U.S.A.

Professor M. BRENNER, Institut für Organische Chemie der Universität, Basle.

Dr. E. BRICAS, Laboratoire de Chimie Biologique, Paris.

Professor E. DANE, Universität, München.

Dr. D. F. ELLIOTT, National Institute for Medical Research, London.

Dr. C. P. FAWCETT, National Institute for Medical Research, London.

Professor J. S. FRUTON, Department of Physiological Chemistry, Yale University.

Dr. R. GEIGER, Farbwerke Hoechst, Frankfurt/Main.

Professor St. GOLDSCHMIDT, Organisch Chemisches Institut der Technische Hochschule, München.

Dr. St. GUTTMANN, Sandoz AG, Basle.

Dr. B. A. HEMS, Glaxo Research Ltd., Greenford.

Dr. P. HERMANN, Physiologisch-chemisches Institut der Martin-Luther-Universität, Halle.

Dr. D. B. HOPE, Department of Pharmacology, Oxford University.

Dr. A. JÖHL, J. R. Geigy AG, Basle.

Dr. H. KAPPELER, Ciba AG, Basle.

Professor E. D. KAVERZNEVA, Institute of Organic Chemistry, U.S.S.R. Academy of Sciences, Moscow.

Professor G. W. KENNER, Department of Organic Chemistry, Liverpool University.

Dr. K. E. Th. KERLING, Organic Chemistry Department, University of Leiden.

Dr. L. KISFALUDY, Gedeon Richter Factory, Budapest.

Dr. H. D. LAW, Miles Laboratories Ltd., Stoke Poges.

Dr. K. MEDZIHRADSZKY, Institute of Organic Chemistry, University of Budapest.

Dr. J. S. MORLEY, I.C.I. Pharmaceuticals Ltd., Alderley Park.

Dr. H. NESVADBA, Sanabo, Vienna.

Dr. G. G. F. NEWTON, Sir William Dunn School of Pathology, Oxford.

Dr. H. NIEDRICH, Institut für Medizin und Biologie der Deutschen Akademie der Wissenschaften, Institut für Pharmakologie, Berlin-Buch.

Dr. Yu. A. OVCHINNIKOV, Institute for Chemistry of Natural Products, U.S.S.R. Academy of Sciences, Moscow.

Dr. H. J. PANNEMAN, N.V. Organon, Oss.

Dr. A. PATCHORNIK, The Weizmann Institute of Science, Rehovoth.

Dr. I. PHOTAKI, Laboratory of Organic Chemistry, University of Athens.

Dr. J. PLESS, Sandoz Ltd., Basle.

Dr. P. QUITT, F. Hoffmann-La Roche & Co. AG, Basle.

Dr. M. ROTHE, Organisch-Chemisches Institut, Johannes Gutenberg Universität, Mainz.

Dr. J. RUDINGER, Institute of Organic Chemistry and Biochemistry, Czechoslovak Academy of Science, Prague.

Professor H. N. RYDON, The Washington Singer Laboratories, Exeter University.

Dr. E. SCHNABEL, Deutsches Wollforschungsinstitut der Technische Hochschule, Aachen.

Dr. E. SCHRÖDER, Schering AG, Berlin-West.

Dr. F. dos S. P. SERRAO, Department of Chemistry, University of Oporto.

Dr. L. A. SHCHUKINA, Institute for Chemistry of Natural Products, U.S.S.R. Academy of Sciences, Moscow.

Professor J. C. SHEEHAN, Department of Chemistry, Massachusetts Institute of Technology.

Dr. R. C. SHEPPARD, Department of Organic Chemistry, Liverpool University.

Professor H. D. SPRINGALL, Department of Chemistry, Keele University.

Dr. G. C. STELAKATOS, Laboratory of Organic Chemistry, University of Athens.

Professor E. TASCHNER, Department of General Chemistry, Institute of Technology, Gdansk.

Dr. G. I. TESSER, Organic Chemistry Department, University of Nijmegen.

Dr. S. G. WALEY, Nuffield Laboratory of Ophthalmology, Oxford University.

Professor F. WEYGAND, Organisch Chemisches Institut der Technisches Hochschule, München.

Professor T. WIELAND, Organisch Chemisches Institut der Universität, Frankfurt/Main.

Dr. M. W. WILLIAMS, Dyson Perrins Laboratory, Oxford University.

Dr. E. WÜNSCH, Max-Plank-Institut für Eiweiss- und Lederforschung, München.

Dr. G. T. YOUNG, Dyson Perrins Laboratory, Oxford University.

Professor L. ZERVAS, Laboratory of Organic Chemistry, University of Athens.

ABBREVIATIONS

THE abbreviations used throughout this volume are those recommended by the Committee on Nomenclature; the symbols and their usage are explained on pages 259–69. The following abbreviations also occur:

DCCI   Dicyclohexylcarbodi-imide

CDI   Carbonyldi-imidazole

DMF   Dimethylformamide

THF   Tetrahydrofuran

SECTION I

SYNTHESIS : METHODS OF PROTECTION

METHODS OF PROTECTION:
AN ASSESSMENT OF THE PRESENT POSITION

H. Kappeler

CIBA Limited, Basle, Switzerland

A VARIETY of methods, which increase in number from year to year, is available nowadays for synthesizing biologically active polypeptides [1] from their constituent amino-acids. Many of these amino-acids contain additional functional groups—such as amino, mercapto, hydroxyl, or carboxyl groups in glutamic or aspartic acid—which add to the difficulty and intricacy of peptide synthesis. These additional functional groups require blocking by suitable protective groups [2] in such a way that they cannot enter into secondary reactions during the planned steps of the synthesis.

As we all know very well from our own experience, these protective groups must possess a number of very definite and well-marked properties. It should be possible to introduce them by means of a simple chemical reaction and also to split them off again under as mild conditions as possible. The optical activity of the peptides must be preserved, and the peptide bond must not be attacked during this process. The derivatives obtained should be readily crystallizable and stable towards the other reagents used in the particular synthesis. When planning the synthesis of a complex polypeptide, therefore, it is of cardinal importance to select the protective groups in such a way as to ensure a selective splitting and to bring them into harmony with the coupling reactions at every stage of the synthesis. Looking at the syntheses of biologically active polypeptides [1] which have been carried out to date, it is striking to note how few of the many known protective groups have been utilized; after all, some of those that have been introduced greatly improve our chances of synthesizing complicated polypeptides.

I do not intend to go into the description of all known methods available for the protection of functional groups. I simply describe our experience in the selection of protective groups.

In our attempts to synthesize the β-melanophore stimulating hormone [3], we selected the following known protective groups: benzyloxycarbonyl for N^{α}-amino groups, tosyl for the N^{ε}-amino function of lysine[6] and [17], the nitro group for arginine[11], and amide for the protection of the side chain carboxyl groups at Asp[1] and Glu[8]. For Asp[18] we used the dimethylester.

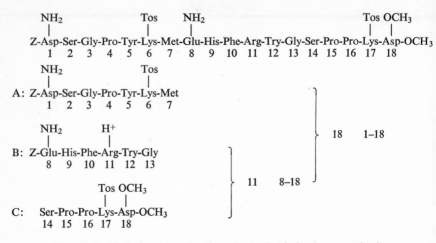

FIG. 1. Synthetic, protected β-melanophore-stimulating hormone (beef).

R. Schwyzer *et al.*, *Helv. Chim. Acta* **42**, 1702 (1959).

The condensation was carried out according to the following scheme:

$$B + C \longrightarrow B - C$$
$$A + [B - C] \longrightarrow A–B–C$$

The peptide A [4] was obtained as a benzyloxycarbonyl derivative in crystalline form, while the t-butyloxycarbonyl derivatives proved to be non-crystalline. B [5] was synthesized by various methods, use also being made of a number of amino-acid derivatives. The use of free arginine, which was not protected at the guanidino group, proved difficult at the dipeptide and tripeptide stages; the increased appearance of by-products, as well as the high degree of water solubility and salt formation at the arginine side chain, complicated our work. On the other hand, free arginine unprotected at the guanidino group proved satisfactory at the hexapeptide B stage. We were thus able to make the pentapeptide ester hydrochloride C [6] react directly with the peptide sequence B. Guttmann and Boissonnas [7] also successfully used free arginine in their α-MSH synthesis.

An attempt was also made to incorporate N^{im}-benzylhistidine [8] into the peptide. The peptides obtained, however, were all sparingly soluble in organic solvents, and this greatly impaired the subsequent course of the synthesis. The use of coloured protective groups, such as phenylazobenzyloxycarbonyl or *p*-methoxyphenylazobenzyloxycarbonyl [9], at the glutamine residue likewise yielded sparingly soluble peptide derivatives.

Since glutamine is the *N*-terminal amino-acid in the peptide sequence 8–18, bases readily yield the pyroglutamic acid derivative, which can no longer be used for the subsequent reactions. I should like to refer in this connection to the excellent paper which Rudinger published in the *Record of Chemical Progress* [10], and in which he enumerated the possibilities of using pyroglutamic acid derivatives as intermediate products for peptide synthesis.

When the amide is employed as a protected form of β- and γ-carboxyl groups in aspartic and glutamic acid respectively, there is the additional danger that the corresponding β- and γ-peptide derivatives will also be formed as a result of cyclic imide formation [11] and subsequent splitting, as Riniker, Brunner and Schwyzer [12] recently demonstrated in the case of Val[5]-hypertensin-II-asp[1]-β-amide.

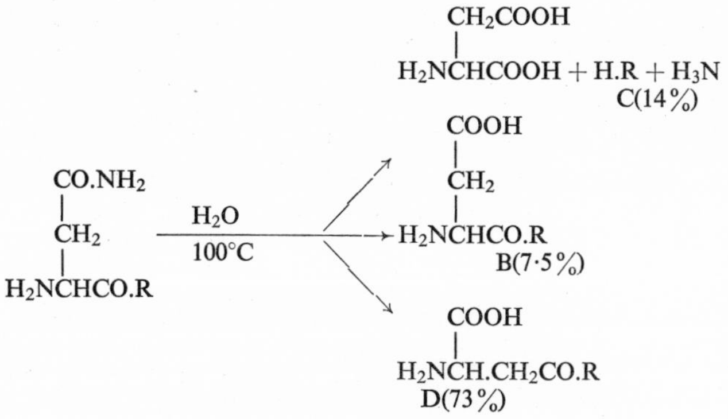

$$CH_2COOH$$
$$|$$
$$H_2NCHCOOH + H.R + H_3N$$
$$C(14\%)$$

$$COOH$$
$$|$$
$$CH_2$$
$$|$$
$$H_2NCHCO.R$$
$$B(7 \cdot 5\%)$$

$$CO.NH_2$$
$$|$$
$$CH_2 \quad \xrightarrow[100°C]{H_2O}$$
$$|$$
$$H_2NCHCO.R$$

$$COOH$$
$$|$$
$$H_2NCH.CH_2CO.R$$
$$D(73\%)$$

α, β rearrangement.   R = -Arg-Val-Tyr-Val-His-Pro-Phe
yields (%) in brackets

FIG. 2. β-Asp[1], Val[5]-Hypertensin II.
B. Riniker, H. Brunner and R. Schwyzer, *Angew. Chem.* **74**, 469 (1962).

No such isomerization was observed when the benzyloxycarbonylhexapeptide methyl ester corresponding to B was saponified with an excess of alkali.

Mild saponification of the dimethylester at aspartic acid[18] in the peptide A–B–C (Fig. 1) yielded most unsatisfactory results.   Similarly, reduction of the benzyloxycarbonyloctadecapeptide with sodium in liquid ammonia for the purpose of removing the N^α-benzyloxycarbonyl group at the asparagine[1] and the N^ε-tosyl groups at the lysine [6] and [17] failed to provide a uniform peptide, so that this method of synthesis could not be pursued any further.

In our experiments—as I shall show later on with reference to a further example—the treatment of large protected peptide derivatives with sodium in liquid ammonia did not lead to the desired peptides.   Guttmann and Boissonnas [7], Hofmann and co-workers [13], as well as Li and co-workers [14], had the same experience with protected α-MSH- and ACTH-derivatives.   They isolated products in which most of the hormonal activity was destroyed.

These and other experiments with small peptide sequences [5, 15] prompted us to look for a combination of protective groups which could be split off again in a mild manner, with a large degree of selectivity and which would enable us to synthesize the nonadecapeptide [16] containing the first 19 amino-acids of the ACTH molecule.

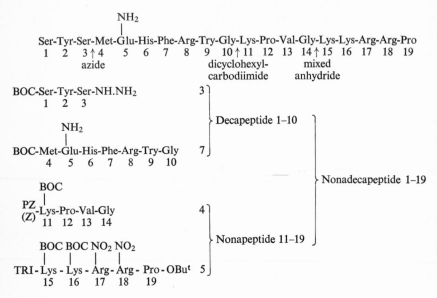

FIG. 3.   Scheme for the synthesis of β^{1-19}-corticotropin.
R. Schwyzer, W. Rittel, H. Kappeler and B. Iselin, *Angew. Chem.* **72**, 915 (1960).

To accomplish this, we used an amino protective group at the ε-amino function of lysine, which can be split off under mild conditions.   For this purpose N^ε-t-butyloxycarbonyl lysine and derivatives were synthesized by Schwyzer and Rittel [17].   This group is easily split off at room temperature by trifluoracetic acid and by 1 N or concentrated mineral acid.   To protect the carboxyl group of the proline in position 19 we selected the t-butylester [18] described by Taschner, Roeske and by Anderson and co-workers.   This ester is much more stable than a corresponding n-alkyl ester towards alkaline reagents.   When aqueous or anhydrous trifluoracetic acid or diluted mineral acid is used, the t-butyl ester is cleaved more slowly than the butyloxycarbonyl group.   On the other hand, the t-butyl esters of amino-acids and peptides were not split at all by hydrochloric t-butanol solution, while butyloxycarbonyl groups were split only slowly [19].   To protect the α-amino function of the peptide sequences, butyloxycarbonyl groups were employed for serine[1] and methionine[4], while the benzyloxycarbonyl or phenylazobenzyloxycarbonyl group was used for lysine[11].   The latter groups were split off together with the two N^{ω}-nitro groups at the arginine [17] and [18] by catalytic hydrogenation at the nonapeptide stage.

In the sequence 15–19 neither a urethane group nor the butyloxycarbonyl group could be used for N^{α}-protection because the removal of these groups would split off either the nitro groups at the arginine or the N^{ε}-butyloxycarbonyl groups at the lysine. Fortunately, Rittel [17] discovered that the trityl group on the α-amino function may be selectively removed from peptides containing t-butyloxycarbonyl and t-butylester groups, and this combination was used for the synthesis of the above-mentioned sequence.

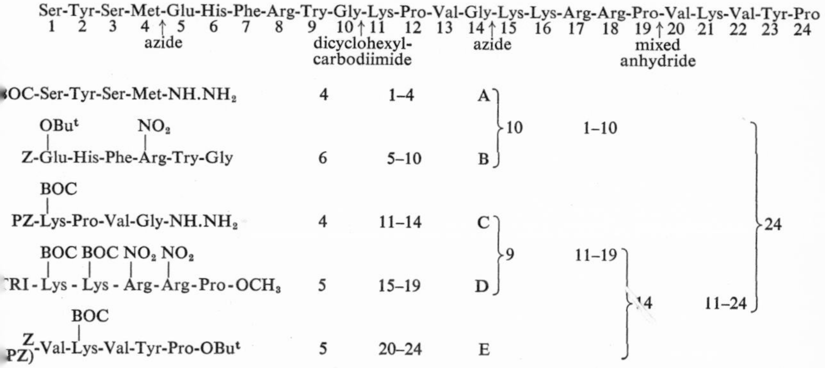

Ser-Tyr-Ser-Met-Glu-His-Phe-Arg-Try-Gly-Lys-Pro-Val-Gly-Lys-Lys-Arg-Arg-Pro-Val-Lys-Val-Tyr-Pro
1   2   3   4 ↑ 5   6   7   8   9   10↑11 12 13 14↑15 16 17 18 19↑20 21 22 23 24
            azide   dicyclohexyl-   azide   mixed
                                carbodiimide   anhydride

FIG. 4.   Scheme for the synthesis of β^{1-24}-corticotropin.

H. Kappeler and R. Schwyzer, *Helv. Chim. Acta* **41**, 491 (1961).

The γ-carboxyl group of the glutamic acid [5] was protected by the amide.

A good yield of free β^{1-19}-corticotropin-Glu^5-γ-amide was obtained by dissolving the protected peptide derivative in anhydrous or 90 per cent trifluoracetic acid.

The same peptide sequence was synthesized simultaneously by Li and co-workers [14]. In contrast to our synthesis, they employed the tosyl group to protect the N^{ε}- and N^{ω}-functions at the lysine and arginine respectively. N^{ε}-tosyl-arginine and its use for peptide synthesis was first described by Schwyzer and Li [15a]. The last stage, the reductive removal of the protective groups with the aid of sodium in liquid ammonia, produced a yield of approximately 2 per cent, whereas our cleavage yield with trifluoracetic acid was quantitative.

The experience we acquired with the synthesis of the protected β-MSH derivative and of the β^{1-19}-ACTH peptide prompted us to attempt the synthesis of the β^{1-24}-ACTH peptide [20]. As Bell and co-workers [21] demonstrated, this peptide sequence still displays full ACTH activity.

In the meantime, Hofmann and co-workers [22] synthesized the sequences 1–23 of this hormone and reported that the peptide exhibited full ACTH activity.

The protective groups for the various peptide sequences are largely the same as in the nonadecapeptide. In this case, the decapeptide derivative 1–10 [23] had to be built up from the sequence BOC-Ser-Tyr-Ser-Met-NH. NH_2 and the hexapeptide derivative Glu(OBu^t)-His-Phe-Arg-Try-Gly for the following reasons:

For the synthesis of the hexapeptide B we selected N^ω-nitro-arginine and, for the first time, glutamic acid-γ-t-butyl ester.

The further planning of the synthesis called for catalytic reduction of the nitro group at the hexapeptide stage, which is not possible if methionine is present in the sequence.

The sequence 11–24 was built up in the same manner as the sequence 11–19 in the nonadecapeptide. The methyl ester was used instead of proline t-butyl ester in position 19 and was readily removed by alkaline saponification at the nonapeptide stage. The t-butyl ester was, however, employed at proline[24]. At lysine[11] the phenylazobenzyloxycarbonyl group rendered excellent service as a coloured α-amino protective group. It permitted rapid purification of the respective nonadeca- and tetradecapeptide derivatives in crystalline form. Together with the nitro groups at the two arginines [17] and [18], the phenylazo-benzyloxycarbonyl group is cleaved from the tetradecapeptide 11–24 by catalytic hydrogenation, using 10 per cent palladium on carbon as catalyst, in 90 per cent acetic acid for 5 hr at 5 atm, then for 19 hr under normal conditions. Under these conditions the N^ε-butyloxycarbonyl groups are not split off. Dinitrophenylation [24] of the hydrogenated tetradecapeptide t-butyl ester and subsequent total hydrolysis shows only N^α-dinitrophenyl lysine. Besides the benzyloxycarbonyl pentapeptide t-butyl ester 20–24, the corresponding phenylazobenzyloxycarbonyl derivative was also produced. For the subsequent experiments, however, the benzyloxycarbonyl derivative was used. Condensation of the phenylazobenzyloxycarbonyl dipeptide with the tripeptide ester in the presence of dicyclohexylcarbodiimide yielded more by-products than did the benzyloxycarbonyl derivative. Finally, the butyl-oxycarbonyl and t-butyl ester protective groups were again readily split off at room temperature with 90 per cent trifluoracetic acid, and 98–100 per cent of free tetracosapeptide was obtained.

When preparing free β^{1-23}-corticotropin amide, Hofmann and co-workers [22] had to treat the protected β^{1-23}-corticotropin-Tyr^{23}-amide with boiling 0·1 N hydrochloric acid for 1 hr in order to remove the protective groups, i.e. the N^α-acetyl group at the serine[1], the amide at the glutamic acid[8] and the N^ε-formyl groups at the lysine. This operation left the Tyr^{23} amide bond intact. The yield was 20–30 per cent.

The butyloxycarbonyl group was also successfully used by Costopanagiotis and Schwyzer [25] to protect N^α- and N^ε-amino functions in an α-MSH synthesis.

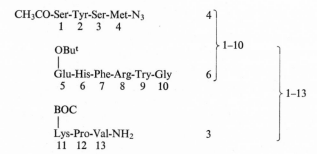

CH$_3$CO-Ser-Tyr-Ser-Met-Glu-His-Phe-Arg-Try-Gly-Lys-Pro-Val-NH$_2$
　　　1　　2　　3　　4　　5　　6　　7　　8　　9　　10　11　12　13

BOC-Ser-Tyr-Ser-Met-OCH$_3$

CH$_3$CO-Ser-Tyr-Ser-Met-N$_3$ 4
　　　1　　2　　3　　4

　　OBu^t
　　　| 1–10
　　Glu-His-Phe-Arg-Try-Gly   6
　　　5　　6　　7　　8　　9　　10   1–13

　　BOC
　　　|
　　Lys-Pro-Val-NH$_2$ 3
　　11　12　13

FIG. 5.   α MSH.

R. Schwyzer and A. Costopanagiotis (1962).

In order to examine further combinations of protective groups in connection with the step-by-step build-up of fairly large peptide sequences, Schwyzer and Sieber [26] tried the synthesis of β^{1-21}-corticotropin and of Abut^4-β^{1-21}-corticotropin in the following way:

BZL	BZL	BZL		OBZL			Z$_2$
|	|	|	R-Met-Y	|			|
R-Ser-Y	R-Tyr-Y	R-Ser-Y		R-Glu-Y	R-His-Y	R-Phe-Y	R-Arg-Y
1	2	3	R-Abut-Y	5	6	7	8
			4				

		Z				Z	Z
		|				|	|
R-Try-Y	R-Gly-Y	R-Lys-Y	R-Pro-Y	R-Val-Y	R-Gly-Y	R-Lys-Y	R-Lys-Y
9	10	11	12	13	14	15	16

Z$_2$	Z$_2$		PZ(MZ)
|	|		|
R-Arg-Y	R-Arg-Y	R-Pro-Y	H-Val-Lys-OBZL
17	18	19	20　21

R = BOC-.   Y = mixed anhydride.   Abut = α-aminobutyric acid.

FIG. 6.   Scheme for the synthesis of β^{1-21}-corticotropin and Abut^4-β^{1-21}-corticotropin.
R. Schwyzer and P. Sieber (1961).

The N^α-amino function was protected by the butyloxycarbonyl group, which was split off again with anhydrous trifluoracetic acid after each step in the synthesis. The guanidino group of arginine was protected with bis-benzyloxycarbonyl [27] and the N^ε-amino group of lysine with benzyloxycarbonyl, except that on lysine[21] the coloured phenylazobenzyloxycarbonyl group was introduced. The terminal carboxyl group of lysine[21] and the γ-carboxyl group of the glutamic acid[8] were esterified with benzyl alcohol. Serine and tyrosine were employed for the synthesis as O-benzyl derivatives. The build-up was accomplished by using mixed anhydrides with triethylamine as base and isobutyl chloroformate as the second acid component. The yields of all steps in the synthesis were between 80 and 95 per cent. The purity of the peptide derivatives, prolonged by one amino-acid at each step, was tested by dinitrophenylation of the terminal group. Splitting off the protective groups of the β^{1-21}-corticotropin derivative with sodium in liquid ammonia yielded an unsatisfactory mixture of numerous peptides.

Contrary to expectation, the catalytic hydrogenation of the aminobutyric[4]-derivative with 10 per cent palladium on carbon in acidic dioxan solution could not be accomplished. The benzyloxycarbonyl residues at the guanidino groups of the arginines can, under these conditions, only be removed extremely slowly and incompletely. Hydrogenation of both tyrosine[2] and tryptophan[9] residues occurred.

The sequence 17–21 [26] was also built up in the same way, using N^{α}-butyloxycarbonyl-N^{ω}-nitroarginine in place of N^{α}-butyloxycarbonyl-N^{ω}-bisbenzyloxycarbonyl arginine. In this case, however, considerably more byproducts occurred during the synthesis.

A further combination of protective groups can be seen in the step-by-step build-up of the sequence 11–24 of β^{1-24}-corticotropin [26]. Lysine was intro-

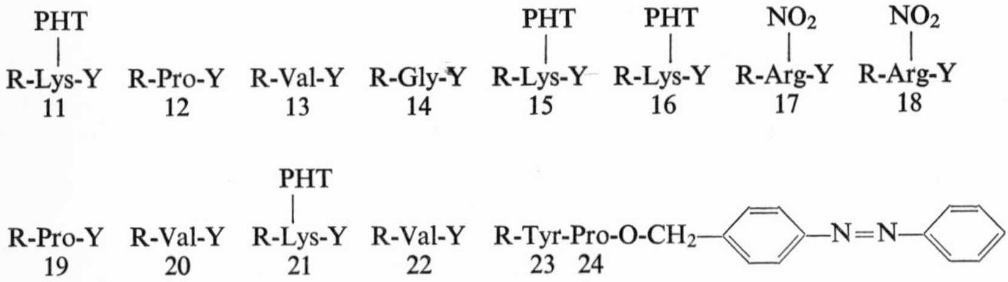

				PHT	PHT	NO₂	NO₂

PHT				PHT	PHT	NO$_2$	NO$_2$
R-Lys-Y	R-Pro-Y	R-Val-Y	R-Gly-Y	R-Lys-Y	R-Lys-Y	R-Arg-Y	R-Arg-Y
11	12	13	14	15	16	17	18

PHT
|
R-Pro-Y   R-Val-Y   R-Lys-Y   R-Val-Y   R-Tyr-Pro-O-CH₂—⟨benzene⟩—N=N—⟨benzene⟩
  19   20   21   22   23 24

R = BOC-.   Y = mixed anhydride.

FIG. 7.   Step-by-step synthesis of sequence 11–24 (β^{1-24}-corticotropin).
R. Schwyzer and P. Sieber (1962).

duced as N^{α}-butyloxycarbonyl-N^{ε}-phthaloyl derivative [28], arginine as N^{α}-butyloxycarbonyl-N^{ω}-nitroarginine, and a coloured phenylazobenzylester as carboxyl protecting group. The N^{α}-butyloxycarbonyl-N^{ε}-phthaloyllysine was prepared in the following manner.

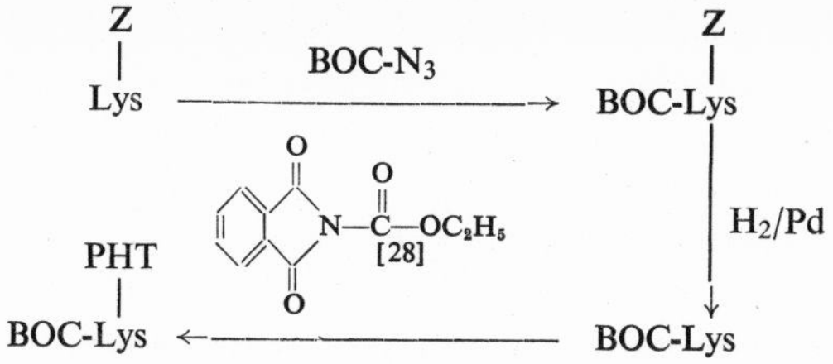

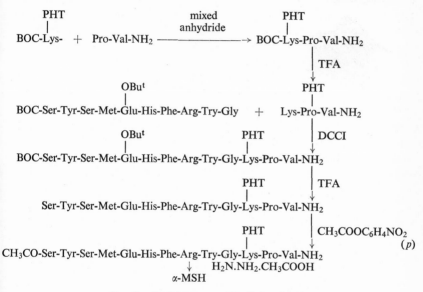

FIG. 8.

Schwyzer and Sieber [25] applied these results to an additional synthesis of α-MSH.

FIG. 9. R. Schwyzer and P. Sieber (1961).

The phthaloyl group was satisfactorily split off by applying 2 moles of methanolic hydrazine acetate solution (pH 6) for 5 hr at 50°C. This obviates the alkaline treatment which may be harmful.

The yields of these methods of synthesis are good and fairly large amounts of α-MSH have been prepared. This contrasts with the syntheses reported hitherto. The preparation of Hofmann and co-workers [29] still contains the N^ε-formyl group at the lysine, while the hydrogen bromide-splitting used by Guttmann and Boissonnas [7] for his protected α-MSH peptide would probably be unsatisfactory when applied to fairly large amounts of peptide. It was possible for the first time to state a value for the specific rotation of the α-MSH: $[\alpha]_D^{25} = -58\cdot5 \pm 2\cdot5°$ ($c = 1$ in 10 per cent acetic acid).

In conclusion, I should like to make a few remarks about the hydrogenation of peptides containing butyloxycarbonyl and t-butyl esters as protective groups besides nitroarginine.

The introduction of butyloxycarbonyl and t-butyl ester into peptides with nitroarginine bars the use of mineral acid during hydrogenation. We were therefore compelled to carry out the catalytic hydrogenation in aqueous acetic acid. In this solvent the hydrogenation was often extremely slow and sometimes also incomplete, as could be seen from the ultraviolet absorption of nitroarginine [30]. Repeated hydrogenation was therefore necessary on every occasion. In many cases the relevant hydrogenation products showed a positive reaction with Folin reagent even in the absence of Folin-positive groups like hydrazino-, tryptophyl-, etc. Whether this phenomena is due to the presence of aminoguanidino groups or not is still an open question, as similar peptides which had been prepared without using nitroarginine also give a positive reaction. This rendered it even more difficult to detect the complete hydrogenation of the nitro group at the arginine.

If, besides nitroarginine, tryptophan was also incorporated into the peptide, the ultraviolet spectra revealed increasing hydrogenation of the tryptophan following prolonged hydrogenation under the above-mentioned conditions.

The use of the combination butyloxycarbonyl, t-butyl ester and nitroarginine still requires detailed investigation in order to obtain optimal conditions.

REFERENCES

1. *Oxytocin:* V. du VIGNEAUD *et al., J. Amer. Chem. Soc.* **75,** 4879 (1953);
   Vasopressin: V. du VIGNEAUD *et al., J. Amer. Chem. Soc.* **78,** 2905 (1956);
   Gramicidin: R. SCHWYZER *et al., Angew. Chem.* **68,** 518 (1956);
   Angiotensin: F. M. BUMPUS *et al., Science* **125,** 886 (1957); W. RITTEL *et al., Angew. Chem.* **69,** 179 (1957);
   α-MSH: St. GUTTMANN *et al., Helv. Chim. Acta* **42,** 1257 (1957); K. HOFMANN *et al., J. Amer. Chem. Soc.* **82,** 3732 (1960);
   Bradykinin: R. A. BOISSONNAS *et al., Experientia* **16,** 326 (1960);
   ACTH-Peptide: R. A. BOISSONNAS *et al., Experientia* **12,** 446 (1956); C. H. LI *et al., J. Amer. Chem. Soc.* **82,** 5760 (1960); *ibid.* **84,** 2460 (1962);
   R. SCHWYZER *et al., Angew. Chem.* **72,** 915 (1960); H. KAPPELER and R. SCHWYZER, *Helv. Chim. Acta* **44,** 1136 (1961); K. HOFMANN *et al., J. Amer. Chem. Soc.* **83,** 487 (1961); *ibid.* **84,** 2054 (1962).
2. JESSE P. GREENSTEIN and M. WINITZ, *Chemistry of Amino Acids,* Vol. II. John Wiley, New York and London.
3. R. SCHWYZER, H. KAPPELER, B. ISELIN, W. RITTEL and H. ZUBER, *Helv. Chim. Acta* **42,** 1702 (1959).
4. B. ISELIN, *Helv. Chim. Acta* **45,** 1499 (1962).
5. H. KAPPELER, *Helv. Chim. Acta* **44,** 476 (1961).
6. R. SCHWYZER, Abstracts, 17th Intern. Congr. Pure and Appl. Chem., p. 130 (1959).
7. St. GUTTMANN and R. A. BOISSONNAS, *Helv. Chim. Acta* **42,** 1257 (1957).
8. A. H. COOK, I. HEILBRON and A. P. MAHADEVAN, *J. Chem. Soc.* **1949,** 1061; B. G. OVERELL and V. PETROW, *ibid.* **1955,** 232.

9. R. Schwyzer, P. Sieber and K. Zatskó, *Helv. Chim. Acta* **41,** 491 (1958).
10. J. Rudinger, *Record Chem. Progr.* (*Kresge-Hooker Sci. Lib.*) **23,** 3 (1962).
11. E. Sondheimer and R. W. Holley, *J. Amer. Chem. Soc.* **76,** 2467 (1954).
12. B. Riniker, H. Brunner and R. Schwyzer, *Angew. Chem.* **74,** 469 (1962).
13. K. Hofmann and H. Yajima, *J. Amer. Chem. Soc.* **83,** 2289 (1961).
14. C. H. Li, J. Meienhofer, E. Schnabel, D. Chung, Tung-Bin Lo and J. Ramachandran, *J. Amer. Chem. Soc.* **82,** 5760 (1960).
15. (a) R. Schwyzer and C. H. Li, *Nature* **182,** 1669 (1958).
    (b) H. Kappeler and R. Schwyzer, *Helv. Chim. Acta* **43,** 1453 (1960).
16. R. Schwyzer, W. Rittel, H. Kappeler and B. Iselin, *Angew. Chem.* **72,** 915 (1960).
17. R. Schwyzer and W. Rittel, *Helv. Chim. Acta* **44,** 159 (1961).
18. R. W. Roeske, *Chem. and Ind.* (1959) 1121; G. W. Anderson and F. M. Callahan, *J. Amer. Chem. Soc.* **82,** 3359 (1960); A. Vollmar and M. S. Dünn, *J. Org. Chem.* **25,** 387 (1960).
19. B. Iselin, private communication.
20. H. Kappeler and R. Schwyzer, *Helv. Chim. Acta* **44,** 1136 (1961).
21. R. G. Shephard, S. D. Willson, K. S. Howard, P. H. Bell, D. S. Davies, S. B. Davis, E. A. Eigner and N. E. Shakespeare, *J. Amer. Chem. Soc.* **77,** 5067 (1956).
22. K. Hofmann, H. Yajima, N. Yanaihara, T. Y. Liu and S. Lande, *J. Amer. Chem. Soc.* **83,** 487 (1961).
23. R. Schwyzer and H. Kappeler, *Helv. Chim. Acta* **44,** 1991 (1961).
24. H. Fraenkel-Conrat *et al.*, *Methods of Biochemical Analysis*, Vol. 2, p. 370.
25. R. Schwyzer, A. Costopanagiotis and P. Sieber, *Chimia*, **16,** 295 (1962).
26. R. Schwyzer and P. Sieber, unpublished work.
27. L. Zervas, M. Winitz and J. P. Greenstein, *Arch. Biochem. Biophys.* **65,** 573 (1956); *J. Org. Chem.* **22,** 1515 (1957).
28. Prepared by the method of G. H. L. Nefkens *et al.*, *Nature* **185,** 309 (1960); *Rec. trav. chim.* **79,** 688 (1960).
29. K. Hofmann, H. Yajima and E. T. Schwarz, *J. Amer. Chem. Soc.* **82,** 3732 (1960).
30. J. R. Gamper, *Helv. Chim. Acta* **45,** 1418 (1962).

ÜBER EINE NEUE ART VON
AMINO-SCHUTZGRUPPEN

E. DANE

Institut für Organische Chemie, Universität, München, G.F.R.

β-DICARBONYLVERBINDUNGEN reagieren mit Aminosäuren in methanolischer Kalilauge zu Kaliumsalzen der entsprechenden Azomethine. Diese Azomethine liegen in der Enaminform vor und sind durch eine Wasserstoffbrücke stabilisiert. Sie wurden zur Synthese von mehreren einfachen Peptiden benutzt.

Eine kurze Mitteilung über diese Reaktion ist im Oktober 1962 in der *Zeitschrift für Angewandte Chemie* erschienen.

ON THE PROTECTION OF α-AMINO AND CARBOXYL GROUPS FOR PEPTIDE SYNTHESIS

E. Gazis, B. Bezas, G. C. Stelakatos* and L. Zervas*

Laboratory of Organic Chemistry, University of Athens, Athens, Greece

Although the benzyloxycarbonyl method [1] is the method of choice for the N-protection of amino-acids, other methods, as is known, are in some cases quite helpful, for instance the toluene-p-sulphonyl [2], the phthaloyl [3], the trifluoroacetyl [4], the diphenylphosphoryl [5], and in more increasing significance the trityl method [6, 7, 8].

The preparation of N-trityl-L-amino-acids does not always proceed, as is known, in good yield. On the other hand, coupling with amino-acid esters, with the exception of N-tritylglycine, can only take place either via the carbodiimide method [9], or better via the diphenylphosphoryl method [5].

In order to overcome these difficulties, i.e. the preparation and the coupling of N-tritylamino-acids, we thought that it would be worth while to replace the N-benzyloxycarbonyl group of benzyloxycarbonylamino-acid p-nitrophenyl esters by the trityl group, by tritylating the free p-nitrophenyl esters. As long as the N-trityl group can be removed more easily than the N-benzyloxycarbonyl group, this type of ester could be useful in those cases where the removal of the N-benzyloxycarbonyl group cannot be effected without disturbing sensitive parts of the molecule, neither by catalytic hydrogenolysis nor by hydrogen bromide.

Unfortunately, only N-tritylglycine p-nitrophenyl ester (I) can be coupled with glycine ethyl ester using the standard procedure. As soon as we realized that the use of this type of ester was limited to glycine derivatives and it was not feasible for other amino-acid p-nitrophenyl esters (for instance compound II), we thought that the Schiff bases of the amino-acid p-nitrophenyl esters could be used as intermediates for peptide synthesis; the removal of the arylidene protecting group takes place, as has long been known [10], almost instantly after the addition of one equivalent of hydrochloric acid. These esters are formed very easily and almost quantitatively from benzaldehyde or salicylaldehyde and the corresponding amino-acid esters. These ester derivatives, III, IV (with the exception of the glycine

* This investigation was supported by the Royal Hellenic Research Foundation, to which we are greatly indebted.

P   17   3

$$\text{Ph}_3\text{C.NH.CH}_2\text{.CO.OC}_6\text{H}_4\text{.NO}_2\text{-}(p) \xrightarrow{\text{H}_2\text{NCH}_2\text{.CO.OEt}} \text{Ph}_3\text{C.NH.CH}_2\text{.CO.NH.CH}_2\text{.CO.OEt}$$
(I) m.p. 154°

$$\text{Ph}_3\text{C.NH.CH(CH}_2\text{.C}_6\text{H}_5)\text{CO.OC}_6\text{H}_4\text{.NO}_2\text{-}(p) \xrightarrow{\text{H}_2\text{NCH}_2\text{.CO.OEt}} \text{no coupling}$$
(II) m.p. 80°

$$o\text{-HOC}_6\text{H}_4\text{.CH}=\text{NCH}_2\text{.CO.OC}_6\text{H}_4\text{.NO}_2\text{-}(p) \xrightarrow{\text{H}_2\text{NCH}_2\text{.CO.OEt}}$$
$$\longrightarrow o\text{-HOC}_6\text{H}_4\text{.CH}=\text{NCH}_2\text{.CO.NH.CH}_2\text{.CO.OEt}$$
(III) m.p. 88–90°

$$o\text{-HOC}_6\text{H}_4\text{.CH}=\text{NCH(CH}_2\text{.C}_6\text{H}_5)\text{CO.OC}_6\text{H}_4\text{.NO}_2\text{-}(p) \xrightarrow{\text{H}_2\text{NCH}_2\text{.CO.OEt}} \text{no coupling}$$
(IV) m.p. 106–108°

$$2\text{CCl}_3\text{.CHO} + \text{H}_2\text{NCH(CH}_2\text{.C}_6\text{H}_5)\text{CO.OC}_6\text{H}_4\text{.NO}_2\text{-}(p) \longrightarrow$$
$$\longrightarrow \text{CCl}_3\text{.CH}=\text{NCH(CH}_2\text{.C}_6\text{H}_5)\text{CO.OC}_6\text{H}_4\text{.NO}_2\text{-}(p) + \text{CCl}_3\text{.CH(OH)}_2$$
(V) m.p. 225°

compounds) behave like the corresponding *N*-trityl amino-acid *p*-nitrophenyl esters and they cannot be used for coupling purposes. Apparently, this behaviour may be attributed to steric factors.* In the hope that this draw-back could be overcome, we have already prepared the corresponding trichloroethylidene derivatives (V) which we are studying in our laboratory. As has been shown by Bergmann and Zervas [10], *N*-arylidene amino-acids are usually not stable and they can only be isolated in the form of some of their salts. On the other hand, only a few Schiff bases of free amino-acids are stable, especially *N*-(5-chlorosalicylidene)-L-valine and *N*-(2-hydroxy-1-naphthal)-L-valine [11], which actually have been recently used by Sheehan and Grenda [12] for peptide synthesis.

Another *N*-protecting group which is quite promising, at least in certain cases, is the tritylsulphenyl group. Tritylsulphenyl chloride reacts very easily with amino acid esters, for instance glycine ethyl ester, forming the corre-sponding tritylsulphenyl derivative VI. The *N*-tritylsulphenyl protecting

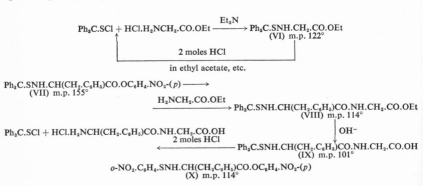

group is split off almost instantly with the theoretical amount of 0·1 N hydro-gen chloride in inert solvents; the products formed are tritylsulphenyl chloride and the hydrochloride of the corresponding amino-acid ester. Both of them are isolated in almost quantitative yields. In contrast to *N*-trityl-L-

---

* Such a steric hindrance is not observed in the case of dipeptide derivatives.

phenylalanine *p*-nitrophenyl ester, the corresponding *N*-tritylsulphenyl derivative VII can be coupled with glycine ethyl ester forming the protected peptide VIII, from which after saponification to compound IX and treatment of the product with two equivalents of hydrogen chloride in the cold, the hydrochloride of the free peptide is obtained. Experiments are in progress in our laboratory to use *N*-(2- or 4-nitrophenylsulphenyl) amino-acid *p*-nitrophenyl esters (X) for the same purposes.

Returning to the problem of preparation of *N*-tritylamino-acids, we would like to report some results related to the tritylation of L-arginine. The tritylation of this particular amino-acid in aqueous solution always gives N^{α}-monotrityl-L-arginine (XI). Boissonnas *et al.* [13] have tritylated L-arginine methyl ester dihydrochloride with 1 mole of trityl chloride and they obtained the corresponding N^{α}-monotrityl derivative (XII). After the saponification of this ester the same trityl-L-arginine (XI) resulted as that obtained by the

direct tritylation of arginine. It is quite interesting that using an excess of trityl chloride along with the proper amount of triethylamine no other trityl group is introduced, as we have found, into the arginine ester molecule. Further tritylation of N^{α}-monotrityl-L-arginine methyl ester is only possible if a strong alkali is simultaneously added, which apparently provides the only way to deprotonize the guanidine group. Saponification of the ester group

* As the monohydrochloride.
† As the dihydrochloride.

under these conditions was not observed because of the steric hindrance exhibited by the guanidine group. Thus, N^{α}, N^{ω}-ditrityl-L-arginine methyl ester (XIII) was obtained, which can be tritylated further in a strongly alkaline solution forming tritrityl-L-arginine methyl ester (XIV). It is very interesting that direct pertritylation of L-arginine methyl ester in the cold and in the presence of the required amount of alkali affords, as we have found, tetratrityl-L-arginine methyl ester (XV); this compound has all of its active hydrogens blocked by trityl groups and it corresponds to a tetra-acylated derivative of arginine p-nitrobenzyl ester [14]. Apparently, during the pertritylation of the free arginine methyl ester, tritylation of the α-amino group is taking place during the very early stages of the reaction. According to this scheme, both the saponification of the ester is hindered and its dis-mutation to α,δ-diguanidinovaleric acid and ornithine is avoided [15]. Selective detritylation of ditrityl- and tritrityl-L-arginine methyl esters (XIII, XIV) with 1 and 2 moles, respectively, of hydrogen chloride in methanol affords compounds for which the analytical data, as well as their behaviour, favour the structures of N^{ω}-monotrityl-L-arginine methyl ester hydrochloride (XVI) and N^{ω},$N^{\omega'}$-ditrityl-L-arginine methyl ester dihydrochloride (XVII). Experiments are in progress in our laboratory for the evaluation in peptide syntheses of all of these tritylated arginines, i.e. compounds XVI and XVII, as well as of others derived from compound XV.

Finally, we would like to describe the way the trityl and tritylsulphenyl groups could be used, in some cases, for the protection of the carboxyl group during peptide synthesis. N-Tritylglycine diethylammonium, or triethyl-ammonium, salt interacts in tetrahydrofuran with trityl chloride forming the corresponding O-trityl ester (XVIII). N-Tritylated amino-acid trityl esters have been isolated during the tritylation of amino-acids in aqueous iso-

$$Ph_3C.NH.CH_2.CO.OH \underset{H_2O,\ CH_3OH}{\overset{Et_2NH,\ Ph_3C.Cl}{\rightleftharpoons}} \underset{(XVIII)\ m.p.\ 174-175°}{Ph_3C.NH.CH_2.CO.O.Ph_3C}$$

$$\Big\downarrow 1\ mole\ HCl$$

$$\underset{(XIX)\ m.p.\ 126-128°}{HCl.H_2NCH_2.CO.O.Ph_3C}$$

$$Z.NH.CH_2.CO.OH \overset{Et_3N,\ Ph_3C.SCl}{\longrightarrow} \underset{(XX)}{ZNH.CH_2.CO.OS.Ph_3C}$$

$$\Big\downarrow H_2NCH_2.CO.OEt$$

$$Z.NH.CH_2.CO.OH + (VI)$$

propanol in the presence of diethylamine, for instance N-trityl-L-alanine trityl ester, m.p. 183–184°. N-Trityl-L-asparagine trityl ester has been also reported in the literature [16]. Addition of one equivalent of 5 N hydro-chloric acid to the acetone solution of XVIII splits off the N-trityl group only, forming glycine trityl ester hydrochloride (XIX). On the other hand, the removal of the O-trityl group can be easily performed either by methanol, or by water in dioxan solution, after standing for several hours at room temperature, or almost instantly by boiling a methanolic solution of the trityl ester. Using methanol, the by-product is the methyl ether of triphenyl-carbinol. Similar experiments using the triethylammonium salt of N-benzyl-oxycarbonylglycine, or that of N-tritylglycine, and tritylsulphenyl chloride were carried out. After filtering off the triethylamine hydrochloride formed, a mixed anhydride (XX) was obtained. On the addition of free glycine ethyl ester, this anhydride reacts quantitatively forming the corresponding N-pro-tected glycine and N-tritylsulphenylglycine ethyl ester (VI).

REFERENCES

1. M. BERGMANN and L. ZERVAS, German Patent No. 556798 (1932); *Ber.* **65**, 1192 (1932).
2. R. SCHÖNHEIMER, *Hoppe-Seyler's Z. physiol. Chem.* **154**, 203 (1926); V. du VIGNEAUD and O. K. BEHRENS, *J. Biol. Chem.* **117**, 27 (1937); J. HONZL and J. RUDINGER, *Collection Czechoslov. Chem. Commun.* **20**, 1190 (1955).
3. J. C. SHEEHAN and V. S. FRANK, *J. Amer. Chem. Soc.* **71**, 1856 (1949); D. A. KIDD and F. E. KING, *Nature* **162**, 776 (1948).
4. F. WEYGAND and E. CSENDES, *Angew. Chem.* **64**, 136 (1952); *Chem. Ber.* **87**, 248 (1954); F. WEYGAND and G. ADERMANN, *ibid.* **93**, 2334 (1960).
5. A. COSMATOS, I. PHOTAKI and L. ZERVAS, *Chem. Ber.* **94**, 2644 (1961).
6. A. HILLMANN-ELIES, G. HILLMANN and H. JATZKEWITZ, *Z. Naturforsch.* **8b**, 445 (1953).
7. L. VELLUZ, G. AMIARD and R. HEYMÈS, *Bull. soc. chim. France* **1955**, 1283; G. AMIARD, R. HEYMÈS and L. VELLUZ, *ibid.* **1955**, 191; *ibid.* **1956**, 97, 698; L. VELLUZ, G. AMIARD, J. BARTOS, B. GOFFINET and R. HEYMÈS, *ibid.* **1956**, 1464.
8. L. ZERVAS, Communications du XIV Congrès International de Chimie Pure et Appliquée, Zürich, 1955, p. 224; D. THEODOROPOULOS, Thesis, University of Athens, 1953; G. C. STELAKATOS, Thesis, University of Athens, 1954; L. ZERVAS and D. M. THEODOROPOULOS, *J. Amer. Chem. Soc.* **78**, 1359 (1956); G. C. STELAKATOS, D. M. THEODOROPOULOS and L. ZERVAS, *ibid.* **81**, 2884 (1959).
9. J. C. SHEEHAN and G. P. HESS, *J. Amer. Chem. Soc.* **77**, 1067 (1955); G. AMIARD, R. HEYMÈS and L. VELLUZ, *Bull. soc. chim. France* **1955**, 1464.
10. M. BERGMANN, H. ENSSLIN and L. ZERVAS, *Ber.* **58**, 1034 (1925); M. BERGMANN and L. ZERVAS, *Hoppe-Seyler's Z. physiol. Chem.* **152**, 282 (1926).
11. F. C. MCINTIRE, *J. Amer. Chem. Soc.* **69**, 1377 (1947).
12. J. C. SHEEHAN and V. J. GRENDA, *ibid.* **84**, 2417 (1962).
13. R. A. BOISSONNAS, St. GUTTMANN, R. L. HUGUENIN, P.-A. JAQUENOUD and Ed. SANDRIN, *Helv. Chim. Acta* **41**, 1852 (1958).
14. L. ZERVAS, M. WINITZ and J. P. GREENSTEIN, *J. Amer. Chem. Soc.* **83**, 3300 (1961).
15. L. ZERVAS and M. BERGMANN, *Ber.* **61**, 1195 (1928).
16. G. AMIARD and R. HEYMÈS, *Bull. soc. chim. France* **1957**, 1373.

THE USE OF THE METHYLTHIOETHYL GROUP FOR CARBOXYL PROTECTION IN PEPTIDE SYNTHESIS

H. N. RYDON and J. E. WILLETT

Washington Singer Laboratories, University of Exeter, England

THE remarkable alkali-lability of the methiodides (I) of β-methylthioethyl esters was discovered by Crane and Rydon [1] and investigated fully by Mamalis and Rydon [2] who showed that, with alkali at room temperature, these compounds broke down according to the equation:

$$R.CO.O.CH_2.CH_2.\overset{+}{S}Me_2\}I^- + OH^- \rightarrow R.CO.O^- + CH_2:CH.\overset{+}{S}Me_2\}I^- + H_2O$$
(I)

The reaction proceeds very rapidly at quite low pH values; thus, the half-change time for the breakdown of the benzoate (I; R = Ph) in 0·01M solution at 25° is about 20 min at pH 10·0 and about 10 min at pH 10·35. Crane and Rydon [1] suggested that this reaction might be useful for the protection of carboxyl groups in synthetic work and we now present a preliminary account of its application in peptide synthesis. The potential usefulness of a carboxyl-protecting group removable under very mildly alkaline conditions, so complementing the acid-labile t-butyl esters [3], is obvious.

The β-methylthioethyl esters (II) of N-benzyloxycarbonyl-, N-trityl-, N-trifluoroacetyl- and N-phthaloyl-glycine were prepared in good yield (60–95 per cent), as crystalline solids (m.p. 34·5°, 78°, 62° and 72°, respectively), by heating the N-protected amino-acid with β-chloroethyl methyl sulphide and triethylamine in refluxing ethyl acetate. The esters were converted by the action of methyl iodide, alone or in acetone or nitromethane, into the methiodides (III); treatment of these, in aqueous solution, with aqueous alkali at pH 9–10 (alizarin yellow G-xylene cyanol FF) rapidly regenerated the N-protected glycines in excellent yield (85 per cent), except in the case of the phthaloyl compound in which some opening of the imide ring occurred. The overall process is as follows:

$$X.NH.CH_2.CO_2H \xrightarrow{\quad Cl.CH_2.CH_2.SMe \quad} X.NH.CH_2.CO.OCH_2.CH_2.SMe$$
(II)

$$X.NH.CH_2.CO_2H + CH_2:CH.\overset{+}{S}Me_2\}I^- \xleftarrow{\quad OH^- \quad} X.NH.CH_2.CO.O.CH_2.CH_2.\overset{+}{S}Me_2\}I^-$$
(III)

with $\downarrow$ MeI

23

Removal of the N-protecting groups was less satisfactory. Attempted removal of the benzyloxycarbonyl group from (II; X = Ph.CH$_2$.O.CO) with hydrogen bromide in acetic acid [4] was complicated by the formation of benzylsulphonium compounds and the situation was not improved by adding diethyl phosphite [5]; treatment with sodium in liquid ammonia was likewise unsuccessful. Attempts to remove the trifluoroacetyl group from (II; X = F$_3$C.CO) with aqueous alkali [6], aqueous ammonia [7] and a basic ion-exchange resin [8] also failed and only a poor yield of N-phthaloyl-glycine was obtained from its methylthioethyl ester by treatment with hydrazine. However, an excellent yield of the toluene-p-sulphonate of glycine β-methylthioethyl ester was obtained by warming the trityl derivative (II; X = Ph$_3$C) with methanolic toluene-p-sulphonic acid; the overall yield, based on glycine, is 60 per cent and ester so prepared was used in the remainder of our work.

Glycine β-methylthioethyl ester was coupled, by a variety of methods, with N-benzyloxycarbonyl-, N-trityl-, N-trifluoroacetyl- and N-phthaloyl-glycine to give the four protected dipeptides (IV).

$$\text{X.NH.CH}_2\text{.CO.NH.CH}_2\text{.CO.O.CH}_2\text{.CH}_2\text{.SMe}$$
$$\text{(IV)}$$

In all, thirteen different coupling reactions were carried out, the methods used comprising the azide, mixed anhydride, activated ester (p-nitrophenyl and cyanomethyl), dicyclohexylcarbodi-imide and bis-o-phenylene pyrophosphite procedures. In no case was any particular difficulty encountered and the yields obtained were comparable to those obtained in couplings involving the esters more usually employed as amine components.

Removal of the protecting groups, both N- and O-, from the resulting dipeptides was rather more satisfactory than was the case with the simple glycine derivatives. Not only was the N-trityl group removed smoothly, in 70 per cent yield, from the dipeptide (IV; X = Ph$_3$C) by the action of warm methanolic toluene-p-sulphonic acid, but the phthaloyl group was also readily removed from the corresponding phthaloyl derivative (IV; X = o-C$_6$H$_4$(CO)$_2$) to give a 60 per cent yield of glycylglycine methylthio-ethyl ester. As before, however, removal of the N-benzyloxycarbonyl and N-trifluoroacetyl groups was unsatisfactory. Removal of the methylthioethyl ester group by conversion into the methiodide, followed by the action of aqueous alkali at pH 9–10, gave good yields (70–80 per cent) of the N-protected dipeptides in the case of the benzyloxycarbonyl-, trityl- and trifluoro-acetyl-compounds; a poor yield (23 per cent) was, however, obtained from the phthaloyl compound owing to ring-opening.

Although much remains to be done to establish the method fully, it seems clear that the methylthioethyl ester group is indeed very suitable for carboxyl protection in peptide synthesis, and we believe that the very mild conditions under which it can be removed will make it of real use in such work, especially in conjunction with trityl N-protection [9, 10]. The reagent β-chloroethyl methyl sulphide, used in the preparation of the esters, is easily prepared [11].

The main difficulty in the procedure is the necessity of preparing the methylthioethyl esters rather circuitously through the N-trityl-amino-acids; this can be a real limitation in the case of those amino-acids, such as leucine and phenylalanine, which give only poor yields on tritylation [10]. For this reason we made numerous attempts to prepare glycine β-methylthioethyl ester directly; the methods tried included the action of β-chloroethyl methyl sulphide on glycine in aqueous solution and on silver glycine, and the esterification of glycine with β-hydroxyethyl methyl sulphide, catalysed by mineral acid, toluene-p-sulphonic acid [12], acetyl chloride [13] and thionyl chloride [14], but in no case was a satisfactory yield obtained.

Recently, in collaboration with Miss M. J. S. A. Amaral and Dr. G. C. Barrett, DL-phenylalanine β-methylthioethyl ester has been obtained by heating the amino-acid, β-chloroethyl methyl sulphide and triethylamine in a sealed tube at 200° and, much more conveniently, by refluxing phenylalanine, β-chloroethyl methyl sulphide and triethylamine in the presence of sufficient water to dissolve the amino-acid. The latter procedure, using benzyl chloride, has also given an 80 per cent yield of L-leucine benzyl ester; the method is, unfortunately, not generally applicable in its present form, since N-alkylation often accompanies ester formation and work is in hand to modify the conditions in such a way as to minimize this undesirable side-reaction. Very recently, in the light of Sheehan's use of substituted salicylylidene derivatives in peptide synthesis, we have prepared the β-methylthioethyl ester of phenylalanine in good yield by treatment of N-salicylidene-phenylalanine with β-chloroethyl methyl sulphide and triethylamine, followed by removal of the salicylidene group by the action of dilute acid.

In addition, work is in progress, likewise in collaboration with Miss Amaral and Dr. Barrett, on the extension of the method to other amino-acids, notably aspartic and glutamic acids, on the use of sulphones [1, 2] instead of sulphonium salts in the removal stage and on other modifications and extensions of the general procedure.

We thank the Department of Scientific and Industrial Research for the award of a Research Studentship (to J. E. W.).

REFERENCES

1. C. W. CRANE and H. N. RYDON, *J. Chem. Soc.* **1947**, 766.
2. P. MAMALIS and H. N. RYDON, *J. Chem. Soc.* **1955**, 1049.
3. R. W. ROESKE, *Chem. and Ind.* **1959**, 1121; G. W. ANDERSON and F. M. CALLAHAN, *J. Amer. Chem. Soc.* **82**, 3359, (1960); E. TASCHNER, Cz. WASIELEWSKI, J. F. BIERNAT and T. SOKOLOWSKA, *Chimia*, **14**, 371, 372 (1960).
4. D. BEN-ISHAI and A. BERGER, *J. Org. Chem.* **17**, 1564 (1952).
5. St. GUTTMANN and R. A. BOISSONNAS, *Helv. Chim. Acta* **41**, 1852 (1958).

6. F. WEYGAND and E. CSENDES, *Angew. Chem.* **64,** 136 (1952).
7. E. E. SCHALLENBERG and M. CALVIN, *J. Amer. Chem. Soc.* **77,** 2779 (1955).
8. F. WEYGAND and M. REIHER, *Chem. Ber.* **88,** 26 (1955).
9. A. HILLMANN-ELIES, G. HILLMANN and H. JATZKEWITZ, *Z. Naturforsch* **8b,** 445 (1953); G. AMIARD, R. HEYMES and L. VELLUZ, *Bull. Soc. Chim. France* **1955,** 191.
10. L. ZERVAS and D. M. THEODOROPOULOS, *J. Amer. Chem. Soc.* **78,** 1359 (1956).
11. W. R. KIRNER and W. WINDUS, *Org. Syntheses,* Coll. **2,** 136 (1943).
12. J. D. CIPERA and R. V. V. NICHOLLS, *Chem. and Ind.* **1955,** 16.
13. W. E. HANBY, S. G. WALEY and J. WATSON, *J. Chem. Soc.* **1950,** 3239.
14. M. BRENNER and W. HUBER, *Helv. Chim. Acta* **36,** 1109 (1953).

ON CYSTEINE AND CYSTINE PEPTIDES

L. ZERVAS,* I. PHOTAKI,* A. COSMATOS and N. GHELIS

Laboratory of Organic Chemistry, University of Athens, Athens, Greece

IT is well known that unsymmetrical open chain derivatives of cystine are not stable but rearrange very easily to the symmetrical ones [1, 2]. The first examples of pure, crystalline unsymmetrical open chain cystine peptides are monoglycyl-L-cystine [2] and γ-L-glutamyl-L-cysteinyl-S-(S-cysteine)-glycine [3a] (Fig. 1). Even at pH 6–7, and much more easily in strong acidic or alkaline media, monoglycylcystine rearranges very easily forming diglycyl-cystine and cystine [2].

```
                              Glu
                              |
Gly—Cys                      └—Cys—Gly
   |                              |
   Cys                           Cys
```

FIG. 1

The existence and the stability of unsymmetrical cystine peptides as in oxytocin and in vasopressin may apparently be attributed to the fact that these compounds are of cyclic structure, the only existing —S—S-bridge of the molecule being implicated in the ring system. Most of the proteins can be considered, in principle, as unsymmetrical polypeptides of cystine. These proteins, i.e. insulin whose structure has been elucidated by Sanger et al. [4] (Fig. 2), are more or less stable, because in this case more than one cystine

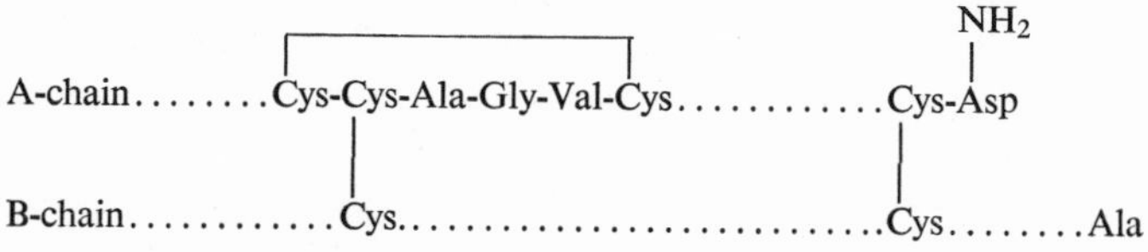

```
                      ┌──────────────┐           NH2
                      │              │            |
A-chain........Cys-Cys-Ala-Gly-Val-Cys...........Cys-Asp
                 |                                  |
B-chain..........Cys.............................Cys........Ala
```

FIG. 2

—S—S-bridge holds the polypeptide chains together, forcing them to partici-pate in a multi-membered ring system.

Whereas the synthesis of common polypeptide chains (i.e. peptides of different amino-acids including cysteine, symmetrical cystine peptides or

* This investigation was supported by the Royal Hellenic Research Foundation, to which we are indebted.

27

oxytocin-type peptides) is, in principle, no more a problem in the peptide chemistry, an inspection of the insulin —S—S-bridge system shows that the unequivocal synthesis of cystine peptides with two or more —S—S-bridges is an extremely difficult task. As we have stated in the Symposia in Basle [5] and in Moscow [6, 7], the solution of this problem could be facilitated if in addition to the existing methods for peptide synthesis, the following requirements were fulfilled [7] (Fig. 3): (a) cysteines bearing different S-protecting

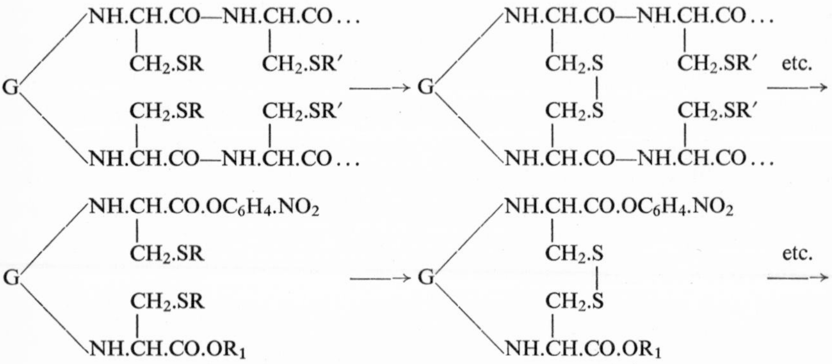

$$G = p—NO_2.C_6H_4.CH_2.OP(O) \quad \text{or} \quad —CO.CH_2.CH_2.CH(NH.Z)CO—$$

FIG. 3

groups selectively removable must be available and (b) procedures must be worked out for preventing the rearrangements during synthesis until their final incorporation in a multi-membered ring system. This could be done by coupling two different peptide chains containing the S-protected cysteines, through their amino ends, with a polyvalent N-protecting group G, i.e. p-nitro- or p-bromobenzyl-phosphoro group or benzyloxycarbonyl-L-glutamoyl group. The selective removal of two S-protecting groups (one from each of the two chains) and the oxidation of the thiol groups thus formed would establish an —S—S-bridge, so that a multi-membered ring is formed and a rearrangement of the cystine peptide chains is prevented. To carry out the —S—S-bridge formation the work of Greenstein [8], du Vigneaud [9] and Rydon [10] would be of great help. By repetition of the selective splitting off of two more S-protecting groups, the formation of a second —S—S-bridge and of an additional ring will be secured. The next step would be the removal of the polyvalent N-protecting group G in such a way that neither the peptide bonds nor the —S—S-bridges would be affected. Certainly, there is also another way for the synthesis of unsymmetrical cystine peptides (Fig. 3). That is, the already mentioned polyvalent N-protecting group could be combined with two S-protected derivatives of cysteine. After the formation of the first —S—S-bridge the peptide chain could be lengthened on both sides, and at a desirable length it could be supplied with new S-protected cysteine derivatives. The second —S—S-bridge could be established either by oxidation of two newly-formed thiol groups of the peptide chains or by a series of reactions [3b] similar to those used by Zahn [3a] for the synthesis of the already mentioned unsymmetrical glutamylcystine peptide.

In the following we shall describe methods which have been developed in our laboratory in order to solve the complicated problems mentioned above, especially the problem of the protection of the thiol group of cysteine during peptide synthesis.

The best known derivative of cysteine with protected thiol group is du Vigneaud's S-benzyl-L-cysteine [11] which has been used by du Vigneaud and his co-workers for the synthesis of glutathione [12], oxytocin and vasopressin [9]. Our problem, however, cannot be solved by using only this compound as long as the S-benzyl group is not removed otherwise than with sodium in liquid ammonia, as this procedure will break an already existing —S—S-bridge. In recent years many other S-protecting groups (i.e. the p-nitrobenzyl [13], tetrahydropyranyl [14], benzylthiomethyl, isobutoxymethyl and p-chlorophenoxymethyl groups [15]), or incorporation of the thiol group by interaction with acetone in a thiazolidine [16] ring, have been proposed or used.

For our purposes S-protecting groups are needed which could be removed not necessarily by hydrogenolysis but also by other chemical means under mild conditions without affecting sensitive parts of the molecule, i.e. peptide bonds, —S—S-bridges, etc. Some progress towards this goal has been made, in our opinion, by the use of S-diphenylmethyl (DPM)-L-cysteine and S-trityl (TRI)-L-cysteine [5, 6, 7]. In order to make the S-DPM and S-TRI-cysteine suitable for peptide synthesis we prepared their esters, as well as their N-formyl, N-benzyloxycarbonyl or N-trityl derivatives [5, 6, 7] (Fig. 4).

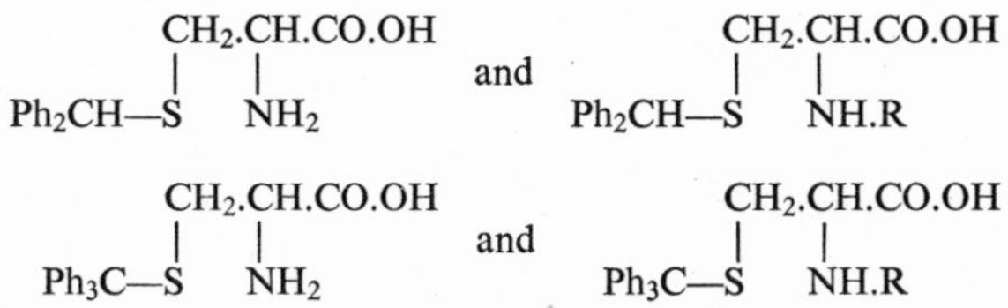

$$
\begin{array}{ccc}
\text{CH}_2.\text{CH}.\text{CO}.\text{OH} & & \text{CH}_2.\text{CH}.\text{CO}.\text{OH} \\
| \quad | & \text{and} & | \quad | \\
\text{Ph}_2\text{CH—S} \quad \text{NH}_2 & & \text{Ph}_2\text{CH—S} \quad \text{NH.R}
\end{array}
$$

$$
\begin{array}{ccc}
\text{CH}_2.\text{CH}.\text{CO}.\text{OH} & & \text{CH}_2.\text{CH}.\text{CO}.\text{OH} \\
| \quad | & \text{and} & | \quad | \\
\text{Ph}_3\text{C—S} \quad \text{NH}_2 & & \text{Ph}_3\text{C—S} \quad \text{NH.R}
\end{array}
$$

R = $C_6H_5.CH_2.OCO$, $(C_6H_5)_3C$, HCO.

FIG. 4

Other S-protecting groups suitable for our purposes are the S-acyl groups [6], which being ester groups can be removed very easily (Fig. 5). Very useful are the S-benzoyl and S-acetyl-L-cysteine and especially their benzyloxycarbonyl derivatives, which can be easily prepared by reduction of N, N'-dibenzyloxycarbonyl-L-cystine with zinc and hydrochloric acid,

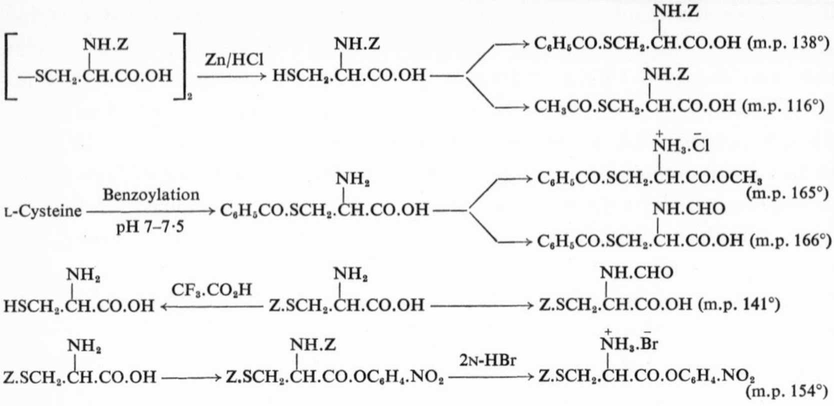

$$\left[\underset{-SCH_2.\overset{|}{C}H.CO.OH}{\overset{NH.Z}{|}}\right]_2 \xrightarrow{\text{Zn/HCl}} \underset{HSCH_2.\overset{|}{C}H.CO.OH}{\overset{NH.Z}{|}} \Big\langle$$

$$\nearrow \; C_6H_5CO.SCH_2.\underset{}{\overset{NH.Z}{\overset{|}{C}}}H.CO.OH \;\; (\text{m.p. } 138°)$$

$$\searrow \; CH_3CO.SCH_2.\underset{}{\overset{NH.Z}{\overset{|}{C}}}H.CO.OH \;\; (\text{m.p. } 116°)$$

$$\text{L-Cysteine} \xrightarrow[\text{pH 7–7·5}]{\text{Benzoylation}} C_6H_5CO.SCH_2.\underset{}{\overset{NH_2}{\overset{|}{C}}}H.CO.OH \Big\langle$$

$$\nearrow \; C_6H_5CO.SCH_2.\underset{\overset{|}{NH.CHO}}{\overset{\overset{+}{N}H_3.\bar{C}l}{\overset{|}{C}}}H.CO.OCH_3 \;\; (\text{m.p. } 165°)$$

$$\searrow \; C_6H_5CO.SCH_2.\underset{}{\overset{NH.CHO}{\overset{|}{C}}}H.CO.OH \;\; (\text{m.p. } 166°)$$

$$\underset{HSCH_2.\overset{|}{C}H.CO.OH}{\overset{NH_2}{|}} \xleftarrow{CF_3.CO_2H} \underset{Z.SCH_2.\overset{|}{C}H.CO.OH}{\overset{NH_2}{|}} \longrightarrow \underset{Z.SCH_2.\overset{|}{C}H.CO.OH}{\overset{NH.CHO}{|}} \;\; (\text{m.p. } 141°)$$

$$\underset{Z.SCH_2.\overset{|}{C}H.CO.OH}{\overset{NH_2}{|}} \longrightarrow \underset{Z.SCH_2.\overset{|}{C}H.CO.OC_6H_4.NO_2}{\overset{NH.Z}{|}} \xrightarrow{\text{2N-HBr}} \underset{Z.SCH_2.\overset{|}{C}H.CO.OC_6H_4.NO_2}{\overset{\overset{+}{N}H_3.\bar{B}r}{|}}$$
$$(\text{m.p. } 154°)$$

Fig. 5

followed by acylation of the N-benzyloxycarbonyl-L-cysteine thus formed. On the other hand, free S-benzoyl-L-cysteine, prepared by direct benzoylation of cysteine at pH 7–7·5, can be easily esterified and N-formylated. Furthermore Katchalski's S-benzyloxycarbonyl and N,S-dibenzyloxycarbonyl cysteine [17] can also be used for our purposes, the first of them in form of the N-formyl derivative [6, 18].

We thought that a solution of our problem could also be offered by L-serine, because this amino-acid can be converted easily to cysteine. This is actually the case with N-benzyloxycarbonyl-O-tosyl-L-serine methyl ester, which (as already reported in Basle) reacts very quickly with the sodium salt of trityl thiol forming the corresponding S-tritylderivative [5] (Fig. 6). As

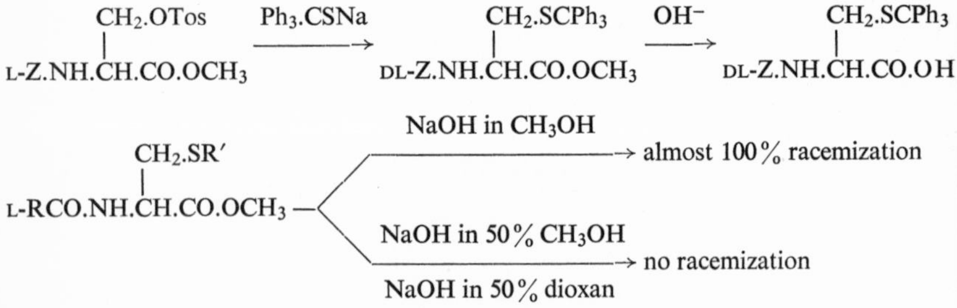

$$\underset{\text{L-Z.NH.CH.CO.OCH}_3}{\overset{CH_2.OT\text{os}}{|}} \xrightarrow{\text{Ph}_3.\text{CSNa}} \underset{\text{DL-Z.NH.CH.CO.OCH}_3}{\overset{CH_2.\text{SCPh}_3}{|}} \xrightarrow{\text{OH}^-} \underset{\text{DL-Z.NH.CH.CO.OH}}{\overset{CH_2.\text{SCPh}_3}{|}}$$

$$\underset{\text{L-RCO.NH.CH.CO.OCH}_3}{\overset{CH_2.\text{SR}'}{|}} \Big\langle$$

$$\xrightarrow{\text{NaOH in CH}_3\text{OH}} \text{almost 100\% racemization}$$

$$\underset{\text{NaOH in 50\% dioxan}}{\xrightarrow{\text{NaOH in 50\% CH}_3\text{OH}}} \text{no racemization}$$

$$R = C_6H_5.CH_2O, \; C_6H_5.$$
$$R' = C_6H_5.CH_2, \; (C_6H_5)_2CH, \; (C_6H_5)_3C.$$

Fig. 6

has been found later, however, during this reaction complete racemization takes place. Since saponification of the product either by methanolic alkali or by alkali in methanol or dioxan-water (1 : 1) leads to fully racemized acid, it is concluded that the racemization occurs prior to the saponification, apparently by a β-elimination mechanism. This conclusion is based on the fact that N-acyl-S-alkyl-L-cysteine esters are fully racemized with alcoholic alkali but not with alkali dissolved in 50 per cent methanol or 50 per cent dioxan. These findings give an explanation for the controversial statements in the literature. Schwyzer [19] found no racemization by saponification of N-benzyloxycarbonyl-S-benzyl-L-cysteine cyanomethyl ester, whereas Maclaren [20] reports racemization by the saponification of N-benzyloxy-carbonylglycyl-S-benzyl-L-cysteine ethyl ester. The explanation is that Schwyzer used alkali dissolved in 30 per cent alcohol whereas Maclaren used alcoholic solutions of alkali.

During our experiments with O-tosylated serine derivatives we observed that these compounds like the corresponding O-diphenylphosphoryl [21] derivatives undergo β-elimination under the action of 0·1 N-alkali, as well as with 1–2 equivalents of diethylamine, forming within a few minutes dehydro-alanine derivatives (Fig. 7). It is interesting that S-dinitrophenyl and S-per-methylated cysteine derivatives (Patchornik et al. [22]) as well as S-cyano-cysteine derivatives (Swan [23]) undergo rapidly with alkali β-elimination with the formation of the same products as in the case of the O-tosyl and

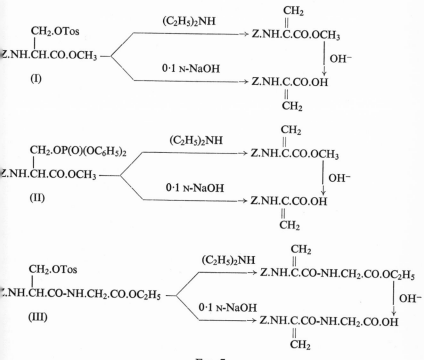

Fig. 7

O-diphenylphosphoryl serine derivatives. Such dehydropeptides are known to undergo easily hydrolysis under mildly basic or acidic conditions [24], or, as has been recently found by Patchornik [22], even by heating with water at 100°. Patchornik [25] has described in the meantime new procedures for the selective breakdown of the double bonds in the dehydropeptides. It is clear that our findings on tosylated or phosphorylated serine peptides may serve for a preferential cleavage of sequences containing serine residues through formation of dehydropeptides. The work of Witkop [26] and of Patchornik and his colleagues [22, 25] for the determination of sequences in a non-enzymatic way acquires herewith a broader application.

Returning to the problem of the S-protection of cysteine during peptide synthesis, we would like to describe the conditions for the splitting off of the S-trityl, S-diphenylmethyl and S-acyl groups, which we have summarized in Fig. 8.

Groups	Reagents	% Cleavage
1. S-Trityl	a. AgNO$_3$-Pyridine	100, at 20° in 1 min
	b. N-HBr in acetic acid	95, at 10° in 3 min
	0·2 N-HBr in acetic acid	75, at 10° in 5 min
	c. Trifluoracetic acid	95, at 70° in 30 min
	d. Na-NH$_3$	100
2. S-Diphenylmethyl	a. Trifluoracetic acid	98, at 70° in 15 min
	b. 2 N-HBr in acetic acid	5–10, at 20° in 20 min
	c. Na-NH$_3$	100
3. S-Benzoyl	a. 1 equiv. 0·1 N-NaOCH$_3$ in CH$_3$OH	98, at 20° in 5 min
	b. 2 N-ammonia	95, at 20° in 30 min
	c. 2 N-HBr in acetic acid	5–7, at 20° in 30 min
	d. Trifluoracetic acid	2–3, at 20° in 30 min
4. S-Benzyloxycarbonyl	a. 1 equiv. 0·1 N-NaOCH$_3$ in CH$_3$OH	90, at 20° in 30 min
	b. 2 N-HBr in acetic acid	12–14, at 20° in 20 min
	c. Trifluoracetic acid	85–88, at 70° in 30 min

FIG. 8.   Cleavage of S-protecting groups of cysteine.

In Fig. 9 a few examples for the synthesis of some peptides are presented simply to illustrate the possibilities of the incorporation of cysteine into a peptide chain using S-trityl, S-diphenylmethyl or S-acyl cysteines. The syntheses were carried out step by step in order to avoid racemization. Depending on the type and the size of peptide to be synthesized, one has to use N-formyl, N-benzyloxycarbonyl [27], N-trityl [28, 29, 30], N-diphenyl-phosphoryl [31], or N-trifluoroacetyl [32] derivatives of the above S-protected cysteines.

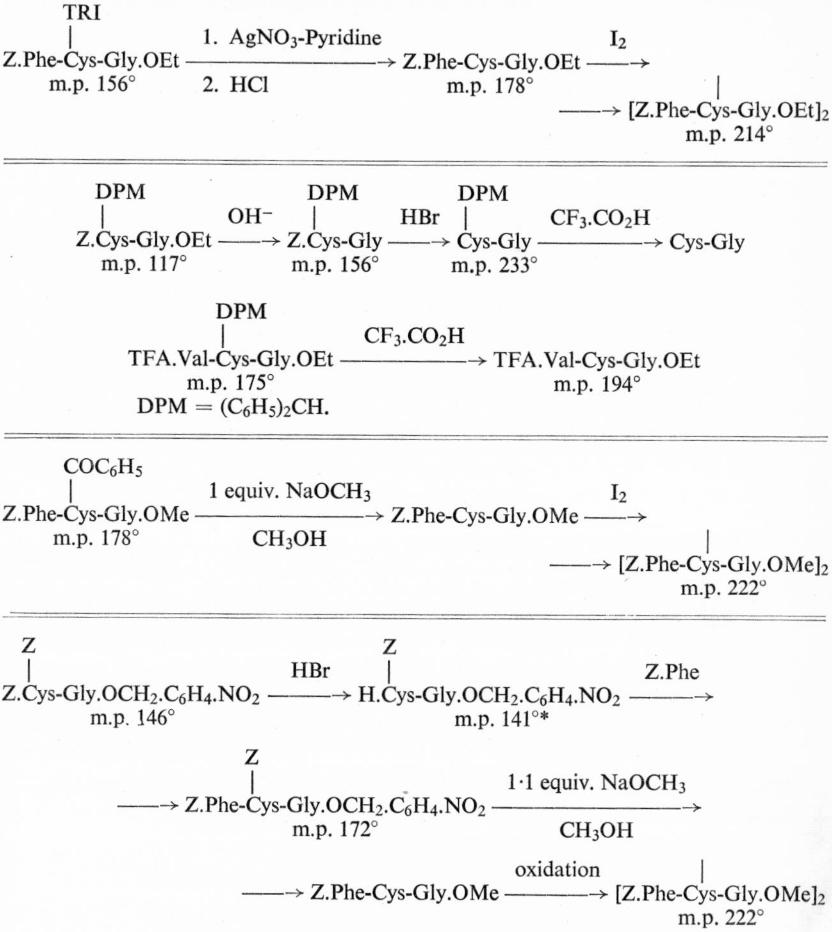

TRI
|
Z.Phe-Cys-Gly.OEt $\xrightarrow[\text{2. HCl}]{\text{1. AgNO}_3\text{-Pyridine}}$ Z.Phe-Cys-Gly.OEt $\xrightarrow{\text{I}_2}$
m.p. 156°   m.p. 178°
|
$\longrightarrow$ [Z.Phe-Cys-Gly.OEt]$_2$
m.p. 214°

DPM   DPM   DPM
| OH$^-$ | HBr | CF$_3$.CO$_2$H
Z.Cys-Gly.OEt $\longrightarrow$ Z.Cys-Gly $\longrightarrow$ Cys-Gly $\longrightarrow$ Cys-Gly
m.p. 117°   m.p. 156°   m.p. 233°

DPM
|
TFA.Val-Cys-Gly.OEt $\xrightarrow{\text{CF}_3\text{.CO}_2\text{H}}$ TFA.Val-Cys-Gly.OEt
m.p. 175°   m.p. 194°
DPM = (C$_6$H$_5$)$_2$CH.

COC$_6$H$_5$
|
Z.Phe-Cys-Gly.OMe $\xrightarrow[\text{CH}_3\text{OH}]{\text{1 equiv. NaOCH}_3}$ Z.Phe-Cys-Gly.OMe $\xrightarrow{\text{I}_2}$
m.p. 178°
|
$\longrightarrow$ [Z.Phe-Cys-Gly.OMe]$_2$
m.p. 222°

Z   Z
| HBr |
Z.Cys-Gly.OCH$_2$.C$_6$H$_4$.NO$_2$ $\longrightarrow$ H.Cys-Gly.OCH$_2$.C$_6$H$_4$.NO$_2$ $\xrightarrow{\text{Z.Phe}}$
m.p. 146°   m.p. 141°*

Z
|
$\longrightarrow$ Z.Phe-Cys-Gly.OCH$_2$.C$_6$H$_4$.NO$_2$ $\xrightarrow[\text{CH}_3\text{OH}]{\text{1·1 equiv. NaOCH}_3}$
m.p. 172°

oxidation |
$\longrightarrow$ Z.Phe-Cys-Gly.OMe $\longrightarrow$ [Z.Phe-Cys-Gly.OMe]$_2$
m.p. 222°

* As the corresponding hydrobromide.

FIG. 9

It is evident that *S*-trityl, *S*-diphenylmethyl and *S*-acyl cysteines are useful intermediates for the synthesis of symmetrical cystine or oxytocin-like peptides. Furthermore, their introduction into peptide chemistry may be considered as the fulfilment of the first requirement mentioned above, for the possibility of the synthesis of unsymmetrical cystine peptides with two at least —S—S-bridges. As an approach to this goal may serve the synthesis of a " key-fragment " of the A-chain of sheep insulin which is now in progress. This fragment (I; Fig. 10) bears an —S—S-bridge and at the same time a thiol group and cannot, at the present, be synthesized otherwise. Its precursor, i.e. the corresponding protected heptapeptide (Fig. 10) has been

P   4

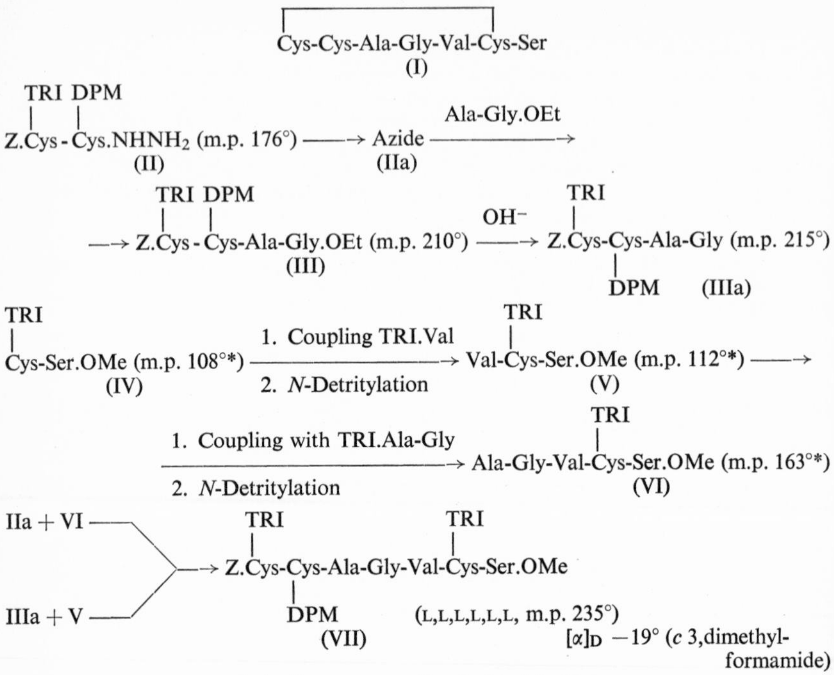

$$
\boxed{\text{Cys-Cys-Ala-Gly-Val-Cys-Ser}}
$$
$$\text{(I)}$$

TRI DPM
 | | Ala-Gly.OEt
Z.Cys - Cys.NHNH$_2$ (m.p. 176°) ——→ Azide ————————→
   (II)   (IIa)

      TRI DPM   TRI
       | | OH$^-$ |
——→ Z.Cys - Cys-Ala-Gly.OEt (m.p. 210°) ————→ Z.Cys-Cys-Ala-Gly (m.p. 215°)
          (III) |
                                              DPM   (IIIa)

TRI   TRI
| 1. Coupling TRI.Val |
Cys-Ser.OMe (m.p. 108°*) ————————————→ Val-Cys-Ser.OMe (m.p. 112°*) ——→
   (IV)   2. N-Detritylation   (V)

                                           TRI
      1. Coupling with TRI.Ala-Gly |
   ————————————————→ Ala-Gly-Val-Cys-Ser.OMe (m.p. 163°*)
      2. N-Detritylation   (VI)

IIa + VI ⎯⎯⎯⎯⎯╲   TRI   TRI
                ╲ | |
                ╲——→ Z.Cys-Cys-Ala-Gly-Val-Cys-Ser.OMe
                ╱ |
IIIa + V ⎯⎯⎯⎯⎯╱   DPM   (L,L,L,L,L,L, m.p. 235°)
                (VII)   [α]$_D$ −19° (c 3,dimethyl-
                                            formamide)

* As the corresponding hydrochlorides.

FIG. 10

synthesized in such a way that racemization is avoided.* We have already started with the transformation of this protected heptapeptide VII to the above " key-fragment " I; the course of the reaction is as follows: (1) saponi-fication; (2) selective removal of the S-trityl groups and of the N-benzyloxy-carbonyl group by means of hydrobromic acid in acetic acid†; (3) oxidation of the thiol groups thus formed; and (4) removal of the diphenylmethyl group with trifluoracetic acid.

REFERENCES

1. F. SANGER, Nature 171, 1025 (1953); A. P. RYLE and F. SANGER, Biochem. J. 60, 535 (1955).
2. L. ZERVAS, L. BENOITON, E. WEISS, M. WINITZ and J. P. GREENSTEIN, J. Amer. Chem. Soc. 81, 1729 (1959).
3. (a) H. ZAHN and H. G. OTTEN, Liebigs Chem., Ann. 653, 139 (1962); (b) H. B. FOOTNER and S. SMILES, J. Chem. Soc., 1925, 2887; C. J. CAVALLITO, J. S. BUCK and C. M. SUTER, J. Amer. Chem. Soc. 66, 1952 (1944).

* The synthesis of another protected heptapeptide of the same type i.e. N,S-dibenzyl-oxycarbonyl-L-cysteinyl-L-(S-trityl)-L-cysteinyl-L-alanyl-glycyl-L-valyl-L-(S-benzoyl)-cysteinyl-L-serine methyl ester, is now in progress.

† This can also be accomplished by removing first the S-trityl groups with silver nitrate and, afterwards, splitting off the N-benzyloxycarbonyl group with hydrobromic acid.

4. H. Brown, F. Sanger and R. Ketai, *Biochem. J.* **60,** 556 (1955).
5. L. Zervas and I. Photaki, *Chimia,* **14,** 375 (1960).
6. L. Zervas, *Collection Czechoslov. Chem. Communs.,* **27,** 2229 (1962).
7. L. Zervas and I. Photaki, *J. Amer. Chem. Soc.,* **84,** 3887 (1962).
8. N. Izumyia and J. P. Greenstein, *Arch. Biochem. Biophys.* **52,** 203 (1954); R. Wade, M. Winitz and J. P. Greenstein, *J. Amer. Chem. Soc.* **78,** 373 (1956).
9. V. du Vigneaud, C. Ressler, J. M. Swan, C. W. Roberts and P. G. Katsoyannis, *J. Amer. Chem. Soc.* **76,** 3115 (1954); V. du Vigneaud, D. T. Gish, P. G. Katsoyannis and G. P. Hess, *ibid.* **80,** 3355 (1958); V. du Vigneaud, D. T. Gish and P. G. Katsoyannis, *ibid.* **76,** 4751 (1954).
10. G. S. Heaton, H. N. Rydon and J. A. Schofield, *J. Chem. Soc.* **1956,** 3157; D. Jarvis, H. N. Rydon and J. A. Schofield, *J. Chem. Soc.* **1961,** 1752.
11. R. H. Siffert and V. du Vigneaud, *J. Biol. Chem.* **108,** 753 (1935).
12. V. du Vigneaud and G. L. Miller, *J. Biol. Chem.* **116,** 469 (1936).
13. C. Berse, R. Boucher and L. Piche, *J. Org. Chem.* **22,** 805 (1957).
14. G. F. Holland and L. A. Cohen, *J. Amer. Chem. Soc.* **80,** 3765 (1958).
15. P. J. E. Pimlott and G. T. Young, *Proc. Chem. Soc.* **1958,** 257; G. T. Young, *Angew. Chem.* **71,** 741 (1959).
16. J. C. Sheehan and D. D. H. Yang, *J. Amer. Chem. Soc.* **80,** 1158 (1958); F. E. King, J. W. Clark-Lewis and R. Wade, *J. Chem. Soc.* **1957,** 880.
17. A. Berger, J. Noguchi and E. Katchalski, *J. Amer. Chem. Soc.* **78,** 4483 (1956).
18. P. G. Katsoyannis, *J. Amer. Chem. Soc.* **83,** 4053 (1961).
19. B. Iselin, M. Feurer and R. Schwyzer, *Helv. Chim. Acta* **38,** 1508 (1955).
20. J. A. Maclaren, *Australian J. Chem.* **11,** 360 (1958).
21. G. Riley, J. Turnbull, W. Wilson, *J. Chem. Soc.* **1957,** 1373.
22. A. Patchornik, M. Sokolovsky and T. Sadeh, Vth International Congress of Biochemistry, Moscow, 1961, Section I, p. 11.
23. J. M. Swan, *Nature* **180,** 643 (1957).
24. M. Bergmann and K. Grafe, *Hoppe-Seyler's Z. physiol. Chem.* **187,** 187 (1930).
25. A. Patchornik and M. Sokolovsky, *Bull. Research Council Israel,* **11A,** 80 (1962).
26. B. Witkop, *Advances in Protein Chemistry,* **16,** 221–321, Academic Press, New York and London, 1961.
27. M. Bergmann and L. Zervas, German Patent No. 556798 (1932); *Ber.* **65,** 1192 (1932).
28. A. Hillmann-Elies, G. Hillmann and H. Jatzkewitz, *Z. Naturforsch.* **8b,** 445 (1953).
29. L. Velluz, G. Amiard and R. Heymès, *Bull. Soc. chim. France* **1955,** 1283; G. Amiard, R. Heymès and L. Velluz, *ibid.* **1955,** 191; *ibid.* **1956,** 97, 698; L. Velluz, G. Amiard, J. Bartos, B. Goffinet and R. Heymès, *ibid.* **1956,** 1464.
30. (a) L. Zervas, Communications du XIV Congrès International de Chimie Pure et Appliquée, Zürich 1955, p. 224; D. Theodoropoulos, Dissert., Univ. Athens 1953; G. C. Stelakatos, Dissert., Univ. Athens 1954;
   (b) L. Zervas and D. M. Theodoropoulos, *J. Amer. Chem. Soc.* **78,** 1359 (1956); G. C. Stelakatos, D. M. Theodoropoulos and L. Zervas, *ibid.* **81,** 2884 (1959).
31. A. Cosmatos, I. Photaki and L. Zervas, *Chem. Ber.* **94,** 2644 (1961).
32. F. Weygand and E. Csendes, *Angew. Chem.* **64,** 136 (1952); F. Weygand, G. Klipping and D. Palm, *Chem. Ber.* **93,** 2619 (1960).

PROTECTION OF THE THIOL GROUP IN CYSTEINE WITH THE TERTIARY BUTYL RESIDUE

A. CHIMIAK

Department of General Chemistry, Technical University, Gdańsk, Poland

THE known methods for the protection of the thiol group in cysteine do not always give satisfactory results. For this reason any new thiol-protecting group may be of interest.

We have observed [1] that carboxyl groups can be alkylated with tert. butyl acetate yielding the corresponding tert. butyl esters. It could be expected that the same method could be also applied for the alkylation of some other acidic groups, and especially for the alkylation of the thiol group.

Cysteine (1 mM) left at 20° with tert. butyl acetate (15 ml) in presence of perchloric acid (2·2 mM) for 4 days yielded the tert. butyl ester of S-tert. butylcysteine hydrochloride (m.p. 202°) in fairly good yield.

From this compound the tert. butyl ester group can be removed easily by solvolysis (trifluoroacetic acid or hydrogen bromide in acetic acid at 20°), whereas the removal of the S-tert. butyl thioether group requires more drastic conditions, as for instance heating with hydrogen bromide in acetic acid.

The tert. butyl ester of S-tert. butylcysteine was coupled with phthaloylglycine (active ester or mixed anhydride method) to give the dipeptide ester in good yield.

REFERENCE

1. E. TASCHNER, A. CHIMIAK, B. BATOR and T. SOKOŁOWSKA, Liebigs Ann. Chem. 646, 134 (1961).

SYNTHESIS OF α-ESTERS OF N-SUBSTITUTED GLUTAMIC ACID

G. H. L. Nefkens

Laboratory of Organic Chemistry, R.C. University, Nijmegen, Holland

As yet only one direct method is known for the synthesis of α-esters of N-substituted glutamic acid. This method is based on the reaction of the internal cyclic anhydride of the N-substituted amino-acid with the appropriate alcohol, giving a mixture of α- and γ-esters which might be separated by extraction and crystallization. Weygand [1] isolated the α- and γ-ethyl esters of trifluoroacetylglutamic acid as the crystalline dicyclohexylammonium salts. Very recently Gibian [2] examined the reaction of anhydrides and alcohols in the presence of dicyclohexylamine and obtained a great variety of well-defined products.

We prepared the α-esters of N-substituted-L-glutamic acid in a one-step reaction, based on the higher acidity of the α-carboxyl group as compared to the γ-carboxyl group. The pK difference roughly amounts to 2 units. Addition of a base thus will ionize the α-carboxyl residue a hundred times more than the γ-carboxyl residue, and it can be expected that the addition of an alkyl halide will give the α-ester and the hydrogen halide of the amine used. This salt can be removed by filtration and washing with water. The crude α-ester is obtained usually in crystalline form after addition of dicyclohexylamine to a solution of the acidic ester in an ether–alcohol mixture.

$$
\begin{array}{l}
\text{COOH} \\
| \\
\text{CH}_2 \\
| \\
\text{CH}_2 + \text{BH}^+ + \text{R}'\text{Br} \\
| \\
\text{R.NH.CH} \\
\diagdown\!\!\!\diagup \text{C} \diagup^{\text{O}}_{\diagdown \text{O}^-}
\end{array}
\quad \xrightarrow{\text{DMF}} \quad
\begin{array}{l}
\text{C} \diagup^{\text{O}}_{\diagdown \text{OH}} \\
| \\
\text{CH}_2 \\
| \\
\text{CH}_2 \\
| \\
\text{R.NH.CH} \\
\diagdown\!\!\!\diagup \text{C} \diagup^{\text{O}}_{\diagdown \text{O.R}'}
\end{array}
$$

This reaction leads to neutral products, of course, if *two* equivalents of halide and *two* equivalents of amine are used.

In this way we prepared the α-ethyl, α-benzyl, α-p-nitrobenzyl and α-phthalimidomethyl esters of N-benzyloxycarbonyl and tosylglutamic acid in yields of 50–80 per cent. At room temperature the reaction was allowed to proceed for 12 hr, using dimethylformamide as solvent and triethylamine as the base.

With dicyclohexylammonium salts, the reaction demanded somewhat higher temperatures because of the low solubility of these salts in dimethylformamide. Consequently the reaction time could be reduced greatly: in some instances a period of 15 min at 60°C sufficed.

For the synthesis of methyl esters the use of methyl bromide is unsuitable owing to its volatility. This halide could advantageously be replaced by an equimolecular amount of dimethyl sulfate. In this case, in addition to dimethylformamide, chloroform could be used as a solvent equally well. This method gave only very low yields in the synthesis of tertiary butyl esters. We also investigated the formation of active esters in this way. Phenyl halides and p-nitrophenyl halides either did not react, or only in a very unsatisfactory way. We investigated bromo-, chloro- and fluoro- substituted nitro- and dinitrobenzenes. A proof of structure of some of the mentioned esters was worked out starting from tosylglutamic acid or benzyloxycarbonylglutamic acid (Fig. 1).

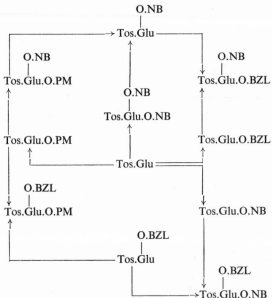

FIG. 1. Proof of structure of α-esters of tosylglutamic acid and benzyl alcohol, p-nitrobenzyl alcohol and phthalimidomethanol.

REFERENCES

1. F. WEYGAND and K. HUNGER, Z. Naturforsch. **13b**, 50 (1958).
2. E. KLIEGER and H. GIBIAN, Liebigs Ann. Chem. **655**, 195 (1962).

ON THE USE OF THE TOSYL GROUP FOR THE PROTECTION OF BASIC AMINO-ACIDS

St. Guttmann

Sandoz Ltd., Basle, Switzerland

Lysine and arginine residues are present in many biologically active peptides. The incorporation of these amino-acids in peptides requires the selective protection of their side chains. The protection of the ε-amino group of lysine has been satisfactorily improved in the recent years. On the contrary, protection of the guanidino group of arginine still presents difficulties, which will be discussed in this paper.

At present there exist four possibilities for protecting the guanidino group of arginine:

(a) Suppression of its basicity by forming salts with strong mineral acid, such as hydrochloric or hydrobromic acids, has been widely used in the synthesis of large peptides [1–8]. This method of protection avoids complications from the introduction and removal of protecting groups, but the peptides obtained are often soluble in water and very difficult to purify.

(b) The nitro group has also been extensively used [7, 9–12]. Its high stability permits the selective removal of other protecting groups. Unfortunately its own removal by catalytic hydrogenation proceeds only very slowly and often incompletely, especially in the case of large peptides, and complicated purification procedures are necessary.

(c) The benzyloxycarbonyl group [13] does not allow selective removal of other groups. It can only be used when arginine is in N-terminal position.

(d) The toluene-p-sulfonyl group is easily introduced. It is very stable and allows selective removal of all other protective groups of the molecule. Since it was proposed for protection of the guanidino group of arginine [14, 15], the tosyl group has been used in the synthesis of MSH- and ACTH-peptides [15, 16], of bradykinin [17], of kallidin [18] and of arginine-vasopressin [19]. It appears to be an almost " universal " protective group for the guanidino group of arginine, as well as for amino groups which should only be liberated at the last step of the synthesis of a peptide. Its removal is easily accomplished by treatment with sodium in liquid ammonia [20].

41

Nevertheless, it has recently been reported that during the treatment of the protected tridecapeptide of an α-MSH analogue [21, 22] by sodium in liquid ammonia, certain peptide bonds were cleaved, most probably at the C-terminal sequence: Gly-Lys-Pro-Val-NH$_2$.

As, on the other hand, the use of the tosyl group for the protection of the basic side groups presents many advantages, it seemed to us worth while to investigate conditions in which this group can be used, without complications.

TABLE 1. STABILITY OR CLEAVAGE OF VARIOUS PEPTIDES UNDER THE INFLUENCE OF SODIUM IN LIQUID AMMONIA UNDER " STANDARD CONDITIONS "

Peptide	Peptide bonds cleaved
Z-Lys-Pro-Val-NH$_2$	None
Tos | Z-Lys-Pro-Val-NH$_2$	None
Z | Z-Lys-Pro-Val-NH$_2$	None
H-Try-Gly-Lys-Pro-OH	↓ Lys-Pro
Z-Gly-Lys-Pro-Val-NH$_2$	↓ Lys-Pro
Tos | Z-Gly-Lys-Pro-Val-NH$_2$	↓ Lys-Pro
Z | H-Gly-Lys-Pro-Val-NH$_2$	↓ Lys-Pro

We have therefore examined the behaviour of a large number of peptides under conditions normally used for the removal of the tosyl group. The investigated peptides were first dissolved in liquid ammonia without any special precautions for ensuring anhydrous conditions. Sodium was immersed into the solution until a deep blue colour resulted. After 3 min the colour was discharged by addition of acetic acid. These conditions will be referred subsequently as " standard conditions ".

Peptides representing the C-terminal sequence of α-MSH were first investigated (Table 1). It is surprising that no cleavage of peptide bonds occurs in tripeptides with the sequence Lys-Pro-Val. If lysine is not in the

N-terminal position, cleavage occurs between lysine and proline. It makes no difference if the ε-amino group of lysine is free or if it is protected by a group removable by sodium in liquid ammonia, or if the carboxyl group of proline is free or substituted. It should be noted that under " standard conditions " the extent of cleavage was never found to be above 50 per cent.

In order to establish whether the presence of lysine or of proline is responsible for this cleavage, another series of peptides containing no Lys-Pro sequence was treated by sodium in liquid ammonia. It was found that in the absence of this sequence no cleavage occurs (Table 2).

TABLE 2. STABILITY OF VARIOUS PEPTIDES UNDER THE INFLUENCE OF SODIUM IN LIQUID AMMONIA UNDER " STANDARD CONDITIONS "

Peptide	Peptide bonds cleaved
Tos | Z-Pro-*Lys*-Gly-NH$_2$	None
Tos Tos | | Z-Gly-*Lys* - *Lys*-OH	None
Tos | H-Val-Pro-*Lys*-Gly-NH$_2$	None
H-Val-*Lys*-Val-Tyr-Pro-OH	None
H-Val-Tyr-*Pro*-OH	None
H-Arg-Arg-*Pro*-OH	None
NO$_2$ | H-Phe-Ser-*Pro*-Phe-Arg-ONB	None
H-Val-His-*Pro*-His-Leu-ONB	↓ His-Pro $< 1\%$

Peptides containing the Lys-Pro sequence were then submitted to the action of sodium in liquid ammonia for various periods of time, the excess of sodium being discharged by addition of acetic acid. It was found (Table 3, curve A) that the partial cleavage occurs only at the beginning of the treatment and that prolongation of the treatment do not increase the cleavage.

This fact strongly suggests that the observed cleavage is caused neither

by sodium nor by ammonia. This hypothesis is confirmed by the results
obtained when treating

Z-Gly-(ε-Tos)-Lys-Pro-Val-NH$_2$ (Table 3, curve B)

or

Gly-(ε-Z)-Lys-Pro-Val-NH$_2$ (Table 3, curve C)

by sodium in liquid ammonia under strictly anhydrous conditions (substances, apparatus and ammonia were all thoroughly dried immediately
before the treatment). In the case of the first peptide which contains a tosyl

TABLE 3

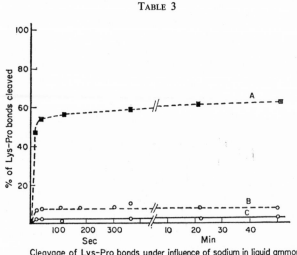

Cleavage of Lys-Pro bonds under influence of sodium in liquid ammonia
A) H-Gly-(ε-z)-Lys-Pro-Val-NH$_2$ under "standard conditions"
B) z-Gly-(ε-Tos)-Lys-Pro-Val-NH$_2$ under anhydrous conditions
C) H-Gly-(ε-z)-Lys-Pro-Val-NH$_2$ under anhydrous conditions

group (curve B), almost 10 per cent of the Lys-Pro bonds were cleaved. The
second peptide which bears no tosyl group was left practically unaffected.
It can therefore be concluded that traces of water (which can be present in
the apparatus or in the substances when working under " standard conditions ") as well as tosyl groups (in the case of tosylated peptides) are at the
origin of the cleavage of Lys-Pro bonds under the action of sodium in liquid
ammonia.

In order to ascertain the exactness of this supposition, both tetrapeptides,
Gly-(ε-Z)-Lys-Pro-Val-NH$_2$ and Z-Gly-(ε-Tos)-Lys-Pro-Val-NH$_2$ were
treated with sodium in liquid ammonia in presence of increasing amounts of
water or of toluene-p-sulfonamide. For both peptides the degree of cleavage
increases with the amount of water or toluenesulfonamide, respectively
(Table 4). About the same results were obtained when N-tosylglutamic acid
was used instead of tosylamide. These results show clearly that the presence

of water as well as that of toluenesulfonyl derivatives is responsible for the cleavage of the Lys-Pro bond.

We have also observed that the Arg-Pro bond, although less susceptible than the Lys-Pro bond, is cleaved when significant amounts of water, or of ammonium chloride, are present during the treatment by sodium in liquid ammonia. The bonds between other amino-acids and proline were found to suffer a certain cleavage under these conditions.

TABLE 4

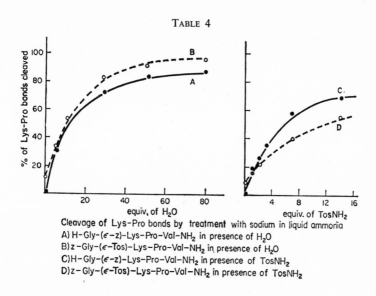

Cleavage of Lys-Pro bonds by treatment with sodium in liquid ammonia
A) H-Gly-(ϵ-z)-Lys-Pro-Val-NH$_2$ in presence of H$_2$O
B) z-Gly-(ϵ-Tos)-Lys-Pro-Val-NH$_2$ in presence of H$_2$O
C) H-Gly-(ϵ-z)-Lys-Pro-Val-NH$_2$ in presence of TosNH$_2$
D) z-Gly-(ϵ-Tos)-Lys-Pro-Val-NH$_2$ in presence of TosNH$_2$

Another side reaction observed during the treatment by sodium in liquid ammonia is the partial deamidination of arginine, which converts it to ornithine. The results obtained when treating arginine itself or some of its derivatives by sodium in liquid ammonia under " standard conditions " are listed in Table 5. When the α-amino group of arginine is not acylated, the extent of the deamidination is not negligible. If the α-amino group of arginine is acylated, or protected by a benzyloxycarbonyl group, the amount of ornithine obtained becomes insignificant. The fact that the benzyloxy-carbonyl group confers the same protection as an acyl group can be explained by admitting that the action of sodium in liquid ammonia splits only the benzyl group and that the resulting sodium or ammonium carbamate is stable under those conditions.

These results lead to the following conclusions:
(a) The cleavage of the Lys-Pro bond observed during the treatment of peptides containing this sequence by sodium in liquid ammonia is a function of the amount of water or of tosyl groups present. This cleavage occurs only when lysine is not in an N-terminal position.

TABLE 5. DEAMIDINATION OF ARGININE DERIVATIVES UNDER
TREATMENT BY SODIUM IN LIQUID AMMONIA

Amino-acid derivative or peptide	Extent of deamidination
Tos | H-Arg-OH	> 20%
Tos | Z-Arg-OH	1–2%
H-Arg-Pro-OH	> 20%
Tos | Z-Arg-Pro-OH	< 1%
Tos Tos | | Z-Arg-Pro-Pro-Gly-Phe-Ser-Pro-Phe-Arg-OH	< 2%

(b) No significant deamidination of arginine or its peptides occurs during the treatment by sodium in liquid ammonia when its α-amino group is substituted by a benzyloxycarbonyl group or by another amino-acid residue.

REFERENCES

1. D. T. GISH and F. C. CARPENTER, *J. Amer. Chem. Soc.* **75,** 5872 (1953).
2. V. du VIGNEAUD, D. T. GISH and P. G. KATSOYANNIS, *J. Amer. Chem. Soc.* **76,** 4751 (1954).
3. R. A. BOISSONNAS, St. GUTTMANN, J.-P. WALLER and P.-A. JAQUENOUD, *Experientia* **12,** 446 (1956).
4. V. du VIGNEAUD, D. T. GISH, P. G. KATSOYANNIS and G. P. HESS, *J. Amer. Chem. Soc.* **80,** 3355 (1958).
5. R. A. BOISSONNAS, St. GUTTMANN, P.-A. JAQUENOUD, ED. SANDRIN and J.-P. WALLER, *Helv. Chim. Acta* **44,** 121 (1961).
6. St. GUTTMANN, *Helv. Chim. Acta* **44,** 721 (1961).
7. R. SCHWYZER, W. RITTEL, H. KAPPELER and B. ISELIN, *Angew. Chem.* **72,** 915 (1960).
8. K. HOFMANN, H. YAJIMA, N. YANAIHARA, T. LIU and S. LANDE, *J. Amer. Chem. Soc.* **83,** 487 (1961).
9. M. BERGMANN, L. ZERVAS and H. RINKE, *Hoppe-Seyler's Z. Physiol. Chem.* **224,** 40 (1934).
10. K. HOFMANN, A. R. RHEINER and W. D. PECKHAM, *J. Amer. Chem. Soc.* **78,** 238 (1956).
11. R. SCHWYZER, B. ISELIN, H. KAPPELER, B. RINIKER, W. RITTEL and H. ZUBER, *Helv. Chim. Acta* **41,** 1274 (1958).
12. R. A. BOISSONNAS, St. GUTTMANN and P.-A. JAQUENOUD, *Helv. Chim. Acta* **43,** 1349 (1960).
13. L. ZERVAS, M. WINITZ and J. P. GREENSTEIN, *J. Amer. Chem. Soc.* **81,** 2878 (1959).
14. R. SCHWYZER and H. C. LI, *Nature,* **182,** 1669 (1958).

15. E. SCHNABEL and H. C. LI, *J. Amer. Chem. Soc.* **82,** 4576 (1960).
16. C. H. LI, J. MEYENHOFER, E. SCHNABEL, D. CHUNG, T.-B. LO and J. RAMACHANDRAN, *J. Amer. Chem. Soc.* **83,** 4449 (1961).
17. St. GUTTMANN, J. PLESS and R. A. BOISSONNAS, *Helv. Chim. Acta* **45,** 170 (1962).
18. J. PLESS, E. STÜRMER, St. GUTTMANN and R. A. BOISSONNAS, *Helv. Chim. Acta* **45,** 394 (1962).
19. R. L. HUGUENIN and R. A. BOISSONNAS, *Helv. Chim. Acta* **45,** 1629 (1962).
20. V. du VIGNEAUD and O. K. BEHRENS, *J. Biol. Chem.* **117,** 27 (1937).
21. K. HOFMANN, *Ann. N.Y. Acad. Sci.* **88,** 689 (1960).
22. K. HOFMANN and H. YAJIMA, *J. Amer. Chem. Soc.* **83,** 2289 (1961).

ERFAHRUNGEN ÜBER DAS VERHALTEN GESCHÜTZTER PEPTIDE BEI DER REAKTION MIT NATRIUM IN FLÜSSIGEM AMMONIAK

S. BAJUSZ

Forschungsinstitut für pharmazeutische Industrie, Budapest

und

K. MEDZIHRADSZKY

Institut für organische Chemie der Universität, Budapest, Ungarn

DIE Abspaltungsmethode der p-Tosyl-, Benzyl- und Benzyloxycarbonyl-Schutzgruppe durch Reduktion mittels Natrium in flüssigem Ammoniak wurde seit den grundlegenden Untersuchungen von du Vigneaud und Mitarbeitern [1] im Laufe von Peptidsynthesen oft angewandt. Man hat zu dieser Methode, wenn es sich um die Abspaltung der Benzyl- und Benzyloxycarbonyl-Gruppe handelte, eher nur dann gegriffen, wenn die hydrogenolytische Spaltung dieser Gruppen Schwierigkeiten bot, was z.B. bei Peptiden mit schwefelhaltigen Aminosäuregliedern nicht selten der Fall war. Übrigens hat die später entwickelte Spaltung der Benzyloxycarbonyl-Gruppe mit Eisessig-Bromwasserstoff [2], weiterhin die Anwendung anderer Schutzgruppen (z.B. Formyl- [3], t-Butyloxycarbonyl [4]) anstatt der Tosylgruppe den Gebrauch der reduktiven Spaltung mit Natrium stark zurückgedrängt. Dies umsomehr, da aus einigen misslungenen Versuchen darauf geschlossen wurde, dass bei diesem Eingriff fallweise auch die unerwünschte Spaltung der Peptidbindung erfolgen kann.

Seit einigen Jahren beschäftigen wir uns mit der Synthese von Polypeptiden mit adrenocorticotroper Wirksamkeit und haben im Laufe dieser Untersuchungen zum vorübergehenden Schutz der ε-Amino-Gruppe des Lysins die Tosyl-Gruppe herangezogen. Wir haben zu dieser Schutzgruppe nicht letzten Endes wegen der vorteilhaften Eigenschaften, so z.B. der guten Kristallisierungsfähigkeit der Derivate gegriffen. Inzwischen berichtete K. Hofmann [5] darüber, dass bei der, mit Hilfe der Natrium-Ammoniak Methode durchgeführten Enttosylierung eines geschützten Tridecapeptids, dessen Sequenz auch im β-Corticotropin vorkommt, auch die Peptidkette in weitgehendem Mass einen Abbau erlitt. Auch haben andere Forscher, obzwar auf weniger konkrete Art, auf präparative Schwierigkeiten hingedeutet, die bei der Anwendung der du Vigneaud'schen Methode fallweise auftreten. Hingegen steht es aber auch fest, dass einige Forschergruppen die Methode mit recht ermutigenden Ergebnissen anwenden konnten, wenn auch das nach der Abspaltung der Schutzgruppen anfallende Produkt in jedem Falle noch einer sehr gründlichen Reinigung bedurft hat.

Wir haben uns das Ziel gesetzt den gegensätzlichen Meinungen über die Leistungsfähigkeit der Methode etwas näher nachzusehen und haben deshalb das Verhalten möglichst weitgehend variierter Modellpeptide bei der reduktiven Abspaltung ihrer Schutzgruppen systematisch untersucht. Voraus sei bemerkt, dass die Untersuchungen noch nicht abgeschlossen sind und das Verhalten einiger Peptidbindungen noch eingehender untersucht werden muss.

Vorerst versuchten wir zu ermitteln, welche Natriummengen von gewissen Oligopeptidderivaten bzw. Schutzgruppen verbraucht werden. Diese Frage erschien uns hauptsächlich deshalb wichtig, weil es angezeigt war einen Überschuss an Natrium, der etwa eine schädliche Wirkung ausüben könnte, möglichst zu vermeiden. Die Angaben über die mindest nötigen Natriummengen sind in der Literatur auch dort sehr abweichend, wo es sich um Derivate handelt, welche dieselben Funktionen und diese in gleicher Zahl enthalten. Auch ist es auffallend, dass man über den Mechanismus der reduktiven Abspaltung noch wenig unterrichtet ist, und überdies auch die Spaltprodukte noch nicht ganz eindeutig identifiziert sind.

Nun haben wir bei einigen Aminosäurederivaten die Natriummenge ermittelt, die mindest nötig ist, um eine mehr als 10 Minuten dauernde Blaufärbung des Reaktionsgemisches hervorzurufen. Wir konnten auf diese Weise feststellen, dass z.B. Benzyloxycarbonyl-Aminosäuren 2, Tosylaminosäuren 2,5–3,5 Atome Natrium pro Mol verbrauchen, viel weniger also als die Berechnung ergibt, wenn man die sauren Gruppen und die entstandenen Spaltprodukte (z.B. Toluol, p-Methylthiophenol) in Betracht zieht. Der Natriumverbrauch scheint auch von der Zuführungsgeschwindigkeit abzuhängen und es ist zu vermuten, dass nach einer schnellen Abspaltung der Schutzgruppen eine allmähliche Reduktion der Spaltprodukte einsetzt. Da geschützte Polypeptide höheren Molekulargewichtes fallweise schwer entfernbares Wasser binden, so scheint es in solchen Fällen einstweilen angezeigt zu sein, zum allmählichen Zusatz des Natriums bis zur beständiger Blaufärbung zu greifen. Immerhin kann bei dieser Arbeitsweise eine unvollständige Abspaltung der Schutzgruppen befürchtet werden.

Wie bereits erwähnt, wird in der Literatur bisher nur über einen einzigen konkreten Fall einer Peptidkettenspaltung berichtet. Es handelt sich um die Angabe von K. Hofmann [5] dass das Produkt, welches nach der mit Natrium in flüssigem Ammoniak bewirkten Enttosylierung eines geschützten Tridekapeptids der 1–13 Sequenz des β-Corticotropins anfiel, als Haupt komponente ein Oligopeptid enthielt, in welchem die drei entständigen Aminosäuren, d.h. Lysin, Prolin und Valin nicht mehr anwesend waren:

Z-Ser-Tyr-Ser-Met-Glu(NH₂)-His-Phe-Arg-Try-Gly-Lys(Tos)-Pro-Val-NH₂

Da bei einem reduktiven Abbau nicht nur mit der Sprengung gewisser Peptidbindungen, sondern auch mit der weitergehenden Umwandlung der Bruchstücke gerechnet werden muss, lässt sich die Angabe von Hofmann auf zweierlei Art erläutern. Entweder erfolgte die Spaltung der Gly-Lys Bindung, wobei der Glycin-Rest ungeschädigt als C-terminales Glied hinterblieb, oder es kam zur Spaltung der Lys-Pro Bindung unter gleichzeitiger Schädigung des Lysin-Restes. Um hier eine Entscheidung zu treffen, haben wir einige, Gly-Lys und Lys-Pro Bindungen enthaltende, analysenreine Peptide der Behandlung mit Natrium im flüssigem Ammoniak unterworfen. Wir konnten feststellen, dass die geschützten Peptide, bzw. Peptidhydrazide

Z-Gly-Lys(Tos)-Lys(Tos)-NH.NH₂
Z-Gly-Lys(Tos)-Pro-NH₂
Z-Val-Lys(Tos)-Pro
Z-Phe-Leu-Lys(Tos)-Val-Lys(Tos)-Pro
Z(Cl)-Pro-Val-Gly-Lys(Tos)-Lys(Tos)-NH.NH₂

nur eine quantitative Abspaltung ihrer Schutzgruppen, hingegen keine weitere Veränderung erlitten. Es ist zu betonen, dass die untersuchten Peptidderivate kristallin, analysenrein und chromatographisch einheitlich waren und wir immer in wasserfreiem Ammoniak, unter einem trockenen Stickstoffstrom gearbeitet haben. Die nach der Reaktion gewonnenen Produkte haben wir absichtlich nicht isoliert, sondern den nach der Vertreibung des Ammoniaks gewonnenen salzhaltigen Rückstand unmittelbar der Papierelektrophorese unterworfen. Das Elektropherogramm bewies in jedem Fall die Einheitlichkeit des Umsetzungsproduktes.

Damit haben wir unsere Untersuchungen nicht abgeschlossen, sondern auch auf Peptide anderer Sequenz erstreckt. So haben wir gefunden, dass das kristalline, analysenreine Benzyloxycarbonyl-heptapeptid-hydrazid, das die Sequenz 1–7 des β-Corticotropins enthält,

Z-Ser-Tyr-Ser-Met-Glu-His-Phe-NH.NH₂

ohne weitere Schädigung entcarbobenzoxyliert werden konnte. Dasselbe war auch der Fall beim kristallinen, analysenreinen Dipeptidderivat

Z-Arg-Try

Bloss in einem einzigen Fall erschienen im Elektropherogramm des nach der Reduktion gewonnenen Rohproduktes zwei ninhydrinpositive Flecken. Dies war beim Benzyloxycarbonyl-nonapeptid-hydrazid, das die Sequenz 1–9 des β-Corticotropins enthält, zu beobachten:

Z-Ser-Tyr-Ser-Met-Glu-His-Phe-Arg-Try-NH.NH₂

Da dieses Derivat zwar analysenrein und chromatographisch einheitlich, jedoch scheinbar amorph war, konnte im voraus nicht ausgeschlossen werden, dass es eine in geschützter Form nicht nachweisbare Verunreinigung enthielt. Deshalb wurde in einem Kontrollversuch das Nonapeptidderivat der Hydrogenolyse unterworfen, und das Elektropherogramm des so gewonnenen Rohproduktes zum Vergleich herangezogen.

Das durch Hydrogenolyse gewonnene Produkt ist als einheitlich zu betrachten; es zeigt eine positive Ninhydrin-, Ehrlich- und Sakaguchi-Reaktion und stellt somit das freie Nonapeptidhydrazid dar. Genau an demselben Ort erscheint auch der eine und intensivste Fleck im Elektropherogramm des nach der Reduktion mit Natrium anfallenden Rohproduktes, und da auch diese Komponente eine positive Ninhydrin-, Ehrlich- und Sakaguchi-Reaktion zeigt, so kann sie mit dem bei der Hydrogenolyse gewonnenen Produkt als identisch betrachtet werden. Hingegen erschienen im Elektropherogramm des Rohproduktes der mit Natrium bewirkten Reduktion noch zwei weitere Flecken. Der eine zeigt bloss eine positive Ninhydrin- und Sakaguchi-Reaktion, jedoch keine Ehrlich-Reaktion mehr und entspricht also einem Produkt, das kein Tryptophan enthält. Der andere Fleck zeigt eine intensive Ehrlich-Reaktion, hingegen keine Ninhydrin- und Sakaguchi-Reaktion und rührt also von einer Substanz her, die ein Umwandlungsprodukt des Tryptophans mit noch freier α- oder β-Stellung im Pyrrolring darstellen dürfte.

Aus den Ergebnissen der bisher durchgeführten Untersuchungen lässt sich somit feststellen, dass bei der reduktiven Abspaltung von Schutzgruppen im Sequenzbereich Gly–Lys–Pro bei den angewandten Peptiden keine Schädigung der Peptidbindungen erfolgte, und dies auch bei vielen anderen Peptidbindungen nicht der Fall war. Ein partieller Abbau war bisher nur am C-terminalen Ende eines Nonapeptid-Derivats zu beobachten, das als Endglied Tryptophanhydrazid enthielt. Es soll durch weitere Untersuchungen entschieden werden, ob und wie die Hydrazid-Gruppe bei dieser Spaltreaktion mitwirkt, weiterhin ob auch die Peptidbindung eines Tryptophan-Zwischengliedes einer Peptidkette bei der Reduktion mit Natrium in flüssigem Ammoniak gefährdet ist.

REFERENZEN

1. V. du VIGNEAUD und O. K. BEHRENS, J. Biol. Chem. **117**, 27 (1937).
2. D. BEN-ISHAI und A. BERGER, J. Org. Chem. **17**, 1564 (1952).
3. K. HOFMANN, E. STUTZ, G. SPÜHLER, H. YAJIMA und E. T. SCHWARTZ, J. Amer. Chem. Soc. **82**, 3727 (1960).
4. F. C. McKAY und N. F. ALBERTSON, J. Amer. Chem. Soc. **79**, 4686 (1957).
5. K. HOFMANN und H. YAJIMA, J. Amer. Chem. Soc. **83**, 2289 (1961).

DISCUSSION ON METHODS OF PROTECTION

H. C. BEYERMAN:

In continuation of our investigation of t-butoxy as a hydroxyl-protecting group for use in peptide synthesis with hydroxyamino-acids [1, 2] we investigated the acid-catalysed addition of isobutene to L-cysteine [2].

It proved possible to obtain in this way S-t-butyl-L-cysteine t-butyl ester hydrochloride, m.p. 198–199° (dec.); picrate, m.p. 115° (dec.). Treatment with trifluoroacetic acid at room temperature yielded S-t-butyl-L-cysteine, m.p. 196–197° (dec.), $[\alpha]_D$ − 24° (c 1·99 in water); hydrochloride, m.p. 202–203°, $[\alpha]_D$ + 5° (c 2·1 in 5N HCl).

The structure of the alkyl-residue in the product of the reaction and assumed to be S-t-butyl-L-cysteine had to be proved, because the thiol-group might have given an isobutyl residue by a radical mechanism, well known with —SH groups. Proof was found in the nuclear magnetic resonance spectrum.

It is interesting that the S-t-butyl bond is rather stable to acid treatment; e.g. S-t-butyl-L-cysteine hydrochloride may be crystallized from 4N HCl. This is explained by the difficult protonation of the sulphur atom in thio-ethers, in contrast to oxygen-ethers.

The sulphur-t-butyl bond could be conveniently split, however, with an excess of aqueous mercuric chloride at 50° for about one day, or room temperature for about a week, or several minutes of boiling. The mercaptide was decomposed with hydrogen sulphide in the usual way. Recovery of optically pure L-cysteine was 82·5 per cent based on L-cysteine as starting material. The S-benzyl group is not changed under these conditions. Therefore the S-t-butyl group seems promising as an additional sulphur-protecting group.

Addition of isobutene in the way described could also be done with peptides, e.g. L-cysteinylglycine, which yielded S-t-butyl-L-cysteinylglycine t-butyl ester, from which S-t-butyl-L-cysteinylglycine was obtained.

A few peptides were made by coupling N-protected amino-acids with S-t-butyl-L-cysteine t-butyl ester (the latter compound as such decomposes slowly on standing, but the hydrochloride is stable).

REFERENCES

1. H. C. BEYERMAN and J. S. BONTEKOE, Proc. Chem. Soc. 1961, 249.
2. H. C. BEYERMAN and J. S. BONTEKOE, Rec. trav. chim. 81 (1962), footnote 9, in print.

G. T. YOUNG:

We now have considerable experience of the incorporation of S-benzylthiomethyl-cysteine [1] into peptides, and in view of the statement by Katsoyannis [2] that exposure of S-benzylthiomethylcysteine-containing peptides to hydrogen bromide in acetic acid should be avoided, I should like to report our findings, which differ from those of Katsoyannis.

The action of 2N-hydrogen bromide in acetic acid on S-benzylthiomethyl-L-cysteine for 1 hr at room temperature (Katsoyannis' experiment was for 45 min) causes the appearance of a very faint spot (R_F 0·09) on a chromatogram using n-butanol–water–acetic acid (Partridge system) as solvent, but chromatographically, analytically and optically pure S-benzylthiomethyl-L-cysteine can be recovered in 95 per cent yield. After 15 hr treatment the spot at R_F 0·09 is stronger, but an 84 per cent yield of amino-acid can be recovered.

It is not unexpected that during the decarbobenzoxylation of derivatives of *S*-benzyl-thiomethylcysteine by hydrogen bromide in acetic acid, side reactions should be encountered, presumably analogous to those occurring with derivatives of methionine. We have for some time now been using the modified procedure devised by St. Guttmann and Boissonnas [3] for such cases, i.e. by carrying out the reaction in the presence of methyl ethyl sulphide. Under these conditions, *N*-benzyloxycarbonyl-*S*-benzylthiomethylcysteine gives a 92 per cent yield of chromatographically, analytically and optically pure *S*-benzyl-thiomethyl-L-cysteine, and so far as we have had no case when we have been unable to use hydrogen bromide in acetic acid successfully. Decarbobenzoxylation of Z-Gly-Cys(BTM) proceeds in 81 per cent yield; Z-Cys(BTM)-Gly (71 per cent); Z-Cys(BTM)-ONP (70 per cent; brief treatment at 70° proved best in this case); Z-Arg(NO₂)-Cys(BTM) (95 per cent).

So far, therefore, we have found the grouping to be very adequately stable for use under appropriate conditions, but a much more real difficulty is in the removal stage. In our exploratory work we used mercuric chloride in N-hydrochloric acid, and synthesized analytically pure diglycyl-L-cysteine and L-cystinyldiglycine. *S*-Benzylthiomethyl-L-cysteine itself gives a 55 per cent yield of L-cystine under these conditions, and a considerable amount of thiazolidine-4-carboxylic acid is formed, and we have spent much time and effort in trying to reduce this side reaction. So far, our best procedure uses mercuric acetate in 80 per cent formic acid to decompose the mercaptal, and an excess of ethanedithiol is present when the mercury mercaptide is decomposed by hydrogen sulphide. In this way, the yield of cystine has been raised to 80 per cent; the removal is very rapid (*ca.* 5 min) and the formation of thiazolidine-4-carboxylic acid is largely suppressed. The use of this procedure with dipeptides has so far proved less satisfactory, and our investigation is continuing.

REFERENCES

1. P. J. E. PIMLOTT and G. T. YOUNG, *Proc. Chem. Soc.* **1958**, 257; G. T. YOUNG, *Angew. Chem.* **71,** 741 (1959).
2. P. G. KATSOYANNIS, *J. Amer. Chem. Soc.* **83,** 4053 (1961).
3. St. GUTTMANN and R. A. BOISSONNAS, *Helv. Chim. Acta* **41,** 1852 (1958).

A. PATCHORNIK:

Protolytic enzymes like trypsin or chymotrypsin do not split the peptide bond at proline residues. Specific non-enzymatic cleavages of peptide bonds can be used to cleave such sequences. At the Weizmann Institute of Science, Rehovoth, Israel, we are studying non-enzymatic cleavages of peptide chains having the sequence X-Pro-Y (X and Y represent amino-acid residues). We have used sodium in liquid ammonia for the chemical cleavage of the Lys-Pro bond in ribonuclease. The protein was treated with excess of sodium for 5–10 min. The yield of cleavage of the Lys-Pro bond was shown to be 42 per cent by subsequent estimation of free proline liberated by the specific enzyme, proline iminopeptidase [1].

REFERENCE

1. S. SARID, A. BERGER and E. KATCHALSKI, *J. Biol. Chem.* **234,** 1740 (1959).

ST. GUTTMANN:

With regard to the comment by Dr. Patchornik, I would like to say that we have observed that, in the presence of 5 to 20 equivalents of ammonium chloride, in a sequence X-Lys-Pro-Y, the Lys-Pro bond is quantitatively cleaved. Other X-Pro bonds, especially Arg-Pro, Ser-Pro, His-Pro and Tyr-Pro are also cleaved, maybe to a less extent. No splitting of other peptide bonds than X-Pro have been observed. This way of splitting could be used for the " non-enzymatical " cleavage of X-Pro bond in structural studies. X-Pro bonds are known to resist to enzymic attack.

G. T. YOUNG:

We have continued our investigations of the electrolytic removal of the nitro-group from nitroarginyl derivatives [1]. We were particularly interested in Professor Schwyzer's results [2], which suggested that the intermediate aminoguanidine may contaminate the product. Certainly, a positive Folin-Ciocalteu test is found throughout the reduction, but this test is both very sensitive and very general; for example, if arginine itself is placed in the electrolytic cell, a Folin positive solution is obtained. We follow the reduction by means of paper electrophoresis at pH 11·5 (or at pH 6), and the reduction is stopped as soon as nitroarginyl derivative is absent. In three cases, we have determined the yield of analytically pure product obtained in this way: L-arginine acetate (90 per cent); L-arginyl-L-leucine acetate (95 per cent); L-arginyl-L-valine acetate (85 per cent). The reduction succeeds in the case of nitro-arginyl-S-benzylcysteine, showing that the presence of sulphur does not interfere. In every case the reduction product gives only one ninhydrin-positive spot after electrophoresis at pH 11·5, and after chromatography on paper using n-butanol–water–acetic acid or phenol–water as solvents.

REFERENCES

1. M. E. CLUBB, P. M. SCOPES and G. T. YOUNG, *Chimia* **14**, 373 (1960).
2. C. GROS, M. P. de GARILHE, A. COSTOPANAGIOTIS and R. SCHWYZER, *Helv. Chim. Acta* **44**, 2042 (1961).

T. WIELAND:

In toxins of *Amanita phalloides* a peptide bond which connects a branched γ-hydroxy-amino-acid with the amino-group of alanine is very easily split by acids (50 per cent tri-fluoroacetic acid, 30 min, 20°) or base (2N ammonium hydroxide, 12 hr, 20°). It is proposed to use this auxiliary effect of the tert. γ-hydroxyl group to make protecting groups of the acyl type, which are removable under mild conditions.

G. C. BARRETT:

The papers presented at this Symposium by Dr. Stelakatos, Professor Rydon, Dr. Tesser and Dr. Block describe reactions with benzyl, trityl, tert.-butyl, and β-methylthio-ethyl halides. There is a similarity in the reaction conditions used, which give rise to the carbonium ion of each of the above reagents:

$$Ph.CH_2.Cl \rightleftharpoons Ph.CH_2^+ \quad Cl^-$$
$$Ph_3C.Cl \rightleftharpoons Ph_3C^+ \quad Cl^-$$
$$Bu^t.Cl \rightleftharpoons Bu^{t+} \quad Cl^-$$
$$CH_3.S.CH_2.CH_2.Cl \rightleftharpoons CH_3.\overset{+}{S}\diagup\overset{\textstyle CH_2}{\diagdown CH_2} \quad Cl^-$$

In each of the very different investigations reported, an organic base (triethylamine, etc.) was used, either one equivalent (Tesser), or in excess. Two-phase systems (water–organic base) were used by Rydon, by Stelakatos, and, essentially, by Block, although Stelakatos used aqueous sodium hydroxide-triethylamine in studies on tritylation of the strongly basic arginine side chain.

In principle, amino-acid esters can be prepared in these systems. tert.-Butyl esters were reported to be obtained in small yield by Tesser, and we have obtained leucine tert.-butyl ester in 2 per cent yield with tert.-butyl chloride in aqueous triethylamine. Methyl bromide (Tesser) failed to yield the α-methyl ester of aspartic acid, because the reagent does not ionize as readily as the classic S_N1 reagents discussed here.

The reactions, as reported, can lead to mixtures of all the possible alkylation products. Small differences in the conditions determine the nature of the products, and each amino-acid will give alkylated products in differing proportions, but the simple experimental procedure can provide useful intermediates (e.g. leucine benzyl ester, by the method reported by Rydon).

G. T. YOUNG:

The determination of the optimum time required for decarbobenzoxylation by hydrogen bromide in acetic acid may conveniently be found by the following procedure, due to M. Welford and B. O. Handford and based on the discovery of Barltrop and Schofield [1] that benzyloxycarbonyl groups may be removed by ultraviolet radiation. At various time intervals aliquots are removed and added to a test tube containing an excess of Dowex-3 acetate resin and covered with n-butanol–water–acetic acid (62:26:12, " BWA "); in this way the reaction is stopped by removal of the hydrogen bromide, and the presence of salts (which interfere with paper chromatography) is avoided. An aliquot of the solution is then spotted on paper, and chromatographed with BWA as solvent. After drying, the paper is exposed to ultraviolet light under standard conditions, which removes the benzyloxycarbonyl group from the benzyloxycarbonyl peptide on the paper, and the chromatogram is then developed with ninhydrin as usual. It is advisable to spray an identical chromatogram with ninhydrin but without irradiation, to confirm that no spot appears in the same position as that of the benzyloxycarbonylpeptide. Some trial of the irradiation procedure is required, as over-long exposure causes much background colour to develop with ninhydrin. We support the paper in a concave fashion, 9 cm from a Hanovia 501/1 120 W lamp, for 90 min exposure. A similar procedure can of course be used with DSC plates; in this case prolonged exposure produces no background colour with ninhydrin, and up to 4 hr irradiation has been used with advantage.

REFERENCE

1. J. A. BARLTROP and P. SCHOFIELD, *Tetrahedron Letters*, **697** (1962).

H. N. RYDON:

By way of a link between the methods of protection we have just been discussing and the methods of coupling we are about to discuss, I should like to present the results of an examination of the methods of protection and coupling used in 91 papers published since 1 January 1960. The table shows against each method the percentage of these papers in which it was employed.

	%
Benzyloxycarbonyl for N-protection	90
Dicyclohexylcarbodiimide for coupling	68
Methyl ester for carboxyl protection	54
Azide for coupling	43
Mixed anhydride for coupling	42
Nitrophenyl ester for coupling	24
Ethyl ester for carboxyl protection	22
Benzyl ester for carboxyl protection	22
Nitrobenzyl ester for carboxyl protection	11
Trityl for N-protection	10

Although clearly influenced by chemical conservatism and liable to change with time, this peptide synthesis " top ten " does show the sort of competition any new method has to overcome.

SECTION II

SYNTHESIS: METHODS OF COUPLING

METHODS OF COUPLING:
PROGRESS SINCE 1958 [1]

T. WIELAND

Institut für organische Chemie, Universität Frankfurt a.M.

AT the 1st European Peptide Symposium in Prague in 1958, a review was given of all known methods of peptide coupling which made use of activation of the carboxylic group [2]. Methods of coupling, at that time, were divided into "carboxyl-activating" and "amino-group-activating" because both of them seemed to be of equal importance. However, in the course of the following years it appeared that more weight has been given to the carboxyl side. Therefore I do not intend to make the same classification as was made in 1958. This time the subtitles will be treated according to more detailed chemical features—as follows

1. Chlorides,
2. Hydrazides and azides,
3. Unsaturated compounds,
4. Activated esters,
5. Derivatives of phosphorus,
6. Azoles, and
7. Different methods which do not fit under (1)–(6).

1. CHLORIDES

These derivatives were the first activated carboxylic groups to be used for peptide synthesis by Emil Fischer. Today they are of significance as unisolated intermediates in two methods of peptide synthesis. The first comes from Heslinga and Arens [3], who achieved peptide coupling by heating α,α-*dichloro-diethyl ether* (II) or α-*chlorovinylethyl ether* (I) with acylamino-acids and amino-acids (or peptide) esters. It is supposed that in this reaction acid chlorides are formed according to the following scheme:

$$H_2C=C\overset{OC_2H_5}{\underset{Cl}{\diagdown}}$$
(I)

or

$$H_3C-C\overset{OC_2H_5}{\underset{\underset{Cl}{|}}{\diagdown}}$$
(II)

$$+ AcNH.CH(R)CO_2H \longrightarrow H_3C.\overset{OC_2H_5}{\underset{\underset{\overset{|}{O}}{|}}{\overset{|}{C}}}-Cl \longrightarrow$$

$$H_3C.CO_2.C_2H_5$$
$$+$$
$$Cl.C.CH(R)NHAc$$
$$\underset{O}{\|}$$

$$H\overset{Cl}{\underset{\underset{Cl}{|}}{\overset{|}{C}}}.OCH_3 \qquad (CH_3)_2\overset{+}{N}=CHCl \quad Cl^-$$
(III)   (IV)

The more easily accessible unsymmetric *dichloro-dimethyl ether* (III) permits, according to Rieche *et al.* [4], the same reaction. A detailed investigation was carried out by Poduska and Gross [5].

The second peptide synthesis by means of chlorides, due to Zaoral and Arnold [6], makes use of *dimethyl-chloromethylenimmonium chloride* (IV) as a chlorinating agent, which arises from dimethylformamide and phosgene. The chloride (IV) effects peptide coupling at 0° with good yields. The question of racemization has not been investigated in detail.

2. HYDRAZIDES AND AZIDES

The azide method of peptide coupling has been watched with more attention in the past years, because it does not cause any racemization. One difficulty here is that the formation of hydrazides of higher peptides from esters by reaction with hydrazine sometimes takes an extremely slow course and gives low yields. According to Weygand [7] or Schwyzer [8] a properly substituted hydrazine is introduced in the first step into a corresponding *N*-acylated amino-acid: *Tritylhydrazine* combined with trifluoroacetyl-amino-acids [7] or butyloxycarbonyl-hydrazine with benzyloxycarbonyl-amino-acids [8] affords protected hydrazides (V, VI), whose other protecting group can be removed selectively; if necessary the hydrazide is set free under acidic conditions:

$$TFA.NH\text{-}\text{-}\text{-}C\overset{O}{\underset{NH.NH.TRI}{\diagdown}} \xrightarrow{OH^-} H_2N\text{-}\text{-}\text{-}C\overset{O}{\underset{NH.NH.TRI}{\diagdown}}$$
(V)

$$Z.NH\text{-}\text{-}\text{-}C\overset{O}{\underset{NH.NH.BOC}{\diagdown}} \xrightarrow{H_2} H_2N\text{-}\text{-}\text{-}C\overset{O}{\underset{NH.NH.BOC}{\diagdown}}$$
(VI)

$$\xrightarrow{H^+} H_3\overset{+}{N}\text{-}\text{-}\text{-}C\overset{O}{\underset{NH.NH_2}{\diagdown}}$$

Hydrazides are formed easily also from thiophenol esters of peptides, whose alkyl esters are quite inert to hydrazinolysis [9].

Recently, Brenner *et al.* [10] were able to expand the principle of *amino-acyl insertion* to derivatives of hydrazine. *N,N′-Diaminoacylhydrazines*, whose one amino-acyl group is protected by a suitable residue (VII), suffer a nearly quantitative rearrangement to peptide hydrazides (VIII), if organic acids or bases are present. Finally the hydrazine residue is removed by oxidation with hypobromous acid.

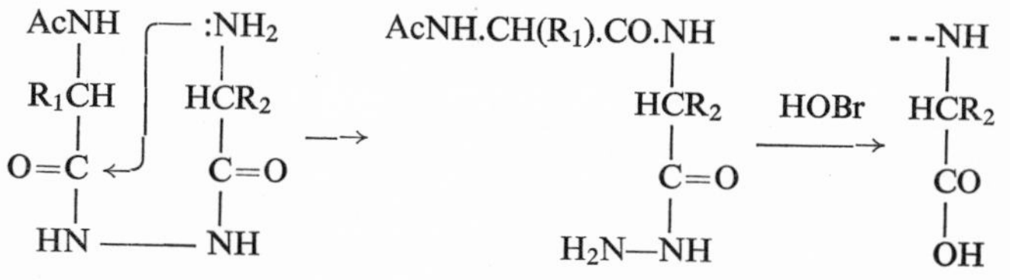

$$
\begin{array}{ccc}
\text{(VII)} & \text{(VIII)} \\
\end{array}
$$

An interesting peptide synthesis starting from hydrazides of benzyloxycarbonyl-amino-acids or benzyloxycarbonyl-peptides occurs if these are oxidized with *N*-bromosuccinimide in the presence of amino-acid or peptide esters (Patchornik *et al.* [11]). In this reaction presumably an acyldiazonium ion (IX) is formed, whose acyl group is activated.

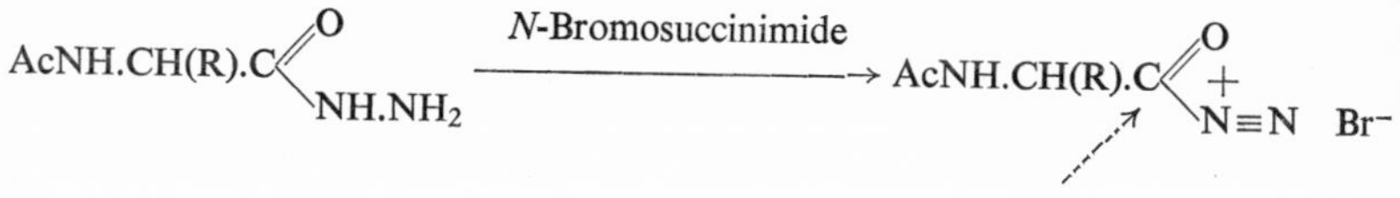

$$
\text{AcNH.CH(R).C}\begin{matrix}\nearrow\text{O}\\\searrow\text{NH.NH}_2\end{matrix} \xrightarrow{\textit{N}\text{-Bromosuccinimide}} \text{AcNH.CH(R).C}\begin{matrix}\nearrow\text{O}\\\searrow\text{N}\equiv\text{N}\end{matrix} + \quad \text{Br}^-
$$

(IX)

3. UNSATURATED COMPOUNDS

Compounds with polarizable double bonds can accept acylamino-acids to give " activated " intermediates. To this class belong the *carbodiimides* of Sheehan [12], the most common representative of which so far is dicyclohexylcarbodiimide. The extremely insoluble dicyclohexyl-urea, formed in peptide syntheses from this reagent, can be separated from poorly soluble peptides only with difficulty. Ureas, which are readily soluble in water or aqueous diluted acids, are formed from basic carbodiimides (X) as *N-ethyl-N'-(3-dimethylaminopropylcarbodiimide* [13] or the homologous *N-tert.butyl-*derivative [14]

$$
\text{(X)} \quad \begin{array}{l} \text{RN=C=N.CH}_2.\text{CH}_2.\text{CH}_2.\text{N(CH}_3)_2 \\ \text{R = C}_2\text{H}_5 \text{ [13]} \quad \text{or} \quad \text{R = C(CH}_3)_3 \text{ [14]} \end{array}
$$

The dehydrating action of dicyclohexylcarbodiimide was utilized by Sheehan [15] to prepare activated amino-acids which react with amines to form peptide bonds: *Tritylserine-β-lactone* (XI), *p-Nitrobenzyloxycarbonyl-histidine-lactam* (XII) and *N-benzyloxycarbonyl-β,β-dimethylcysteine-β-thio-lactone* (XIII).

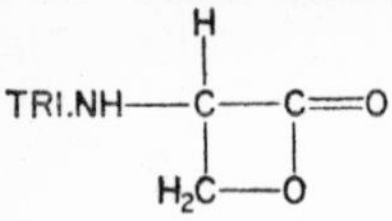

(Structural formulas XI, XII, XIII)

$$TRI.NH—C—C=O$$ (with $H_2C—O$ ring) (XI)

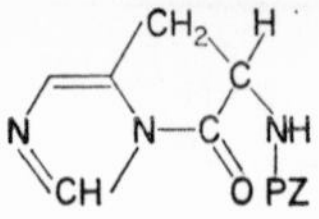

(XII) structure with CH_2, N, CH, N—C, NH, O PZ

$$Z.NH—C—C=O$$ (with $H_3C—C—S$, CH_3) (XIII)

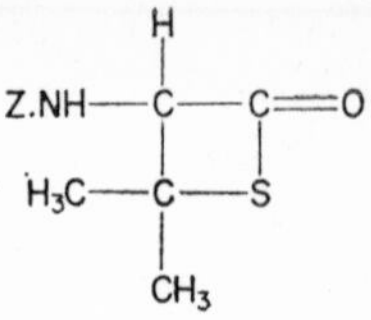

Carbodiimide itself, perhaps tautomeric with cyanamides, and unsymmetrical di-alkylated cyanamides, cause peptide synthesis between the usual
components when heated to 100° without any solvent, according to Losse [15].
The same author also successfully made use of *diphenylketene* in peptide
synthesis [16]. Here even at −15° a mixed anhydride with acylamino-acids
is formed (XIV) which, on account of steric hindrance, reacts with amino-
acid esters only at the desired acyl moiety.

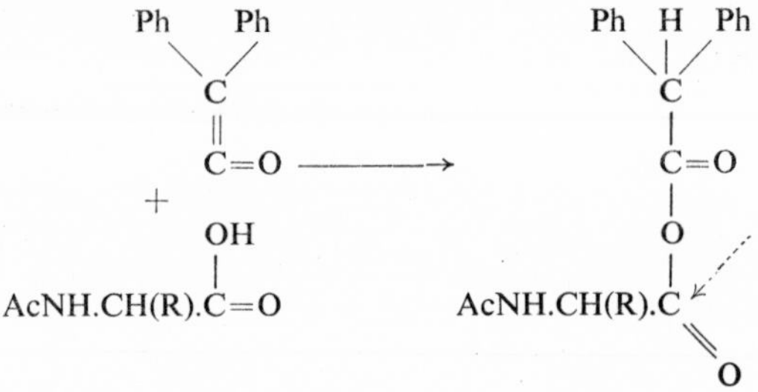

$$Ph \quad Ph$$
$$\backslash \diagup$$
$$C$$
$$\|$$
$$C=O \longrightarrow$$
$$+$$
$$OH$$
$$|$$
$$AcNH.CH(R).C=O$$

$$Ph \quad H \quad Ph$$
$$\backslash \ | \ \diagup$$
$$C$$
$$|$$
$$C=O$$
$$|$$
$$O$$
$$|$$
$$AcNH.CH(R).C$$

(XIV)

N-Ethyl-5-phenylisoxazolium-3'-sulfonate (XV), a new peptide-forming reagent suggested by R. B. Woodward *et al.* [17], is effectively a derivative of
ketene. The actual acylating compound, however, is the energy-rich *O-acyl
enol* (XVI) [18], a product of an internal acyl-migration occurring after the
addition of an acylamino-acid to the first formed oxo-ketenimine.

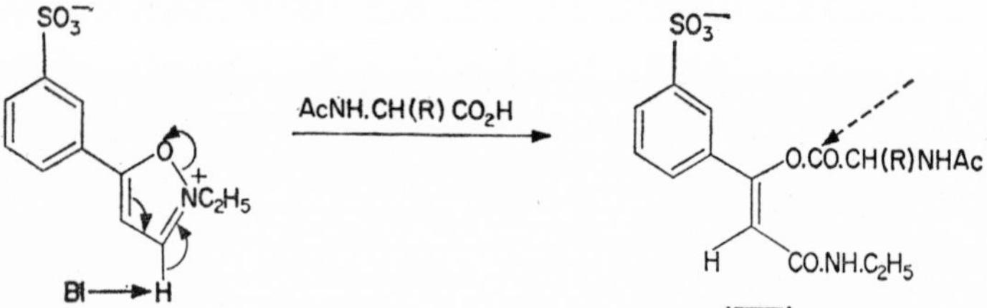

(Structure XV) SO_3^- ... NC_2H_5 ... Bl——H

$$\xrightarrow{AcNH.CH(R) CO_2H}$$

(Structure XVI) SO_3^- ... $O.CO.CH(R)NHAc$ ... H ... $CO.NH.C_2H_5$

(XV)   (XVI)

4. ACTIVATED ESTERS

In this class aryl esters further play an important role. In a manner
analogous to the introduction of other substituted phenyl residues, the
p-methanesulfonylphenyl-group also can be attached by reaction of acylamino

acids with the sulfurous or phosphorous esters. This aryl group is recommended by Schwyzer and Sieber [20] because of its resistance to catalytic hydrogenation. In its presence N-protecting groups can be removed by hydrogen. p-Nitrophenyl esters, and certainly other aryl esters too, can be prepared, according to experiments of K. Vogeler in my laboratory [21] by heating acylamino-acids with *di(p-nitrophenyl) carbonate*, $(pNO_2.C_6H_4O)_2C=0$. Furthermore, 2,4,6-trichlorophenyl esters [22] are activated esters, suitable for peptide synthesis.

In the field of non-aromatic activated esters, only the *vinyl esters* (XVII) have been described since 1958. Weygand and Steglich [23] obtained these compounds from acylamino-acids by transvinylation with vinyl acetate and catalytic amounts of palladous chloride. The so-called *hydroxyphthalimide esters* (XVIII) of Nefkens [24], likewise activated compounds, are not esters but derivatives of hydroxylamine. They are prepared by condensation of acylamino-acids and N-hydroxyphthalimide with dicyclohexylcarbodiimide.

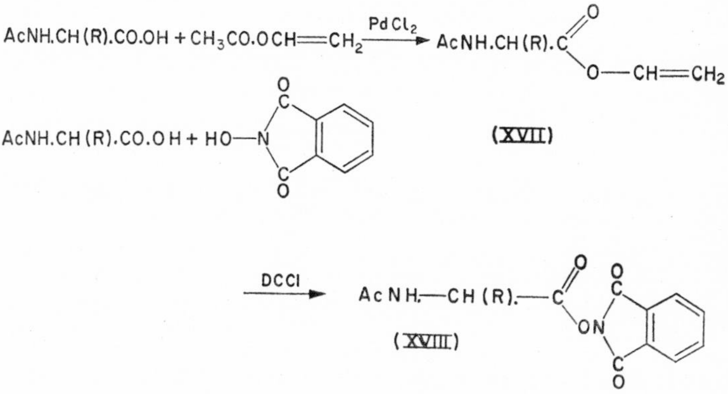

Whereas thus far all peptide syntheses with activated esters have been carried out in the presence of a base, Weygand and Steglich [25] have found that activated esters, especially benzyloxycarbonyl-amino-acid thiophenyl esters, react with free amino-acids when heated in glacial acetic acid. In this solvent, the zwitterionic form of free amino-acids seems partially neutralized. Reaction time and yields strongly depend on steric factors; phthaloylamino-acids give only moderate yields [26].

5. DERIVATIVES OF PHOSPHORUS

To the several derivatives of phosphorous and phosphoric acids which have been recommended in peptide chemistry [1] diphenyl phosphorochloridate has now been added [27]. Phosphoric oxide in diethyl phosphite was suggested as a peptide-forming reagent earlier by Schramm and Wissmann [28]. The actual dehydrating species is assumed to be a mixture of ethyl polyphosphates. The reaction is emphatically recommended by Erlanger and Kokowski [29] for preparation of large amounts of dipeptides because it allows application of very concentrated solutions of the participants. As for tripeptides, the danger of racemization must not be overlooked.

As new derivatives of phosphorous acid, *bis-o-phenylene pyrophosphite* of Rydon [30] and *diethyl ethylene pyrophosphite* of Anderson [31] may be mentioned. In the latter case, imidazole had a significant improving action. The imidazolide of ethylenephosphorous acid (XIX), synthesized after this observation [32], turned out to be a very good condensing agent.

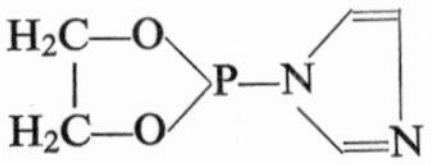

$$\begin{array}{c} H_2C-O \\ | \\ H_2C-O \end{array} \!\!\!\! \begin{array}{c} \\ \diagup P-N \\ \end{array} \!\!\!\! \begin{array}{c} \diagup \!\!=\!\!| \\ \diagdown \!\!=\!\! N \end{array} \quad (XIX)$$

6. AZOLES

As to the mechanism of this promoting action of imidazole, no details have been given, but it is not improbable that (XIX) transfers its imidazole to the carboxyl group of the acylamino-acid. This would give the *amino-acid-imidazolide* as the actual acylating compound. These imidazolides (XX), already mentioned in the last review [2], now are accessible from acylamino-acids and

(1) carbonyldiimidazole,
(2) phenylphosphoric acid diimidazolide [33], or
(3) thionyl-diimidazole [34]. (XXI)

In the last case no intermediate needs to be isolated, but one obtains a peptide from imidazole, thionyl chloride, acylamino-acid and amino-acid ester [35]:

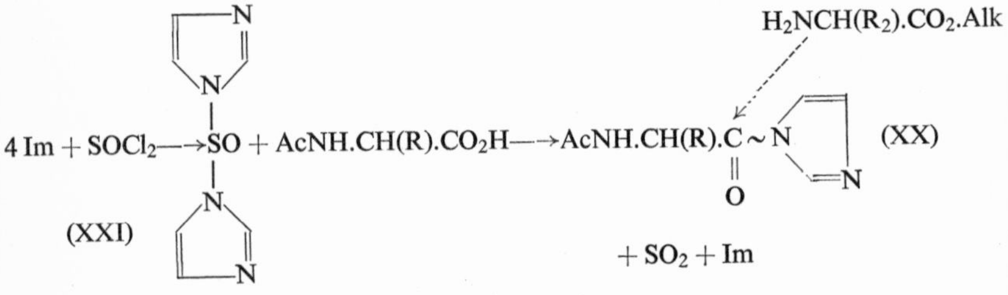

$$4\,Im + SOCl_2 \longrightarrow SO + AcNH.CH(R).CO_2H \longrightarrow AcNH.CH(R).C \!\sim\! N \quad (XX)$$

$$H_2NCH(R_2).CO_2.Alk$$

$$+ SO_2 + Im$$

Im = imidazole

As is well known [36], imidazole distinctly catalyses the hydrolysis of reactive esters. This property, for which intermediate formation of an acylimidazole is discussed, can be utilized for a new peptide synthesis using *acylamino-*

acid-alkyl esters, according to experiments of K. Vogeler in my laboratory. Thus, benzyloxycarbonylalanine methyl ester gives over 60 per cent dipeptide, when heated with finely powdered sodium glycinate at 80° in molten imidazole for several hours. The yield increases if, instead of the sodium salt, the tert. butylester of glycine is employed.

$$\text{Z.NH.CH(CH}_3\text{).C}\begin{smallmatrix}\diagup\text{O}\\\diagdown\text{OCH}_3\end{smallmatrix} + \text{H}_2\text{N.CH}_2\text{.CO}_2\text{.Na}$$

$$\xrightarrow[> 60\%]{\text{Im}} \text{Z.NH.CH(CH}_3\text{)CO.NH.CH}_2\text{.CO}_2\text{H}$$

$$\text{Z.NH.CH(CH}_3\text{).C}\begin{smallmatrix}\diagup\text{O}\\\diagdown\text{OCH}_3\end{smallmatrix} + \text{H}_2\text{N.CH}_2\text{.CO.OBu}^\text{t}$$

$$\xrightarrow[75-80\%]{\text{Im}} \text{Z.NH.CH(CH}_3\text{).CO.NH.CH}_2\text{.CO.OBu}^\text{t}$$

Under the same conditions no peptide synthesis occurs without imidazole. The heterocyclic base also catalyses significantly the hydrazinolysis of alkyl esters. On this occasion it was observed that the phthaloyl-residue is removed from *N* rather rapidly by heating the phthaloylamino-acid with imidazole.

A further azole, useful as carbonyl-di-compound in peptide chemistry, is 1,2,4-*triazole*, suggested by Beyermann *et al.* [37].

7. DIFFERENT METHODS

(a) Oxazolidones

Under dehydrating conditions oxazolidones are produced from *N*-acyl-amino-acids and aldehydes. These heterocyclic compounds, " activated " amino-acid derivatives, are available for peptide syntheses according to Micheel *et al.* Optimal yields are obtained if *chloral* as an aldehyde reacts with tosyl- or benzyloxycarbonyl-amino-acids and acetic anhydride plus catalytic amounts of thionyl chloride [38, 39] to give the most reactive oxazolidone (XXIIa). E. Dane *et al.* [40] found that chloral will react even with free amino-acids under dehydrating conditions forming 1,3-*oxazolidone-5-derivatives* (XXIIb), whose *N*-atom bears an additional hydroxytrichloroethyl residue. The latter compounds (XXIIb) are split by, for example, glycine ethyl ester with formation of *N*-formylpeptide esters.

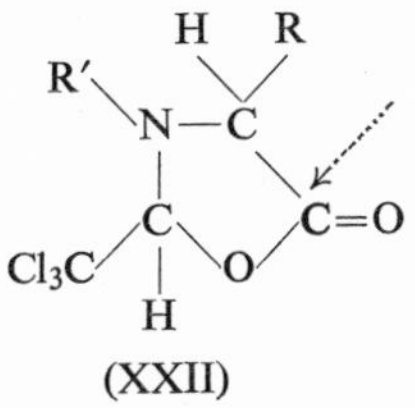

a: $R' = \text{Tos, Z}$

b: $R' = -\text{CH(OH).CCl}_3$

(XXII)

The hydroxytrichloroethyl group is converted to formyl (and chloroform) by the action of alkali.

$$\underset{\underset{\text{OH}}{|}}{\overset{\overset{\text{H}}{|}}{\text{Cl}_3\text{C.C.NH.R}}} \xrightarrow{\text{OH}^-} \text{Cl}_3\text{CH} + \overset{\overset{\text{H}}{|}}{\text{O}=\text{C.NH.R}}$$

(b) Derivatives of Carbonic Acid

In spite of the danger of racemization, the method of *mixed carbonic-carboxylic anhydrides* is one of the most widely used methods of coupling in peptide chemistry. Racemization is wholly or nearly prevented, at least in the formation of the test-peptide Z-Gly-L-Phe-Gly-OEt of Anderson, if the reaction is carried out in minimal time and at $-15°$ with tetrahydrofuran as solvent. Other well-known derivatives of carbonic acid are the *benzyloxycarbonyl compounds*. Like the other *urethanes*, N-phenyloxycarbonyl- and nitrophenoxycarbonylamino-acids [41], they lose their OH-containing component on heating with formation of the $(O=C=N—)$ isocyanato group, which with an acylamino-acid undergoes a Goldschmidt peptide synthesis [42]. Benzyloxycarbonylglycine ester on heating with phthaloylalanine above 150° yields phthaloyl-Ala-Gly ester with elimination of carbon dioxide [21]. Similarly α-*isothiocyanato-acid esters* (XXIV) give peptides, splitting off carbonyl sulphide. The sulfur compounds (XXIV) are obtained from amino-acid esters and CS_2 with alkali by taking out H_2S from the primarily formed dithiocarbamates [15] (XXIII).

$$\underset{\underset{\text{O}}{||}}{\text{Ph.CH}_2\text{.O.C.NH.CH(R).CO}_2\text{.C}_2\text{H}_5} \xrightarrow[-\text{PhCH}_2\text{OH}]{\Delta} \text{O}=\text{C}=\text{N.CH(R).CO}_2\text{.C}_2\text{H}_5$$

$$\underset{\underset{\text{(XXIII)}}{}}{\overset{\overset{\text{SH}}{|}}{\text{S}=\text{C.NH.CH(R).CO}_2\text{C}_2\text{H}_5}} \xrightarrow{-\text{H}_2\text{S}} \text{S}=\text{C}=\text{N.CH(R).CO}_2\text{.C}_2\text{H}_5 \quad \underset{+ \text{Z.NH.CH(R').CO}_2\text{H} \xrightarrow{-\text{COS}} \text{Dipeptide}}{\overset{\text{(XXIV)}}{}}$$

(c) Passerini-Reaction

I. Ugi [43] published a remarkable application of the Passerini reaction, in which in the presence of an amine two peptide linkages are formed at one time. As an example, the reaction of isocyanoacetic acid-tert.butyl ester, phthaloylglycine, benzylamine and acetaldehyde (Schiff base) may be formulated. At first an *O*-acylpeptide (XXV) is formed, which is converted by $O→N$ migration of the phthaloylglycyl residue to the *N*-benzylated tripeptide (XXVI):

As you have seen, in the field of peptide synthesis much progress has been made since 1958. It has become possible to synthesize peptides with more than twenty amino-acids in a definite sequence, but I think that peptide chemistry still needs new methods. The problems are well known: avoiding racemization, finding better solvents, increasing yields and evolving methods for establishing secondary and tertiary structures in an unambiguous way. Let me conclude by thankfully mentioning Dr. H. Determann, who helped in preparing this comprehensive treatise and carried out some of the experiments referred to in this paper.

REFERENCES

1. Recent summaries: J. P. GREENSTEIN and M. WINITZ, *Chemistry of Amino Acids*, J. Wiley, New York, 1961. N. F. ALBERTSON, Synthesis of Peptides with Mixed Anhydrides, in A. Cope, *Organic Reactions*, J. Wiley, New York, 1962, Vol. 12, p. 157.
2. T. WIELAND, *Collection Czechoslov. Chem. Commun.* **24**, 6 (1959).
3. L. HESLINGA and J. F. ARENS, *Rec. trav. chim. Pays-Bas* **76**, 982 (1957).
4. A. RIECHE and H. GROSS, *Chem. Ber.* **92**, 83 (1959).
5. K. PODUSKA and H. GROSS, *Chem. Ber.* **94**, 527 (1961).
6. M. ZAORAL and Z. ARNOLD, *Tetrahedron Letters* **14**, 9 (1960).
7. F. WEYGAND and W. STEGLICH, *Chem. Ber.* **92**, 313 (1959).
8. R. SCHWYZER, *Angew. Chem.* **71**, 742 (1959); *Chimia* **14**, 366 (1960).
9. T. WIELAND and B. HEINKE, *Liebigs Ann. Chem.* **615**, 184 (1958).
10. M. BRENNER and W. HOFER, *Helv. chim. Acta* **44**, 1794 (1961); **44**, 1798 (1961). R. WEBER, W. HOFER, W. HEER and M. BRENNER, *ibid.* **44**, 2154 (1961).
11. Y. WOLMAN, P. M. GALLOP and A. PATCHORNIK, *J. Amer. Chem. Soc.* **83**, 1263 (1961).
12. J. C. SHEEHAN and G. P. HESS, *J. Amer. Chem. Soc.* **77**, 1067 (1955).
13. J. C. SHEEHAN, P. A. CRUICKSHANK and G. L. BOSHART, *J. Org. Chem.* **26**, 2525 (1961).
14. H. B. KÖNIG and F. MOOSMÜLLER, D.B.P. 1070639 (Dec. 1959) *C.A.* **55**, 25779 (1961).
15. G. LOSSE and H. WEDDIGE, *Angew. Chem.* **72**, 323 (1960); *Liebigs Ann. Chem.* **636**, 144 (1960).
16. G. LOSSE and E. DEMUTH, *Chem. Ber.* **94**, 1762 (1961).

17. R. B. WOODWARD, R. A. OLOFSON and H. MAYER, *J. Amer. Chem. Soc.* **83**, 1010 (1961).
18. R. B. WOODWARD and R. A. OLOFSON, *J. Amer. Chem. Soc.* **83**, 1007 (1961).
19. B. ISELIN, W. RITTEL, P. SIEBER and R. SCHWYZER, *Helv. Chim. Acta* **40**, 373 (1957).
20. R. SCHWYZER and P. SIEBER, *Helv. Chim. Acta* **41**, 2190 (1958).
21. T. WIELAND, B. HEINKE, K. VOGELER and H. MORIMOTO, *Liebigs Ann. Chem.* **655**, 189 (1962).
22. G. KUPRYSZEWSKI, *Roczniki Chem.* **35**, 595 (1961).
23. F. WEYGAND and W. STEGLICH, *Angew. Chem.* **73**, 757 (1961).
24. G. H. L. NEFKENS and G. J. TESSER, *J. Amer. Chem. Soc.* **83**, 1263 (1961).
25. F. WEYGAND and W. STEGLICH, *Chem. Ber.* **93**, 2983 (1960).
26. F. WEYGAND and J. KAELICKE, *Chem. Ber.* **95**, 1031 (1962).
27. A. COSMATOS, J. PHOTAKI and L. ZERVAS, *Chem. Ber.* **94**, 2644 (1961).
28. G. SCHRAMM and H. WISSMANN, *Chem. Ber.* **91**, 1073 (1958).
29. B. F. ERLANGER and N. KOKOWSKI, *J. Org. Chem.* **26**, 2534 (1961).
30. P. C. CRAFTS, J. H. H. MARKES and H. N. RYDON, *J. Chem. Soc.* **1959**, 3610.
31. G. W. ANDERSON and A. C. MCGREGOR, *J. Amer. Chem. Soc.* **79**, 6180 (1957).
32. G. W. ANDERSON, *Ann. N. Y. Acad. Sci.* **88**, 677 (1960).
33. F. CRAMER and H. SCHALLER, *Chem. Ber.* **94**, 1636 (1961).
34. H. A. STAAB and K. WENDEL, *Chem. Ber.* **93**, 2902 (1960). H. A. STAAB, *Angew. Chem.* **74**, 407 (1962).
35. T. WIELAND and K. VOGELER, *Angew. Chem.* **73**, 435 (1961).
36. M. L. BENDER in Mechanism of catalysis of nucleophilic reactions of carboxylic acid derivatives, *Chem. Rev.* **60**, 53 (1960).
37. H. C. BEYERMANN and W. MAHSSEN VAN DEN BRINK, *Rec. trav. chim. Pays-Bas* **80**, 1372 (1961).
38. F. MICHEEL and W. MECKSTROTH, *Chem. Ber.* **92**, 1675 (1959).
39. F. MICHEEL and H. HANEKE, *Chem. Ber.* **92**, 309 (1959); **95**, 1009 (1962).
40. E. DANE, R. HEISS and H. SCHÄFER, *Angew. Chem.* **71**, 339 (1959); D.B.P. 1079648 (Apr. 60) *C.A.* **55**, 25784 (1961).
41. Y. ISHIZUKA, *C.A.* **53**, 5149 (1959).
42. St. GOLDSCHMIDT and M. WICK, *Z. Naturforsch.* **5b**, 170 (1950).
43. I. UGI, *Angew. Chem.* **74**, 9 (1962).

USE OF SOME NEW ACTIVE ESTERS IN PEPTIDE SYNTHESIS

J. PLESS

Sandoz Ltd., Basle, Switzerland

WE encountered some difficulties when working with p-nitrophenyl esters, introduced into peptide chemistry by Bodanszky [1]. Thus after the peptide coupling reaction it is sometimes difficult to eliminate completely the p-nitrophenol liberated during the reaction. When such a contaminated product is submitted to catalytic hydrogenation, for instance in order to remove a benzyloxycarbonyl group, the p-nitrophenol still present is reduced and gives coloured by-products, which sometimes inactivate the catalyst or hamper the isolation of the free peptide obtained. We therefore decided to undertake a systematic study of the reactivity of new potential active esters, which would not produce undesirable side products on subsequent hydrogenation, and we have compared their reactivity with that of active esters already used in peptide chemistry.

We first determined the dissociation constant (expressed as pK) of several phenols and of other compounds having acidic hydrogen, such as oximes and hydroxamic acids. We expected a significant parallel between the reaction rate of the active esters and the acidity of their hydroxy components. The acidity of a phenol is a function of the stability of its anion. The same electronic effects which favour this stability increase the reactivity of the corresponding phenolic esters towards nucleophilic attack. Esters of slightly acidic phenols with protected amino-acids—as we shall see—react slowly with amines. On the other hand, it is not always desirable to increase the dissociation of the phenol too greatly. For example, 2,4,6-trinitrophenol is a strong acid (pK 0·29) and it might be expected that 2,4,6-trinitrophenyl-benzyloxycarbonyl-L-phenylalaninate would possess a very high reactivity. We found that it is in fact so high that this ester cannot be isolated, and immediately disproportionate to benzyloxycarbonylphenylalanine anhydride.

Thus after having measured the pK values of a great variety of phenols, we condensed the most promising one with benzyloxycarbonyl-L-phenyl-alanine by the dicyclohexylcarbodiimide procedure and compared the rate of the coupling of these esters with benzylamine, in dioxan-water. By using an excess of benzylamine the reaction remained of first order and the half-reaction time could be used as a measure of the reactivity. These values were calculated from the change of the optical density of the reaction mixture as a function of time, by Dr. K. Stich in our physico-chemical department. To confirm that the reaction was taking place as expected, we also allowed these phenolic esters to react on a preparative scale with benzyl-

TABLE 1

Z – Phe – O – X + H₂N–CH₂–⟨⟩ → Z–Phe–NH–CH₂–⟨⟩					
X =	pK	$t/2$ (min)	X =	pK	$t/2$ (min)
⟨⟩–N(CH₃)₂ 3)	—	No reaction	⟨⟩–Cl	12·09	360
⟨⟩–⟨⟩	13·00	Very slow	I,⟨⟩–I (I)	8·24	350
⟨⟩–F	13·10	Very slow	Cl⟨⟩	11·98	264
⟨⟩–Cl	12·51	700	⟨=N⟩	11·55	172
F,⟨⟩	12·15	555	⟨⟩–C(=O)–CH₃	11·18	157
⟨⟩–F	12·42	500	⟨=N–CH₃⟩⊕	6·75	?

TABLE 2

Z – Phe – O – X + H₂N–CH₂–⟨⟩ → Z – Phe – NH – CH₂–⟨⟩					
X =	pK	$t/2$ (min)	X =	pK	$t/2$ min)
Cl,⟨⟩,Cl	10·70	44·4	Br,⟨⟩–Br,Br	8·29	72·0
⟨⟩–C(=O)–OC₂H₅ 3)	11·35	42·1	⟨⟩–NO₂ 1)	9·41	5·7
Cl,⟨⟩–Cl	10·87	38·5	⟨⟩–N=O	8·22	4·3
OCH₃,⟨⟩–C(=O)–H	10·30	31·0	Cl,⟨⟩–Cl,Cl	9·60	2·8
Br,⟨⟩–Br	10·82	31·0	ClCl,⟨⟩–Cl,ClCl 4)	6·25	2·3
Cl,⟨⟩–Cl,Cl 2)	9·65	19·3			

amine and with glycine ethyl ester. The desired products were in all cases isolated in a yield above 75 per cent.

Table 1 gives the structure of those substituted phenyl esters the reactivity of which was found to be definitely lower than that of the corresponding p-nitrophenyl ester. Most of the phenols from which they were obtained have pK values over 11. The low reactivity of the 2,4,6-triiodophenol derivatives, in spite of the great acidity of that phenol itself, can be explained by the steric hindrance caused by iodine atoms in the *ortho* positions.

Table 2 gives the structure of the substituted phenyl esters, having a reactivity comparable to that of *p*-nitrophenyl ester. In this case also the

TABLE 3

Z – Phe – O – X + H$_2$N–CH$_2$–⟨ ⟩ → Z–Phe–NH–CH$_2$–⟨ ⟩					
X =	pK	Yield	X =	pK	Yield
$-NH-\overset{O}{\underset{\ }{C}}-O-CH_2-$⟨ ⟩	14·3	68%	$-NH-\overset{O}{\underset{\ }{C}}-CH_3$	14·5	60%
$-NH-SO_2-$⟨ ⟩	13·1	78%	$-NH-\overset{O}{\underset{\ }{C}}-CH_2-CL$	10·8	Side reaction
$-NH-\overset{O}{\underset{\ }{C}}-$⟨ ⟩	11·4	72%	$-N=\overset{NH_2}{\underset{\ }{C}}-CH_2-CL$	8·8	,,
$-NH-\overset{O}{\underset{\ }{C}}-$⟨ ⟩$-NO_2$	9·9	85%	$-N=\overset{NH_2}{\underset{\ }{C}}-C\overset{CL}{\underset{CL}{{<}}}_{CL}$	Strongly acid	,,

TABLE 4

Z–Phe–O–X+H$_2$N–CH$_2$–⟨ ⟩ → Z–Phe-NH–CH$_2$–⟨ ⟩		
X =	pK	Yield
$-N=CH$ —⟨ ⟩	14·5	90%
$-N=CH$ —⟨ ⟩$\overset{NO_2}{- NO_2}$	12·0	92%
$-N=CH$ —⟨ ⟩$_{=N}$	13·4	83%
$-N=CH$ —⟨ ⟩$_N$	13·1	84%

rate of reaction increases when the pK value of the phenol decreases, unless steric effects interfere. For instance, bromine atoms in both *ortho* positions exert a more pronounced hindrance than chlorine atoms in the same positions.

Table 3 includes mixed anhydrides of several hydroxamic acids. Compounds of this type have still not been investigated systematically for their potentialities in peptide synthesis. The dissociation constants of the hydroxamic acids are rather low. Although benzhydroxamic acid has a pK of 11·4, the reaction velocity of the mixed anhydride between phenylalanine and this hydroxamic acid with benzylamine ($t/2 = 44$ min) is similar to that of esters of phenols whose pK is about 10·5. α-Chloroacetic hydroxamic acids were found to have higher dissociation constants than aromatic ones, but their mixed anhydrides with benzyloxycarbonylphenylalanine gave side reactions when they reacted with benzylamine.

This study of mixed anhydrides of hydroxamic acids prompted us to investigate the behavior of the structurally related aldoximes and ketoximes. While we did not succeed in preparing esters of ketoximes, the preparation of esters of benzyloxycarbonylphenylalanine and aldoximes (Table 4) presented no difficulties. Moreover, the latter were found to react with benzylamine and glycine ethyl ester in high yields.

This study has shown that beside the large number of active esters and mixed anhydrides of protected amino-acids which have been already described in the literature, there are still many new ones worthy of further investigation.

REFERENCES

1. M. BODANSZKY and V. du VIGNEAUD, *J. Amer. Chem. Soc.* **81**, 5688 (1959).
2. G. KUPRYSZEWSKI and M. KACZMAREK, *Roczniki Chem.* **35**, 935 (1961).
3. B. ISELIN, W. RITTEL, P. SIEBER and R. SCHWYZER, *Helv. Chim. Acta* **40**, 373 (1957).
4. G. KUPRYSZEWSKI and M. FORMELA, *Roczniki Chem.* **35**, 1533 (1961).

ALKOXYVINYL ESTERS AS COUPLING REAGENTS IN PEPTIDE SYNTHESIS

D. COHEN and H. D. SPRINGALL

Department of Chemistry, The University of Keele, Keele, Staffordshire

THE first acetylenic ether, phenoxyacetylene (HC≡C.O.Ph), was made nearly sixty years ago by Slimmer [1] (1903), but these ethers were not investigated as a class until the work of Jacobs and Cramer [2] (1940).

The most commonly used member of the class, ethoxyacetylene, now available commercially, is most readily made by a modification of the method of Nazarov, Krasnaia and Vinogradov [3] (1958)—a 3-stage preparation from ethyl vinyl ether.

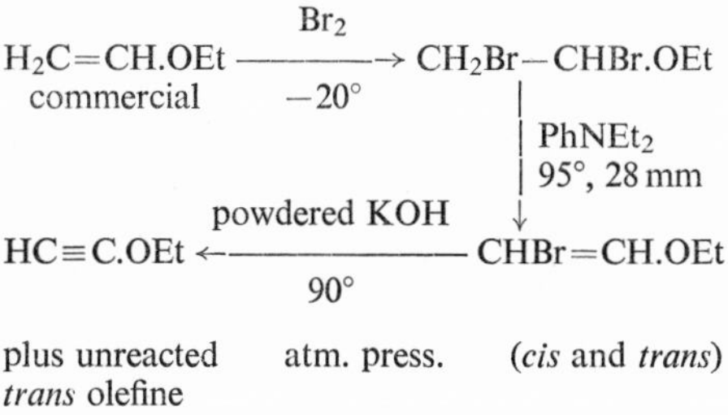

$$H_2C=CH.OEt \xrightarrow[-20°]{Br_2} CH_2Br-CHBr.OEt$$

$$\downarrow \substack{PhNEt_2 \\ 95°, 28\,mm}$$

$$HC≡C.OEt \xleftarrow[90°]{powdered\ KOH} CHBr=CH.OEt$$

plus unreacted   atm. press.   (*cis* and *trans*)
trans olefine

[The modifications to the procedure of Nazarov *et al.*, due to Cohen [4] (1961), consist in the use of (i) low temperature for the initial bromination and (ii) atmospheric pressure for the final dehydrobromination.]

For the past ten years Arens [5] and his colleagues have been examining the synthetic uses of the alkoxyacetylenes, and their thioanalogues, and have discovered a variety of very useful processes.

Among the many reactions of alkoxyacetylenes studied by Arens was that with carboxylic acids [6] in which the overall reaction is

$$2\ R.CO_2H + HC≡C.OEt$$

$$\downarrow$$

$$(R.CO)_2O + CH_3.C.OEt$$

$$\substack{\| \\ O}$$

i.e. the transfer of the elements of water from the $2\ R.CO_2H$ to the HC≡C.OEt. [The process has the practical advantage, over many similar

73

dehydration reactions, that the unwanted product, here ethyl acetate, is very easy to eliminate from the reaction system.] Arens suggested that this reaction proceeds in three stages via the ethoxyvinyl ester (I):

$$HC\equiv C.OEt \xrightarrow{\quad R.CO_2H \quad} H_2C=C\begin{smallmatrix} \diagup OEt \\ \diagdown O.CO.R \end{smallmatrix} \xrightarrow{\quad R.CO_2H \quad} CH_3.C\begin{smallmatrix} \diagup OEt \\ -O.CO.R \\ \diagdown O.CO.R \end{smallmatrix}$$

$$\text{(I)} \qquad\qquad\qquad\qquad \text{(II)} \quad \Big\downarrow$$

$$CH_3.CO.OEt + (R.CO)_2O$$

In the earlier stages of this work, the intermediates were not isolatable. Nevertheless, the reaction was applied to N-protected amino-acids, and peptide links were formed by reaction of the postulated intermediate $I(R = Y.NH.CHR^1)$ with the nucleophilic amino group of the second amino-acid component $NH_2.CHR^2.CO_2R^3$ [7]. Subsequently Arens [8] (1958), isolated the intermediate I $(R = CF_3)$ and, in the approach to peptide synthesis, Sheehan [9] (1958) isolated I $(R = $ ⟨structure⟩ $N.CH_2)$ in 30 per cent yield, by the simple addition of ethoxyacetylene to an aqueous solution of phthaloylglycine *en route* to the synthesis of phthaloylglycyl peptides.

At Yale, Wasserman and Wharton [10] (1958) found it possible to make compounds of type I in virtually quantitative yields by using either a Hg^{++} (as mercuric acetate) catalyst or a 3- or 4-fold molar excess of ethoxyacety-lene in an inert solvent $(CH_2Cl_2, CCl_4, C_6H_6, \text{etc.})$. All these compounds of type I had characteristic i.r. peaks at $5\cdot74$ and $5\cdot96\,\mu$. Many were readily distillable liquids: all were very susceptible to nucleophilic attack, e.g. by alcohols, amines or acids to give esters, amides or unsymmetrical anhydrides respectively. Using benzoic acid labelled with O^{18} Wasserman and Wharton were able to show that the reaction of ethoxyacetylene with acids does in fact give initially an intermediate of the types I and II $(R = Ph, \text{in this case})$.

Wasserman and Cohen [11] by using the Wasserman–Wharton technique, i.e. with the Hg^{++} catalyst or with large excess of ethoxyacetylene, were able to isolate the compound I $(R = $ ⟨structure⟩ $N.CH_2)$, identical with Shee-han's compound, in 80–90 per cent yield. They found that when amino-acids having N-protecting groups of the type $Y.NH.$ were used (in place of the phthaloyl protecting group when there is no residual H-atom on the amino-N-atom), the type I intermediates were always contaminated, to a slight extent, with the corresponding anhydrides, $(Y.NH.CHR.CO)_2O$, but that the intermediates so contaminated could, nevertheless, be used to form peptide links.

Wasserman and Cohen [12] subsequently went on to make and study reactive alkoxyvinyl esters of phosphoric acids (in Yale) and then, by Cohen [13] alone, of sulphonic acids (in Keele) by the Wasserman–Wharton technique. We, recently, have made a further study of the peptide formation reaction, using the same technique. We have applied this to the coupling of benzyloxycarbonylglycyl-L-phenylalanine, with glycine ethyl ester using the conditions specified by Anderson and Callahan [14] for testing a coupling reagent and carrying out a parallel condensation with dicyclohexylcarbodi-imide so that we could (a) compare the effectiveness of ethoxyacetylene and of the di-imide with regard to yield and to racemization of the L-phenyl-alanine residue in the condensation (Z-Gly-DL-Phe-Gly-OEt is very insoluble in cold ethanol), and (b) attempt the isolation, preferably in high yield, of the intermediate I (R = Z-Gly-L-Phe). (Sheehan [9] and Arens [9a] and their co-workers have already shown that under the Arens conditions for the use of ethoxyacetylene there is little, if any, racemization accompanying the use of this reagent in the Anderson-Callahan test.)

Using a mercuric catalyst and 1 mole of ethoxyacetylene as condensing agent in anhydrous tetrahydrofuran, we found that the yield of crude product (Z-Gly-Phe-Gly-OEt) (*ca.* 50 per cent) was considerably lower than with dicyclohexylcarbodi-imide, but there was only about 3 per cent of the DL-form compared with about 10 per cent when the latter was used.

Evaporation of the solution of benzyloxycarbonylglycyl-L-phenylalanine after treatment with ethoxyacetylene gave a white solid which, recrystallized from ethyl acetate–petrol ether, gave a compound (m.p. 120°) with an infra-red spectrum showing the characteristic ethoxy vinyl ester peaks: almost certainly

$$\begin{matrix} \text{Z-Gly-L-Phe-O} \\ \text{EtO} \end{matrix}\Big\rangle\text{C=CH}_2\text{, though not yet analysed}$$

i.e.   I(R = Z-Gly-L-Phe)

We feel that, by increasing the proportion of ethoxyacetylene in the first stage, the yield of the intermediate I (R = Z-Gly-L-Phe) and thence of the final tripeptide derivative could be made very much higher, without sacrifice of optical purity. Experiments along these lines are proceeding.

Note added December 1962

The compound m.p. 120° originally isolated from the reaction of benzyl-oxycarbonylglycyl-L-phenylalanine, Z-Gly-L-Phe-OH, with ethoxyacetylene in the presence of Hg^{++} ion, in tetrahydrofuran solution, was thought to be the reactive intermediate ethoxyvinyl ester of the protected dipeptide Z-Gly-L-Phe.O.C(OEt):CH_2. It has now been found that this ester is very rapidly hydrolysed by traces of moisture and the compound isolated proved to be the original protected dipeptide (occasionally contaminated with varying amounts of the dipeptide anhydride). The infrared spectrum of the reaction system, as reported above, shows the characteristic peaks indicative of the presence of the ethoxyvinyl ester and we have now succeeded in isolating this ester, as a pale yellow liquid, n_D^{25}, 1·4930, by working with a great excess of ethoxyacetylene. (Found: C, 64·68; H, 6·13; N, 6·78 per cent. $C_{23}H_{26}O_6N_2$ requires C, 64·77; H, 6·15; N, 6·57 per cent.)

REFERENCES

1. SLIMMER, *Ber.* **36,** 289 (1903).
2. JACOBS and CRAMER, *J. Amer. Chem. Soc.* **62,** 1849 (1940).
3. NAZAROV, KRAZNAIA and VINOGRADOV, *J. Gen. Chem.* (*U.S.S.R.*), **28,** 451 (1958).
4. COHEN, unpublished work.
5. See, e.g., ARENS, in *Advances in Organic Chemistry*, vol. 2, Ed. Raphael, Taylor and Wynberg, Interscience, New York, 1960, p. 117.
6. HESLINGA and ARENS, *Rec. trav. chim.* **76,** 982 (1957).
7. ARENS, *Rec. trav. chim.* **74,** 769 (1955).
8. BROEKEMA, van der WERF and ARENS, *Rec. trav. chim.*, **77,** 258 (1958).
9. SHEEHAN and HLAVKA, *J. Amer. Chem. Soc.* **80,** 635 (1958).
9a. PANNEMAN, MARX and ARENS, *Rec. trav. chim.* **78,** 487 (1959).
10. WASSERMAN and WHARTON, *Tetrahedron*, **3,** 321 (1958); *J. Amer. Chem. Soc.* **82,** 661 (1960).
11. WASSERMAN and COHEN, unpublished work.
12. WASSERMAN and COHEN, *J. Amer. Chem. Soc.* **82,** 4435 (1960).
13. COHEN, unpublished work.
14. ANDERSON and CALLAHAN, *J. Amer. Chem. Soc.* **80,** 2902 (1958).

NEBENREAKTIONEN BEI DER AZIDSYNTHESE

E. Schnabel

Deutsches Wollforschungsinstitut, Aachen

Die Curtius'sche Azidmethode [1] ist noch immer ein unentbehrliches Verfahren der Peptidchemie; zumal Smart, Young und Williams [2] zeigen konnten, daß eine racemisierungsfreie Kondensation selbst unter Bedingungen möglich ist, bei denen nach fast allen anderen Verfahren mehr oder weniger starke Racemisierung beobachtet wird. Außerdem können als Aminkomponenten auch freie Aminosäuren und Peptide [3] verwendet werden.

Leider hat man schon eine ganze Reihe von Nebenreaktionen beobachtet. Der Curtius Abbau [4] mit den Folgereaktionen wie Oxazolidonbildung beim Serin [5, 6] oder Addition des Isocyanats an die Aminogruppe der Aminkomponente zum Harnstoffderivat [7] führt zu einer Umwandlung der die Azidogruppe tragenden Aminosäure in ein Aldehydderivat (ein Aminal), und bei der Totalhydrolyse wird sie zerstört. Bei einer weiteren Gruppe von Reaktionen bleibt das Kohlenstoffgerüst der betreffenden Aminosäure erhalten. Am wichtigsten ist hier die schon häufig beobachtete und kürzlich von Honzl und Rudinger [8] eingehend untersuchte Amidbildung. Außerdem hat man die Entstehung von symmetrischen Bishydraziden [9] und von Azlactonen [6] beobachtet. Weiter ist die Oxydation von S-Benzylcystein in Peptidderivaten zum Sulfoxyd [8] beschrieben, sowie die Nitrierung von Tyrosin [10] und N-Nitrosierung von Tryptophanderivaten [11]. Diese letzteren Reaktionen können durch die Wahl geeigneter Reaktionsbedingungen unterdrückt werden.

Ein weiterer Nachteil ist die meist verhältnismäßig niedrige Ausbeute bei der Kondensation. Um die oft wertvollere Aminkomponente besser auszunutzen, wird das Azid manchmal in beträchtlichem Überschuß eingesetzt. Zur Untersuchung der dabei aus den Aziden entstehenden Reaktionsprodukte wurden einige Benzyloxycarbonylaminosäureazide für sich unter den Bedingungen der Peptidsynthese reagieren lassen.

Aus Benzyloxycarbonyl-DL-serinazid [12] wurde beim Stehen im Eisschrank das, in der L-Reihe von Fruton [5] beschriebene, Oxazolidonderivat in fast quantitativer Ausbeute erhalten. Schmp. 138° (126–127°).

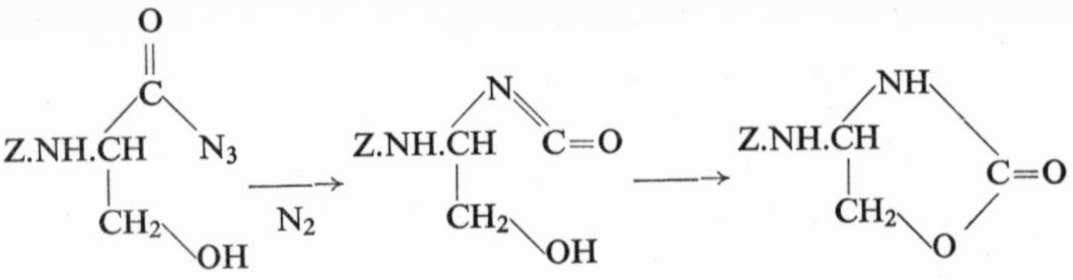

$$\text{Z.NH.CH–N}_3 \ (\text{CH}_2\text{–OH}) \xrightarrow{-\text{N}_2} \text{Z.NH.CH–N=C=O} \ (\text{CH}_2\text{–OH}) \longrightarrow \text{Z.NH.CH} \underset{\text{CH}_2\text{–O}}{\overset{\text{NH}}{\diagdown}} \text{C=O}$$

Das primär aus dem Azid gebildete Isocyanat hatte mit der β-Hydroxy-gruppe zum cyclischen Urethan reagiert. Serin fehlte im Totalhydrolysat und es war nur Benzylamin nachweisbar.

α,β-DL-Bisbenzyloxycarbonylamino-propionsäureazid lieferte in geringer Ausbeute Benzyloxycarbonyl-4-benzyloxycarbonylamino-imidazolidon-(2) einen cyclischen Harnstoff. Schmp. 165–167°.

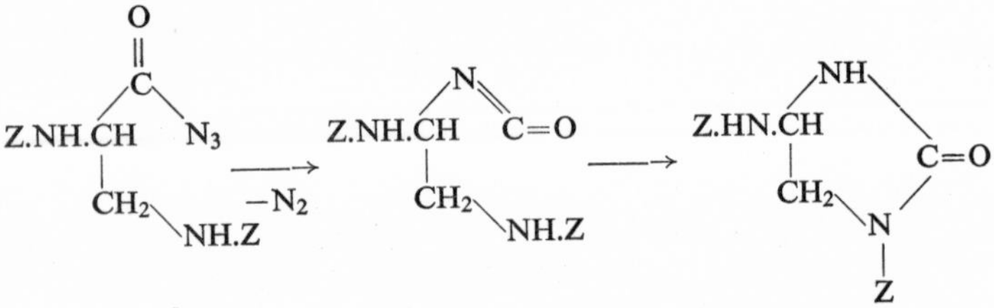

$$\text{Z.NH.CH–N}_3 \ (\text{CH}_2\text{–NH.Z}) \xrightarrow{-\text{N}_2} \text{Z.NH.CH–N=C=O} \ (\text{CH}_2\text{–NH.Z}) \longrightarrow \text{Z.HN.CH} \underset{\text{CH}_2\text{–N(Z)}}{\overset{\text{NH}}{\diagdown}} \text{C=O}$$

Der Mischschmelzpunkt mit authentischem Amid—Schmp. 171–173°—war deprimiert und bei der Totalhydrolyse wurden neben Benzylamin einige weitere Ninhydrin-positive Verbindungen, jedoch nur Spuren von Diamino-propionsäure gefunden. Das Isocyanat hatte mit der β-Benzyloxycarbonyl-amido-gruppe reagiert. Die Reaktion einer Isocyanatgruppierung mit einer Amidgruppe wurde bereits von Goldschmidt und Wick [13] beschrieben, die bei der Darstellung der Isocyanatoverbindungen von Peptidestern die Hydantoine erhielten.

Beim Benzyloxycarbonyl-L-cysteinazid wurde die Bildung des analogen Thiazolidons erwartet. Das Hydrazid wurde ohne Schutz der Mercapto-gruppe unter Stickstoff dargestellt, da sich die Verwendung des Tetrahydro-pyranylrestes [14] nicht bewährte. Mit salpetriger Säure bildete sich eine tiefrote, essigesterlösliche Verbindung. Zur Reduktion von eventuell vor-handenem Disulfid wurde wiederholt mit Thioglykolsäure gewaschen. Bei Zimmertemperatur schieden sich aus der Reaktionslösung unter Entfärbung amorphe Flocken ab. Ein identisches Material wurde aus Dibenzyloxy-carbonyl-L-cystin [15] und Benzyloxycarbonyl-L-cysteinhydrazid nach der gemischten Anhydridmethode dargestellt—Schmp. unter Zersetzung ab 280°. Der Nitroprussid-Test war erst nach Behandeln mit Cyanid positiv. Im Totalhydrolysat waren neben Cystin noch etwa 10% einer Verbindung anwesend, die auch bei der Totalhydrolyse von Dibenzyloxycarbonyl-L-cystin entstand und chromatographisch als S-Benzylcystein identifiziert wurde. Nach Fiesselmann [16] entsteht aus Thioglykolsäurehydrazid in saurer Lösung das symmetrische Bishydrazid, das im Falle des Cystein-derivates durch die salpetrige Säure zum Bis-(dibenzyloxycarbonyl-L-cystin-hydrazid) oxydiert wurde. Beim Öffnen des Reaktionsgefäßes entwich Stickoxyd als stechend riechendes, sich an der Luft braun färbendes Gas.

$$
\begin{array}{l}
\ \ \text{O}\diagdown\qquad\ \ \text{O}\diagup \\
\ \ \text{C.NH.HN.C} \\
2\ \text{Z.HN.CH}\quad\ \text{HC.NH.Z} \quad \xrightarrow[-4\text{NO}+2\text{H}_2\text{O}]{+2\text{N}_2\text{O}_3} \\
\ \ \ \ \text{CH}_2\qquad\ \ \ \text{CH}_2 \\
\ \ \ \ \text{SH}\qquad\ \ \ \text{SH}
\end{array}
$$

Z.NH.CH — HC.NH.Z ... (Strukturformel des Bis-cystinhydrazids)

Da in keinem der untersuchten Fälle das Amid isoliert werden konnte, wurden einige in der Literatur beschriebene Fälle von Amidbildung nachge-arbeitet. Aus Benzyloxycarbonyl-S-benzyl-L-cysteinazid [17] wurden in Übereinstimmung mit Hegedüs [18] unter den angegebenen Bedingungen 22% Amid erhalten und durch Mischschmelzpunkt mit authentischem Material eindeutig identifiziert. Daneben fielen 55% einer Substanz mit einem Schmp. von 225–227° an, deren Elementaranalyse auf ein symme-trisches Harnstoffderivat, den N,N'-Di-(1-benzyloxycarbonylamino-2-thio-benzyl-äthyl-1)-harnstoff, hindeutet.

$$
\begin{array}{l}
2\ \text{Z.HN.CH.N}{=}\text{C}{=}\text{O} \qquad\qquad\ \ \text{Z.HN.CH.NH.C.HN.CH.NH.Z} \\
\ \ \ \ \ \ \text{CH}_2 \qquad \xrightarrow[-\text{CO}_2]{+\text{H}_2\text{O}} \qquad\ \ \text{CH}_2\ \ \ \ \text{O}\ \ \ \ \text{CH}_2 \\
\ \ \ \ \ \ \text{S.BZL} \qquad\qquad\qquad\qquad\ \ \text{S.BZL}\qquad\quad\text{S.BZL}
\end{array}
$$

Offenbar enthielt das Lösungsmittel noch Feuchtigkeit [19]. Im Total-hydrolysat war kein S-Benzylcystein nachweisbar.

Auch beim Stehen von Dibenzyloxycarbonyl-L-lysinazid [20] wurde nach Prelog und Wieland [21] das Amid [22] erhalten—24%—Außerdem fielen 38% eines symmetrischen Harnstoffderivats an—Schmp. 204–207°. In n-Butanol bildete sich kein Amid, sondern das Butylurethan—Schmp. 112–114°—und außerdem 12.5% Harnstoffderivat. Nach der Totalhydrolyse war Lysin nicht mehr nachweisbar.

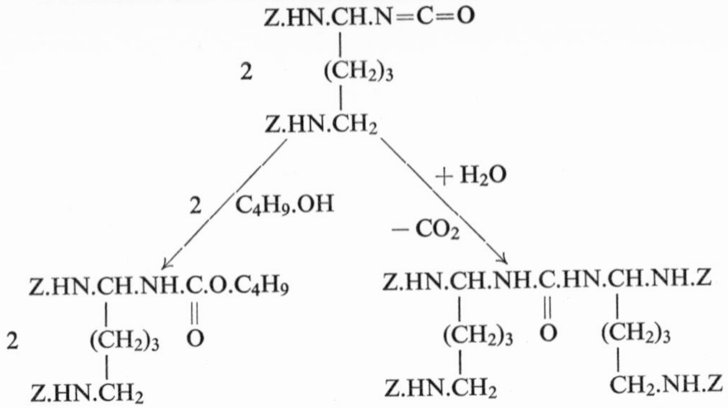

$$Z.HN.CH.N=C=O$$
$$2 \quad (CH_2)_3$$
$$Z.HN.CH_2$$

$$2 \; C_4H_9.OH \qquad + H_2O$$
$$- CO_2$$

$$Z.HN.CH.NH.C.O.C_4H_9 \qquad Z.HN.CH.NH.C.HN.CH.NH.Z$$
$$2 \quad (CH_2)_3 \quad O \qquad\qquad (CH_2)_3 \quad O \quad (CH_2)_3$$
$$Z.HN.CH_2 \qquad\qquad Z.HN.CH_2 \qquad CH_2.NH.Z$$

Wurde das Azid aus Natriumazid und Dibenzyloxycarbonyl-L-lysin [22] nach der gemischten Anhydridmethode nach Weinstock [23] dargestellt und in Äther gehalten, so konnte ebenfalls kein Amid, sondern nur *N,N'*-Bis-(1,5-dibenzyloxycarbonylaminopentyl-1)-harnstoff in 67% Ausbeute erhalten werden.

Abweichende Resultate wurden jedoch beim Abbau von Benzyloxycarbonyl-*S*-benzyl-L-cysteinyl-L-tyrosinazid erhalten. So beschreibt Roberts [24] die Bildung des Amids in Benzylalkohol enthaltender Lösung—Schmp. 212–213°. Das Amid schmilzt jedoch tiefer—197–198°—und die obige Verbindung ist das Benzylurethan;

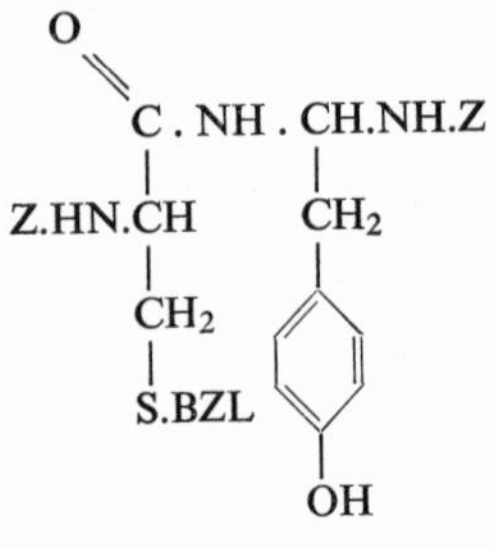

$$O$$
$$C . NH . CH.NH.Z$$
$$Z.HN.CH \qquad CH_2$$
$$CH_2$$
$$S.BZL$$
$$OH$$

Daneben wurde in 6% Ausbeute eine Substanz vom Schmp. 239–242° isoliert, deren Analyse auf das Isocyanatoderivat stimmte. Wahrscheinlich hatte die Isocyanatogruppe intramolekular mit einer reaktiven Gruppe des Moleküls—etwa einer Säureamidbindung, nicht jedoch der phenolischen Hydroxylgruppe—reagiert, oder es war Polymerisation erfolgt. Im Totalhydrolysat beider Verbindungen fehlte Tyrosin.

Um zu untersuchen, ob derartige Nebenprodukte, die vor allem bei der Synthese höherer Peptide nur schwer abgetrennt werden können, den weiteren Gang der Synthese stören, wurde das DL-4-Benzyloxycarbonyl-amino-oxazolidon-(2) in verschiedenen Lösungsmitteln katalytisch hydriert. In inerten organischen Lösungsmitteln wie Dioxan oder tert.-Butanol [25] wurde bei Reaktionstemperaturen oberhalb 50° das Oxazolidon-(2) [26] mit

70% Ausbeute erhalten und durch Vergleich mit einem nach Fränkel und Cornelius [27] synthetisiertem Präparat eindeutig identifiziert. Bei Zimmertemperatur wurde ebenfalls Ammoniak frei, aber es entstand das Bis-[4-oxazolidonyl-(2)]-amin,

$$CH_2.CH.NH.CH.CH_2$$
$$O \quad NH \quad HN \quad O$$
$$C \qquad C$$
$$O \qquad O$$

—Schmp. 133–135°; 55% Ausbeute—ein symmetrisches Aminal, das beim Stehen in methanolischer Lösung unter Ammoniakentwicklung langsam ins 4-Methoxy-oxazolidon-(2) übergeht und durch Wasser ziemlich rasch hydrolysiert wird. Das 4-Methoxy-oxazolidon-(2) ist das Hauptprodukt der Hydrierung in abs. Methanol.

REFERENZEN

1. Th. CURTIUS, *Ber.* **35**, 3226 (1902).
2. N. A. SMART, G. T. YOUNG und M. W. WILLIAMS, *J. Chem. Soc.* **1960**, 3902.
3. Th. CURTIUS und R. WÜSTENFELD, *J. prakt. Chem.* [2] **70**, 73 (1904).
   K. HOFMANN, A. JÖHL, A. E. FURLENMEIER und H. KAPPELER, *J. Amer. Chem. Soc.* **79**, 1636 (1957).
4. Th. CURTIUS, *Ber.* **23**, 3023 (1890).
5. J. S. FRUTON, *J. Biol. Chem.* **146**, 463 (1942).
6. A. STOLL und Th. PETRZILKA, *Helv. Chim. Acta* **35**, 589 (1952).
7. M. A. NYMANN und R. M. HERBST, *J. Org. Chem.* **15**, 117 (1950).
   J. W. HINMAN, E. L. CARON und H. N. CHRISTENSEN, *J. Amer. Chem. Soc.* **72**, 1620 (1950).
   T. E. MAJEWSKI, Dissertation, Univ. of Delaware (1953).
   K. C. HOOPER, H. N. RYDON, J. A. SCHOFIELD und G. S. HEATON, *J. Chem. Soc.* **1956**, 3148.
   K. HEYNS, W. WALTER und F. MÜLLER, *Angew. Chem.* **68**, 617 (1956).
   G. L. TRITSCH und D. W. WOOLLEY, *J. Amer. Chem. Soc.* **82**, 2787 (1960).
   K. HOFMANN, T. A. THOMPSON, H. YAJIMA, E. T. SCHWARTZ und H. INOUYE, *J. Amer. Chem. Soc.* **82**, 3715 (1960).
   E. DYER und S. SHYLUK, *J. Org. Chem.* **26**, 1321 (1961).
   J. RAMACHANDRAN, Univ. of California Berkeley, und ebenso R. Schwyzer, Ciba AG. Basel, beobachteten die Bildung des Harnstoffderivates bei der Kondensation von Z.Val-Lys-Tyr.N₃ mit H.Val-Pro.NH₂ (priv. Mitteilung).
        └—Tos
8. J. HONZL und J. RUDINGER, *Collection Czechoslov. Chem. Commun.* **26**, 2333 (1961).
9. J. I. HARRIS und J. S. FRUTON, *J. Biol. Chem.* **191**, 143 (1951).
   F. SCHNEIDER, *Hoppe-Seyler's Z. physiol. Chem.* **320**, 82 (1960).
10. E. SCHNABEL und H. ZAHN, *Monatsh. Chem.* **88**, 646 (1957).
11. D. BRANDENBURG, Dissertation, T. H. Aachen (1961).
12. R. F. FISCHER und R. R. WHETSTONE, *J. Amer. Chem. Soc.* **76**, 5076 (1954).
13. St. GOLDSCHMIDT und M. WICK, *Liebig's Ann. Chem.* **575**, 217 (1952).
14. G. F. HOLLAND und L. A. COHEN, *J. Amer. Chem. Soc.* **80**, 3765 (1958).
15. M. BERGMANN und L. ZERVAS, *Ber.* **65**, 1192 (1932).
16. H. FIESSELMANN, *Angew. Chem.* **73**, 537 (1961).

17. G. R. Harington und R. V. Pitt Rivers, *Biochem. J.* **38**, 417 (1944).
18. B. Hegedüs, *Helv. Chim. Acta* **21**, 737 (1948).
19. C. Naegeli und A. Tyabji, *Helv. Chim. Acta* **16**, 349 (1933).
20. M. Bergmann, L. Zervas und J. P. Greenstein, *Ber.* **65**, 1692 (1932).
21. V. Prelog und P. Wieland, *Helv. Chim. Acta* **29**, 1128 (1946).
22. M. Bergmann, L. Zervas und W. F. Ross, *J. Biol. Chem.* **111**, 245 (1935).
23. J. Weinstock, *J. Org. Chem.* **26**, 3511 (1961).
24. C. W. Roberts, *J. Amer. Chem. Soc.* **76**, 6203 (1954).
25. P. C. Crofts, J. H. H. Markes und H. N. Rydon, *J. Chem. Soc.* **1959**, 3610.
26. S. Gabriel, *Ber.* **21**, 568 (1888).
27. S. Fränkel und M. Cornelius, *Ber.* **51**, 1662 (1918).

N-CARBOXY-N-TRITYL-α-AMINO-ACID ANHYDRIDES IN PEPTIDE SYNTHESIS

H. BLOCK† and MARGARET E. COX

Courtaulds Limited, Research Laboratories, Lower Cookham Road,
Maidenhead, Berks., England

N-CARBOXY-α-AMINO-ACID anhydrides have been extensively used in the synthesis of poly-α-amino-acids [1]. Their employment without modification in the stepwise synthesis of peptides has also been described [2], but experience in the Courtaulds Research Laboratories, Maidenhead, has been that this method results in polymer contamination and poor yields of the desired peptide. During some researches into the mechanism of polymerization [3] we used N-phenylglycine-N-carboxyanhydride to isolate a suspected intermediate; this reagent was used because of its inability to initiate polymerization further after reaction, a property due to the weak basicity of the resulting substituted aniline group. Use of a substituent which precludes further reaction in the same manner as the phenyl group, but which is easily removable without racemization after reaction, would result in a class of anhydrides suitable for the stepwise synthesis of peptides (reaction 1). Imino-acids

$$
\begin{array}{c}
\text{RCH.CO} \\
| \quad\quad\ \ \ \rangle\text{O} + \text{H}_2\text{N.CHR}'.\text{CO.OR}'' \rightarrow \\
\text{XN . CO}
\end{array}
\quad
\begin{array}{c}
\text{X.NH.CHR.CO.NH.CHR}'.\text{CO.OR}'' + \text{CO}_2 \\
\Big| \text{HA} \\
\downarrow \\
\text{H}_2\text{N.CHR.CO.NH.CHR}'.\text{CO.OR}'' + \text{XA}
\end{array}
\qquad (1)
$$

such as proline, hydroxyproline and sarcosine would require other, conventional coupling procedures.

The use of an acyl group for " X " such as benzyloxycarbonyl, trifluoracetyl, etc., for this purpose would be expected to lead to difficulties in the formation of the N,N-diacyl grouping. Attempts to prepare N-benzyloxycarbonylglycine N-carboxyanhydride by treating N-benzyloxycarbonylglycine with phosgene failed, although the synthesis of the N-acetylglycine derivative by this method has been described [4]. We have had some success using the N-trityl group (X = CPh₃): the N-tritylglycine, N-trityl-L- and N-trityl-D-alanine N-carboxyanhydrides have been prepared and used in the formation of small peptides.

† Now at the University of Liverpool, Liverpool, 7.

The preparative steps necessary in the synthesis of a peptide by this method are: (i) the formation of a *N*-trityl-α-amino-acid or its quarternary ammonium salt, (ii) the preparation of the *N*-carboxyanhydride of this α-amino-acid, and (iii) the reaction of this reagent with an α-amino-acid or peptide ester to give a *N*-trityl-peptide ester, followed by removal of the trityl protecting group. Each of these stages is described separately below.

I. THE SYNTHESIS OF *N*-TRITYL-α-AMINO-ACIDS

There are two general methods for the preparation of *N*-trityl-α-amino-acids [5, 6, 7] employing either the free α-amino-acid or its ester as substrate. We have concentrated on the former, for which the described technique [6, 7] is to treat a solution of the acid in an isopropanol–water mixture with triphenylchloromethane in the presence of diethylamine. When applied by us this method resulted in poor and even zero yields in many cases. In some instances this is partly due to the formation of *N*-trityl-α-amino-acid trityl esters. Examples of this type of compound have been isolated from glycine† and alanine‡ reaction mixtures when ethanol is not used as an aid for chloroform removal in the method of Stelakatos *et al.* [7]. Since these esters are insoluble in both ether and water, they can be isolated by partitioning the reaction product between ice-cold dilute hydrochloric acid and ether.

N-Tritylasparagine trityl ester has been reported [8] as the product of reaction between asparagine and triphenylchloromethane in the presence of triethylamine in an ether–water solvent mixture. These reaction conditions when applied to glycine resulted in a 90 per cent yield of *N*-tritylglycine trityl ester, although in no case were we able to produce *N*-tritylalanine or *N*-tritylphenylalanine trityl esters under these or other similar reaction conditions. A summary of reactions attempted together with yields is given in Table 1.

These *N*-trityl-α-amino-acid trityl esters are a convenient source of the *N*-trityl-α-amino-acids since they behave in a similar way to other trityl esters [9] and undergo alcoholysis on reflux (*ca.* 3 min) in good yield (reaction 2).

$$\text{Ph}_3\text{C.NH.CHR.CO.OCPh}_3 + \text{R'OH} \xrightarrow{\text{reflux}} \text{Ph}_3\text{C.NH.CHR.CO.OH} + \text{Ph}_3\text{COR'}$$
$$\text{R'} = \text{Me or Et} \qquad (2)$$

Hydrolysis under alkaline conditions did not occur for these trityl esters even with prolonged heating, whilst acid hydrolysis, which is very facile, resulted in the formation of free α-amino-acid in all cases.

---

† M.p., 136°.
‡ D-isomer m.p., 185°; $[\alpha]_D^{20}$, + 118·1° (*c* 0·5 in ethyl acetate).

TABLE 1. YIELDS OF *N*-TRITYL-α-AMINO-ACIDS AND *N*-TRITYL-α-AMINO-ACID TRITYL ESTERS FROM A VARIETY OF REACTION CONDITIONS

α-Amino-acid	Yield of *N*-trityl-α-amino-acid diethylammonium salt %	Yield of *N*-trityl-α-amino-acid trityl ester %	Method
Glycine	33	—	I
Glycine	0	19	III
Glycine	—	90	IV
D-Alanine	27	4	III
D-Alanine	0	31	V
D-Alanine	—	0	IV
L-Asparagine	—	72	IV
L-Leucine	22	0	II
L-Leucine	0	0	IV
L-Leucine	29 (crude)	0	III
L-Phenylalanine	28	0	II
α-Methyl L-glutamate	0	—	II
α-Methyl L-glutamate	—	0	IV
L-Valine	20	—	II
L-Tryptophan	0	—	II
S-Benzyloxycarbonyl-L-cysteine†	10	—	II

Methods

I. Method " B " of Zervas and Theodoropoulos [6].
II. Method " B " of Stelakatos, Zervas and Theodoropoulos [7].
III. Method as " II " modified to isolate the trityl ester as described in text.
IV. Water-immiscible solvent such as used by Amiard and Heymes [8].
V. Method as " III " with *N*-ethylpiperidine as reacting base and 3 × molar ratio of triphenylchloromethane to α-amino-acid.

† M.p. of diethylammonium salt, 165°.

II. THE SYNTHESIS OF *N*-TRITYL-α-AMINO-ACID *N*-CARBOXYANHYDRIDES

Conversion in yields of 60 to 70 per cent, of *N*-tritylglycine‡ and *N*-trityl-alanine§ to the *N*-carboxyanhydrides was accomplished by reaction with phosgene in refluxing dioxan or ethyl acetate (reaction 3).

$$Ph_3C.NH.CHR.CO.OH + COCl_2 \longrightarrow \begin{array}{c} RCH.CO \\ | \quad\quad >O + 2HCl \\ Ph_3C.N . CO \end{array} \quad (3)$$

Precautions must be taken to remove the hydrogen chloride with a base such as triethylamine or, preferably calcium carbonate, since failure to do so

‡ *N*-Tritylglycine *N*-carboxyanhydride: m.p., 210° (decomp.).
§ *N*-Trityl-L-alanine *N*-carboxyanhydride: m.p., 208–210° [α]$_D^{20}$, + 34·7 (*c* 0·5 in ethyl acetate).

results in the formation of the unsubstituted α-amino-acid N-carboxyan-hydride (reaction 4, possibly in combination with a hydrogen chloride induced removal of the trityl group from the substrate).

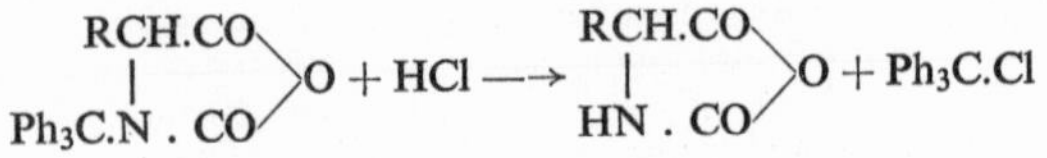

$$\begin{array}{c} \text{RCH.CO} \\ | \\ \text{Ph}_3\text{C.N . CO} \end{array}\!\!\!\!\!\!\!\!\Big\rangle\text{O} + \text{HCl} \longrightarrow \begin{array}{c} \text{RCH.CO} \\ | \\ \text{HN . CO} \end{array}\!\!\!\!\!\!\!\!\Big\rangle\text{O} + \text{Ph}_3\text{C.Cl} \qquad (4)$$

In the synthesis of N-tritylalanine N-carboxyanhydride we have found the N-ethylpiperidinium salt of N-tritylalanine a more useful substrate; it can be prepared in an analogous manner to that appertaining in the synthesis of the diethylammonium salt [6, 7].

There is evidence that side reaction 4, although adequately controlled with the aforementioned bases in the phosgenation of N-tritylglycine and N-trityl-alanine, is a cause of failure in preparing these derivatives with some other N-trityl-α-amino-acids. Attempts to react N-trityl-L-phenylalanine with phosgene using calcium carbonate to remove hydrogen chloride resulted in the formation of L-phenylalanine N-carboxyanhydride in good yield.

TABLE 2

Peptide	Yield of purified product %	M.p. °	$[\alpha]_D^{20}$
N-Trityl-Gly-Gly.OEt	84	162 (Lit. [10], m.p. 159°)	
Gly-Gly.OEt.HCl	70	183–4 (Lit. [11], m.p. 182°)	
N-Trityl-Gly-Gly-Gly.OEt	94	185 (Lit. [10], m.p. 185·5°)	
N-Trityl-Gly-Gly-Gly-Gly.OEt [a]	79	163 (Lit. [10], m.p. 180·5°)	
N-Trityl-Gly-Gly-Gly-Gly-Gly.OEt [a]	70	200–3	
N-Trityl-D-Ala-L-Ala.OMe [a]	70	176–7	+18·6 (c 0·45 in MeOH)
N-Trityl-L-Ala-D-Ala-L-Ala [a, b]	49	140	−26·7 (c 0·35 in ethyl acetate/light petroleum [b.p. < 40°])

[a] Further characterized by satisfactory elemental analysis.
[b] The methyl ester first prepared could not be easily purified. For this reason a portion was saponified with ethanolic potassium hydroxide.

The use of triethylamine led to a mixture of products believed to be small peptide derivatives resulting from the formation and subsequent triethyl-amine-initiated polymerization of L-phenylalanine N-carboxyanhydride. N-Trityl-L-leucine behaved similarly in the presence of triethylamine. It appears that with these α-amino-acids, triethylamine hydrochloride is a strong enough acid to remove the blocking group (reaction 4). The use of a suspension in aqueous sodium hydroxide as the reaction medium in the case of *N*-trityl-L-phenylalanine also failed.

We hope to investigate a wider range of reaction conditions in an effort to overcome these difficulties.

III. THE SYNTHESIS OF PEPTIDES WITH *N*-TRITYL-α-AMINO-ACID *N*-CARBOXYANHYDRIDES

Coupling was performed in high yield by mixing equivalents of an aqueous solution of a peptide or amino-acid ester (pH adjusted to 7 with triethylamine) with a dioxan solution of the *N*-trityl-α-amino-acid *N*-carboxyanhydride. After standing at ambient temperature for periods between 5 and 16 hr the product was fully precipitated by the addition of water. The trityl group was removed with hot 50 per cent acetic acid [6, 7] and the peptide ester used for further coupling or purified. Yields and other data are shown in Table 2.

We wish to thank Professor C. H. Bamford for his advice and encouragement, and for the interest he has shown in this work, and Mr. D. R. Boreham and Mrs. D. Kapur for carrying out some of the experiments here described.

REFERENCES

1. C. H. BAMFORD, A. ELLIOTT and W. E. HANBY, *Synthetic Polypeptides*, Academic Press, New York, 1956; E. KATCHALSKI and M. SELA, *Advances in Prot. Chem.* **13**, 243 (1958); M. A. STAHMANN (Editor), *Polyamino acids, Polypeptides and Proteins*. University of Wisconsin Press, Madison, 1962.
2. J. L. BAILEY, *Nature* **164**, 889 (1949); idem, *J. Chem. Soc.* **1950**, 3461; W. LAGENBECK and P. KRESSE, *J. Prakt. Chem.* **2**, 261 (1955).
3. C. H. BAMFORD, H. BLOCK and A. C. P. PUGH, *J. Chem. Soc.* **1961**, 2057.
4. E. DYER, F. L. McCARTHY, R. L. JOHNSON and E. V. NAGLE, *J. Org. Chem.* **22**, 78 (1957).
5. A. HILLMANN-ELIES, G. HILLMANN and H. JATZKEWITZ, *Z. Naturforsch.* **8b**, 455 (1953); G. AMIARD, R. HEYMES and L. VELLUZ, *Bull. Soc., chim. France* **22**, 191, 1464 (1955); idem, ibid. **23**, 97, 698 (1956); idem, U.S. Patent 2,833,399 (1959); L. VELLUZ, G. AMIARD, J. BARTOS, B. GOFFINET and R. HEYMES, *Bull. Soc., chim. France* **23**, 1464 (1956); R. A. BOISSONNASS, St. GUTTMANN, J. P. WALLER and A. A. JAQUENOUD, *Experientia* **12**, 446 (1956).
6. L. ZERVAS and D. M. THEODOROPOULOS, *J. Amer. Chem. Soc.* **78**, 1359 (1956).
7. G. C. STELAKATOS, D. M. THEODOROPOULOS and L. ZERVAS, ibid. **81**, 2884 (1959).
8. G. AMIARD and R. HEYMES, *Bull. Soc., chim. France* **24**, 1373 (1957).
9. G. S. HAMMOND and J. T. RUDESILL, *J. Amer. Chem. Soc.* **72**, 2769 (1950); C. A. BUNTON and A. KONASIEWICZ, *J. Chem. Soc.* **1955**, 1354.
10. R. SCHWYZER, B. ISELIN, W. RITTEL and P. SIEBER, *Helv. Chim. Acta* **39**, 872 (1956).
11. BEILSTEIN, *Handbuch der Organischen Chemie* (1922 Edition), **IV**, 373.

SYNTHESE VON PROLINPEPTIDEN. IV

AUFKLÄRUNG VON NEBENREAKTIONEN

E. WÜNSCH

Max-Planck-Institut für Eiweiss- und Lederforschung,
Abteilung für Peptidchemie, München

BEI der Reindarstellung von Peptiden der Sequenz Gly-Pro-X hatten wir festgestellt, dass Umkristallisieren aus heissem Wasser/Aethanol zur Abspaltung der Aminosäure X führt; am Beispiel von Gly-Pro-Ala konnte chromatographisch Alanin identifiziert werden, daneben das Diketopiperazin von Glycylprolin. Verantwortlich hierfür war der Lösungsvorgang: der prozentuelle Anteil an Spaltprodukten stieg mit der Erhitzungsdauer.

$$\text{Gly-Pro-X} \xrightarrow[\text{Erhitzen}]{\text{H}_2\text{O}} \boxed{\text{Gly-Pro}} + \text{X}$$

Besonders leicht trat diese Reaktion beim Pro-Pro-Gly auf; wurde das Tripeptid aus Lösungsmittelgemischen umkristallisiert, die etwas Wasser enthielten, zeigten sich im chromatographischen Test wechselnde Mengen an freiem Glycin.†

Im Zuge der Darstellung von Prolinpeptiden, die als Vergleichsmaterial für die Strukturaufklärung des Kollagens bzw. als Substrate der Kollagenase dienen sollten, waren des öfteren grössere Mengen an Nebenprodukten aufgetreten. Bei der Synthese von Z-Gly-Pro-Ala-OMe (m.p. 158–159°) aus Z-Gly-Pro-OH und Alaninmethylester nach dem Sheehanschen Carbodiimid-Verfahren konnten wir aus der Mutterlauge in Mengen bis 10% eine Verbindung mit m.p. 104–105° isolieren, der wir zunächst die Struktur eines Z-Glycyl-prolyl-(dicyclohexyl-)-harnstoffs zuschrieben.

Die chromatographische Untersuchung eines Hydrolysats zeigte jedoch neben Glycin und Prolin nur wenig Cyclohexylamin bzw. Alanin (letzteres sicher aus Spuren restlichen Z-tripeptid-esters); ein " Acylharnstoff " konnte daher nicht vorliegen. Die oben erwähnte leichte Bildung von Diketopiperazinen aus Gly-Pro-X liess den Schluss zu, dass ein aktiviertes Z-Gly-Pro-CO (im vorliegenden Falle das O-Lactim seine Dicyclohexyl-harnstoffs)

---

† Vgl. dazu die Ergebnisse von Rydon u. Smith [2] über die Polymerisation von Prolinpeptid-estern.

bei der Umsetzung mit Aminosäureestern als Nebenreaktion Ringschluss zum Z-diketopiperazin erleiden könnte.

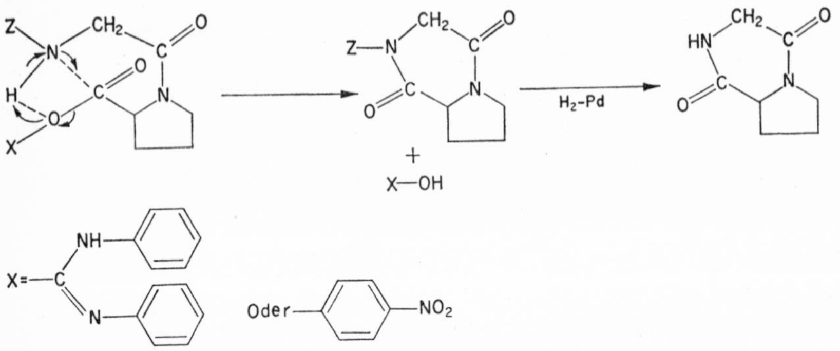

Die Beweisführung dieser Annahme sollte wie folgt gelingen:

1. Bei genannter Umsetzung von Z-Gly-Pro-OH mit sterisch gehinderten Amino-Komponenten müsste sich die Ausbeute an Nebenprodukt erhöhen, ev. dieses zum Hauptprodukt werden. Bei Versuchen mit Valinester und β-Naphtylamin war das auch der Fall.
2. Das isolierte Nebenprodukt müsste nach Entcarbobenzoxylierung (Hydrogenolyse oder Bromwasserstoff-Solvolyse) (Glycyl-prolyl)-diketo-piperazin ergeben: nach beiden Verfahren konnte die "Anhydro-verbindung" auch isoliert und chromatographisch identifiziert werden.†)

Diese Erfahrungen gaben uns die Möglichkeit, ein lange Zeit unerklärliches Problem zu lösen.

Die Synthese von Prolinpeptiden der Formel X-Pro hatten wir seit Jahren sehr erfolgreich mit Hilfe der Goldschmidtschen "Phosphorazo-Methode" ausgeführt [4]. Der Umsatz der als Zwischenprodukt postulierten Chlor-phosphit-prolinester gelang zunächst auch mit Z-dipeptiden, z.B. Z-Leu-Gly-OH; er scheiterte jedoch mit Z-Gly-Gly-OH. Über die üblichen nur als Öle gewonnenen Zwischenstufen, erhielten wir stets ein mit Glycyl-glycin verunreinigtes Glycyl-glycyl-prolin. Analog verlief auch die Synthese von Glycyl-glycyl-sarcosin; das Endprodukt war ein Gemisch von Di- und Tripeptid. Da die Reaktion von Phosphorazokörpern bzw. Chlorphosphit-amiden mit Carbonsäuren in der 1. Stufe zu einem gemischten Anhydrid führt, d.h. im vorliegendem Falle zu einem energiereichen Z-glycyl-glycyl-derivat, schien auch hier eine Nebenreaktion in Richtung Z-diketopiperazin-bildung wahrscheinlich.

† In der Zwischenzeit haben Goodman und Stueben [3] ähnliche Befunde an Hand des Z-Gly-Pro-ONP beschrieben; sie konnten das Z-diketopiperazin rein mit einem m.p. 109–110° erhalten.

Nach hydrogenolytischer Decarbobenzoxylierung des öligen Reaktions-
produkts von Z-Gly-Gly-OH und Prolinmethylester erhielten wir ein
Gemisch zweier Substanzen: 1. eine ninhydrinpositive, die sich als Glycyl-
glycyl-prolinmethylester erwies und 2. eine ninhydrinnegative, die wir
chromatographisch als Diketopiperazin identifizieren konnten.

Auf Grund dieser Ergebnisse besteht generell die Gefahr, dass bei der
Synthese von Prolinpeptiden Nebenreaktionen oben geschilderter Art
ablaufen können, sofern als Voraussetzung gegeben ist: 1. Eine " Aktivier-
ung " eines Acyl-peptids mit carboxylendständigem Prolin und 2. eine
vorausgehend sterisch nicht gehinderte Peptid- bzw. Amid-Bindung.

ZUSAMMENFASSUNG

1. Bei der Synthese von Prolinpeptiden der Sequenz Gly-Pro-X aus
   Z-Gly-Pro-OH und Aminosäureestern nach der Carbodiimid-Methode
   tritt als Nebenreaktion Bildung von Z-(glycyl-prolyl)-diketopiperazin
   auf.
2. Eine ähnliche Reaktion wird beim Umsatz von Z-glycyl-glycin mit
   den sterisch gehinderten Estern von Prolin und Sarcosin nach dem
   " Phosphorazo-Verfahren " beobachtet.

REFERENZEN

1. I. Mitt., E. Wünsch, *Hoppe-Seyler's Z. physiol. Chem.* im Druck.
   II. Mitt., E. Wünsch, ebenda im Druck.
   III. Mitt., E. Wünsch und H. G. Heidrich, ebenda im Druck.
2. H. N. Rydon und P. W. G. Smith, *J. Chem. Soc.* **1956**, 3642.
3. M. Goodman und K. C. Stueben, *J. Amer. Chem. Soc.* **84**, 1279 (1962).
4. E. Wünsch, *Angew.* **71**, 743 (1959); 2. Europ. Peptidsymposium, München, 1959.

BEITRÄGE ZUM REAKTIONSMECHANISMUS DER KUPPLUNG MIT DICYCLOHEXYLCARBODIIMID

L. Kisfaludy und M. Löw

Gedeon Richter Factory, Budapest, Hungary

Ausgehend von der Annahme, daß ein besserer Einblick in den Mechanismus der mit Dicyclohexylcarbodiimid vor sich gehenden Kondensationsreaktion geschützter Aminosäuren und Aminosäureester möglich sein wird, wenn als Aminkomponenten schwächere bzw. stärkere Basen verwendet werden als die Aminosäureester, führten wir Versuche zur Acylierung von Benzylamin und Anilin mit geschützter Aminosäure durch. Die Ergebnisse dieser Versuche sind tabellarisch zusammengefaßt. Aus den Daten der Tabelle können folgende Schlüsse gezogen werden: (a) Wenn eine schwächere Base angewandt wird als der Aminosäureester, entsteht praktisch ein einziges Endprodukt, das Amid, das sich unabhängig von der Vermischungsreihenfolge der Reaktionspartner bildet und herauspräpariert werden kann. (b) Ist die Möglichkeit der Anhydridbildung gegeben, so acyliert dieses die Aminkomponente augenblicklich (in den Fällen 1., 3., und 4.), bei der Anwendung von 0,5 Mol (1) ist also eine 40%ige und beim Arbeiten mit 1 Mol (3) eine *ca.* 80%ige Amidbildung zu erwarten, was durch die Versuchsergebnisse auch bestätigt wurde. (c) Nimmt die Wahrscheinlichkeit der Anhydridbildung ab (die Fälle 2. und 5.) so muß im Falle einer starken Base mit dem Ablauf von zwei konkurrierenden Reaktionen gerechnet werden. Die eine ist der nukleophile Angriff des freien Amins auf die protonierte Form des sich aus dem Dicyclohexylcarbodiimid durch 1,2-Addition bildenden O-Acylcarbamid-Derivates, d.h. die eigentliche Amidbildung, während die zweite die Umwandlung der nicht protonierten Form des O-Acylcarbamid-Derivates in das N-Acyl-Derivat ist. Die letztere Reaktion verläuft langsamer, da das O-Acylcarbamid eine starke Base ist und so überwiegend in der protonierten Form vorliegt. Die Geschwindigkeit der Amidbildung wird bei einer gegebenen Konzentration des protonierten O-Acylcarbamids von der Konzentration der freien Amin-Base determiniert. Das Amin liegt im Reaktionsgemisch größtenteils als geschütztes Aminosäure-Ammoniumsalz vor, da sich das freie Amin nur in der Bildungsrate des protonierten O-Acylcarbamids bildet. Im Falle von Benzylamin führt diese niedrige Amidkonzentration bei der Anwendung eines neutralen Lösungs-

Lösungsmittel	Amid		Acylcarbamid	
	Herauspräp. (%)	Nach UV-Spektrum (%)	Herauspräp. (%)	Nach UV-Spektrum (%)
1. Reihenfolge: 1. Z-Gly-OH; 2. DCCI; 3. Benzylamin; Molverhältnis 1:1:1				
DMF	41–48	62	8,7	21,6
Dioxan	34	49	21	28
Acetonitril	44	44	—	7,3
2. Reihenfolge: 1. Z-Gly-OH; 2. Benzylamin; 3. DCCI; Molverhältnis 1:1:1:1				
DMF	11–18	31	23–30	40
Dioxan	12	—	15	—
Acetonitril	54	55	—	5,8
3. Reihenfolge: 1. Z-Gly-OH; 2. DCCI; 3. Benzylamin; Molverhältnis 2:1:1				
DMF	73	—	—	—
Dioxan	70	—	—	—
Acetonitril	70	—	—	—
4. Reihenfolge: 1. Z-Gly-OH; 2. DCCI; 3. Anilin; Molverhältnis 1:1:1				
DMF	65	—	—	—
Dioxan	77	—	—	—
5. Reihenfolge: 1. Z-Gly-OH; 2. Anilin; 3. DCCI; Molverhältnis 1:1:1				
DMF	70	—	—	—
Dioxan	85	—	—	—

mittels dazu, daß sich das Amid mit ähnlicher Geschwindigkeit bildet wie das N-Acylcarbamid. Wenn mit einer schwachen Base oder mit einer starken Base in basischem Lösungsmittel gearbeitet wird, so verschiebt sich das Protonierungsgleichgewicht zugunsten der nicht protonierten Form und so kommt es bei der so entstehenden höheren Konzentration des freien Amins zu einer Verschiebung des Verhältnisses der Reaktionsgeschwindigkeiten zugunsten des Amids. Dies liefert eine Erklärung dafür, daß sich gemäß den Ergebnissen unserer Versuche im Falle einer schwachen Base praktisch nur das Amid bildet, während beim Arbeiten mit einer starken Base je nach der Qualität des Lösungsmittels auch mehr oder weniger des N-Acylcarbamid-Derivates entsteht.

EINFLUSS DER SUBSTITUIERTEN BENZYLOXY-CARBONYL-GRUPPEN AUF DIE BEI DER KUPPLUNG MIT DICYCLOHEXYLCARBODIIMID AUFTRETENDE RACEMISIERUNG

L. Kisfaludy

Gedeon Richter Factory, Budapest, Hungary

Das Maß der elektronenansaugenden Wirkung der zum vorübergehenden Schutz von Aminogruppen dienenden Acyl-Radikale, die zu einer Lockerung der αC-H Bindung führt, ist vom Gesichtspunkte der Racemisierung von besonderer Bedeutung. Eine der Gründe der ausgedehnten Anwendung des Benzyloxycarbonyl-Radikals ist, daß die elektronenansaugende Wirkung seiner Carbonylgruppe nicht nur in Richtung des N (und αC) sondern auch in Richtung des über eine große Elektronendichte verfügende Sauerstoffatoms zur Geltung gelangt. Auf Grund dieses Gesichtspunktes untersuchten wir den Einfluß der durch uns verwendeten p-Chlorbenzyloxycarbonyl-Schutzgruppe auf die Racemisierung. Unter den $-I$ und $+M$ Effekten des im aromatischen Ring in p-Stellung stehenden Cl-Atoms ist der erstere stärker, was zur Folge hat, daß die C-Atome des Ringes eine partiale positive Ladung erhalten. Das bedeutet aber wiederum, daß die Elektronendichte des mit der Benzylgruppe verbundenen O-Atoms abnimmt und so die elektronenansaugende Wirkung der Carbonylgruppe in Richtung des N (und αC) etwas stärker zur Geltung gelang als im Falle der unsubstituierten Benzyloxycarbonyl-Gruppe.

Um diese Theorie unter Beweis zu stellen, wurde die Methode von Anderson und Callahan gewählt, die das Benzyloxycarbonyl-Glycyl-L-Phenylalanin in Gegenwart von Dicyclohexylcarbodiimid mit Glycinäthylester kuppelten und dabei fanden, daß der geschützte racemische Tripeptidester unter den gegebenen Versuchsbedingungen aus 2%iger äthanolischer Lösung auskristallisiert. Im Durchschnitt der Ergebnisse von drei Versuchen erhielten sie das Racemat bei Raumtemperatur in 7,4% und bei $-5°$ unter 1%. Bei ser Durchführung des gleichen Verfahrens in Gegenwart der p-Chlorbenzyloxycarbonyl-Schutzgruppe erhielten wir den erwähnten racemischen Tripeptidester im Durchschnitt der Ergebnisse von vier Versuchen bei Raumtemperatur in 8,7 und bei $0°$ in 2,5%. Diese experimentellen Ergebnisse erhärten also die obigen theoretischen Überlegungen.

GASCHROMATOGRAPHISCHE UNTERSUCHUNG DER RACEMISIERUNG BEI PEPTIDSYNTHESEN †

F. WEYGAND, A. PROX, L. SCHMIDHAMMER und W. KÖNIG

Organisch-chemisches Institut der Technischen Hochschule, München

AM Beispiel des Diastereoisomerenpaares N-TFA-L-Ala.L-Phe.OCH$_3$ + N-TFA-L-Ala.D-Phe.OCH$_3$ wurde erstmals die gaschromatographische Trennung in die Diastereoisomeren an einer nur 2 m langen gepackten Säule mit Siliconöl als flüssiger Phase beobachtet [1] . Weitere diastereoisomere N-TFA-Dipeptidmethylester lassen sich, wie wir inzwischen festgestellt haben, an Kapillarsäulen nach Golay trennen. Nicht bei allen Verbindungen ist die Trennung an einer 50 m langen Golay-Säule, die mit Polypropylenglykol belegt ist, so gut, wie man es für die Untersuchung der bei Peptidsynthesen auftretenden Racemisierung fordern muß.

Abb. 1, Kurve A, zeigt die Trennung von N-TFA-L-Ala.L-Leu.OCH$_3$ und N-TFA-D-Ala.L-Leu.OCH$_3$, die Kurve B diejenige von N-TFA-L-Val.L-Val.OCH$_3$ und N-TFA-D-Val.L-Val.OCH$_3$ bei 180°. Man erkennt, daß die Auflösung δ [2] im ersten Fall unter den angewandten Bedingungen nur 59%, im zweiten Fall aber 98% beträgt. In Tab. 1 sind weitere δ-Werte angegeben. Aus dem Zusammenhang zwischen Auflösung und Stoffüberlagerung [3] (Tab. 2), die allerdings nur für ideale Gauss-Verteilungskurven gilt, folgt, daß beispielsweise bei einer Auflösung von 90% 0,9% Diastereoisomeres nicht mehr erkannt werden kann. Daher können nur Dipeptide mit einer Auflösung von über 90% zur quantitativen Untersuchung herangezogen werden, wenn die noch nachweisbare Menge an Racemisierungsprodukt weniger als 1% betragen soll. Es ist zu erwarten, daß noch weitere Dipeptide als die in Tab. 1 aufgeführten eine diesbezügliche Auflösung geben werden, denn hinsichtlich der anzuwendenden chromatographischen Bedingungen ergeben sich noch weite Variationsmöglichkeiten. Es sei darauf hingewiesen, daß die Auflösung durch Tailing beeinträchtigt wird. Die Angaben in Tab. 1 und 2 schließen dieses ein.

Bezüglich der gaschromatographischen Diastereoisomerentrennung zur Untersuchung der Racemisierung bei Peptidsynthesen gelten folgende allgemeine Einschränkungen:

† Abkürzungen: NBS = Bromsuccinimid; THF = Tetrahydrofuran; DMF = Dimethylformamid; TÄA = Triäthylamin; i.U. = im Unterschuß (0,9 Äquiv.).

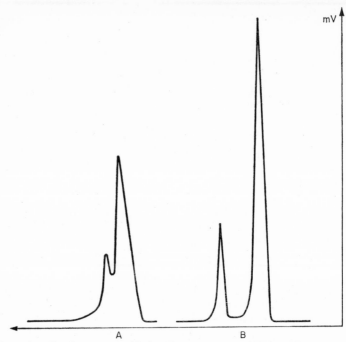

Abb. 1.   Gaschromatographische Trennung von N-TFA-L-Ala.L-Leu.OCH$_3$
und N-TFA-D-Ala.L-Leu.OCH$_3$ (Kurve A) sowie von N-TFA-L-Val.L-Val.OCH$_3$
und N-TFA-D-Val.L-Val.OCH$_3$ (Kurve B).

Tabelle 1.   Trennung von diastereomeren
N-TFA-Dipeptid-methylestern

Golay-S.R., Trenntemp. 180°, Strömungsgeschw.: 2,19 Nml. N$_2$/min
Teilerverh.: 1:15.   Standard: Myristinsäuremethylester = 1,00

Sequenz	diastereom. Verbindg.	q_G†	δ (%)	Sequenz	diastereom. Verbindg.	q_G	δ (%)
Ala-Ala	L-L	0,92	93	Val-Leu	L-L	1,64	87
	L-D	0,86			L-D	1,77	
Ala-Val	L-L	1,07	78	Leu-Val	L-L	1,45	99
	L-D	1,12			L-D	1,58	
Ala-Leu	L-L	1,62	59	Leu-Leu	L-L	2,14	92
	L-D	1,67			L-D	2,29	
Val-Val	L-L	1,08	98	Leu-Ile	L-L	1,99	96
	L-D	1,19			L-D	2,19	
Leu-Ala	L-L	1,27	0	Leu-Pro	L-L	2,58	69
	L-D				L-D	2,64	

† q_G = relative Gesamtretention bezogen auf den Standard.

TABELLE 2. ZUSAMMENHANG ZWISCHEN AUFLÖSUNG
UND STOFFÜBERLAGERUNG

Auflösung δ (%)	Stoffüberlagerung (%)
50	12,5
80	3,2
90	0,9
99	0,0001

Die Methode ist generell auf Dipeptide mit zumindest zwei optisch aktiven Aminosäuren beschränkt.

L.L- und D.D-Verbindungen bzw. L.D- und D.L-Verbindungen können nicht unterschieden werden. Daher kann nicht entschieden werden, welche der beiden Aminosäuren racemisierte. Bei den Dipeptidsynthesen kann jedoch allgemein angenommen werden, daß eine Racemisierung, falls sie erfolgt, nur die N-terminale, aktivierte Aminosäure betrifft.

Die quantitative Auswertung der Fraktogramme geschieht durch integrale Ausmessung der Banden. Die Abb. 2 zeigt die Abhängigkeit der Verhältnisse der Flächeninhalte von der prozentualen Zusammensetzung einer Mischung von N-TFA-L-Val.L-Val.OCH$_3$ + N-TFA-L-Val.D-Val.OCH$_3$, die praktisch linear ist. Dasselbe ergab sich für die N-TFA-Leu.Val.OCH$_3$-Diastereoisomeren. Bei der Methode wird also die Menge an diastereoisomerer

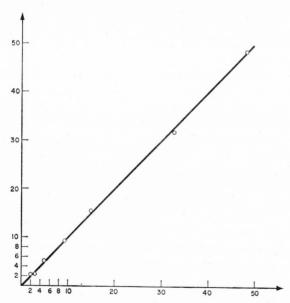

ABB. 2. Eichgerade der Diastereomerentrennung von N-TFA-Val-Val-OCH$_3$.

Verbindung im Gesamtgemisch des gebildeten Peptids prozentual ermittelt. Der Racemisierungsgrad ergibt sich durch Verdoppelung dieser Werte. Der mittlere Fehler der Einzelmessung betrug ±0,4%. Bei der gaschromatographischen Untersuchung findet keine zusätzliche, z.B. thermisch bedingte Racemisierung statt.

Die Empfindlichkeit des Verfahrens übertrifft die aller bisher angewandter Methoden an Stereospezifität, Erfassung des Gesamtmaterials, quantitativer Genauigkeit und der Nachweisgrenze. Wir haben uns bisher darauf beschränkt, die Angaben nur von 1% an aufwärts an diastereoisomerer Verbindung im Gesamtgemisch zu bestimmen. Bei hoher Auflösung, wie bei den Val.Val-Peptiden sind jedoch noch geringere Racemisierungsgrade quantitativ erfaßbar (Abb. 3).

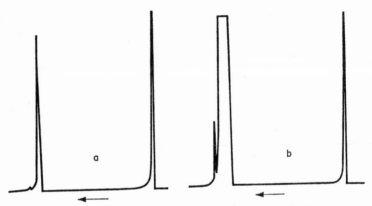

ABB. 3. Trennung von N-TFA-Val-Val-OCH₃ an Golay-Säule R. Nachweis von geringen Mengen L-D-Verbindung in L-L-Verbindung durch entsprechend vergrößerte Substanzaufgabe: (a) 0,2 µl, (b) 1,0 µl. Die Aufgabe erfolgte in 5%iger EtOAc-Lösung. Der zugewogene Teil an D-L-Verbindung bezogen auf das Gesamtgemisch betrug 2%.

Ein großer Vorteil des Verfahrens ist der, daß keinerlei Isolierung des Produktes vorgenommen werden muß. Sie ist im Gegenteil streng zu vermeiden, weil z.B. durch die Abtrennung des Produktes in krist. Form eine Fraktionierung eintreten kann. Nebenprodukte der Synthese oder nicht umgesetzte Ausgangsverbindungen stören nicht, weil sie, wenn überhaupt, an anderer Stelle im Gaschromatogramm erscheinen.

Bei der Untersuchung der Racemisierung bei der Synthese von N-TFA-Dipeptidmethylestern ist nach beendeter Umsetzung keinerlei Aufarbeitung vor der Gaschromatographie erforderlich. Leicht flüchtige Lösungsmittel wurden jedoch i.Vak. bei Zimmertemperatur entfernt, worauf der Rückstand in Essigester aufgenommen und mit verd. Natriumhydrogencarbonatlösung, mit verd. Salzsäure und mit Wasser gewaschen und über Natriumsulfat getrocknet wurde. Nach der Synthese von Benzyloxycarbonyl-dipeptidmethylestern wird ebenso verfahren, der Essigester i.Vak. abdestilliert und der Rückstand durch Erhitzen mit wasserfreier Trifluoressigsäure entcarbobenzoxyliert, sodann mit Trifluoressigsäuremethylester unter Zusatz von Triäthylamin in abs. Methanol N-trifluoracetyliert. Die N-TFA-Dipeptidmethylester wurden in Essigester gelöst, eingespritzt.

Durch Veresterung von reinstem H.L-Val.L-Val.OH mit Methanol.HCl und N-Trifluoracetylierung wurde anschließend gaschromatographisch bewiesen, daß bei beiden Operationen keine Racemisierung stattfindet.†

In der vorliegenden Mitteilung wird hauptsächlich über Racemisierungsuntersuchungen bei der Synthese von Z.Val.Val.OCH$_3$ und N-TFA-Val. Val.OCH$_3$ berichtet. Wir haben diese Sequenz als erste eingehend untersucht, weil die Reaktionsgeschwindigkeit bei der Synthese sterisch gehinderter Dipeptide im allgemeinen viel geringer als bei anderen Sequenzen ist,‡ wodurch die Gefahr der Racemisierung auf der Stufe des aktivierten Derivates erhöht sein sollte. Ferner ist die Auflösung, wie schon oben erwähnt wurde, in diesem Falle besonders gut.

Wenn in den nachstehenden Tabellen der Racemisierungsgrad unter 2% angegeben ist, d.h. die Menge an ermittelter diastereoisomerer Verbindung geringer als 1% ist, so bedeutet das, daß entweder gar keine Racemisierung festzustellen war oder daß sie wirklich geringer als 2% ist. Wir möchten uns in diesen Fällen noch nicht festlegen.

Sämtliche Versuche wurden mit demselben L-Valin ausgeführt. Da bei einigen Synthesen keine Racemisierung gefunden wurde, ergibt sich auch, daß das Ausgangsmaterial frei von Racemat war.

Die gaschromatographischen Untersuchungen wurden mit einem Fraktometer 116 E (Perkin-Elmer u. Co.), ausgerüstet mit einem Kompensationsschreiber (Kompensograph, Siemens u. Halske) und einem Flammenionisationsdetektor, ausgeführt. Es wurde die handelsübliche Golay-Säule R (Polypropylenglykol, 50 m Stahl) von Perkin-Elmer u. Co. verwendet. Die Trenntemperatur betrug 180°, als Trägergas diente Stickstoff. Das Teilungsverhältnis lag zwischen 1:20 und 1:25, die Strömungsgeschwindigkeit betrug 1,27 Nml/min.

RESULTATE

Folgende Verfahren zur Herstellung der Peptidbindung wurden untersucht:

1. Methode der aktivierten Ester (p-Nitrophenylester [4], Cyanmethylester [5], Thiophenylester in Eisessig [6] und Vinylester [7]).

---

† Versuch von Herrn. I. Tomida ausgeführt.
‡ Nach kinetischen Messungen von Herrn D. Hoffter verläuft z.B. die Synthese von N-TFA-Val.Val.OCH$_3$ nach der Vinylester-Methode in Malonester bei 30° 17-mal langsamer als die Synthese von N-TFA-Ala.Val.OCH$_3$.

2. Dicyclohexylcarbodiimid-Methode [8].
3. Azid-Methode [9].
4. Carbonyldiimidazol-Methode [10].
5. Phosphorazo-Methode [11].
6. Methode der gemischten Anhydride [12].
7. Methode nach Woodward [13].
8. Methode nach Patchornik (Hydrazid + Bromsuccinimid) [14].

Bei der Synthese von Z.Val.Val.OCH$_3$ (Tab. 3) ist auffällig, daß bei fast
allen Peptidsynthesen unter den angegebenen Bedingungen nur sehr geringe

TABELLE 3.   RACEMISIERUNGSUNTERSUCHUNGEN BEI PEPTIDSYNTHESEN
DARSTELLUNG VON Z-VAL-VAL-OCH$_3$
(die gaschromatographische Untersuchung erfolgte als N-TFA-Val-Val-OCH$_3$)

Methode	Ester dest.	Ester HCl + N(C$_2$H$_5$)$_3$	Lsgm.	Temp. (°C)	Zeit (h)	Menge an diastereom. Verbindung (%)	Racemisie-rungsgrad (%)
Akt. Ester							
O-C$_6$H$_4$.NO$_2$	+	−	EtOAc	+ 24	48	< 1	< 2
O-C$_6$H$_4$.NO$_2$	−	+	EtOAc	+ 24	48	< 1	< 2
O-CH$_2$.CN	+	−	EtOAc	+ 24	48	kein Peptid!	−
O-CH$_2$.CN	+	−	EtOAc	110	2	kein Peptid!	−
O-CH$_2$.CN	+	−	EtOAc	110	8	1	2
S-C$_6$H$_5$	freie	Aminosre.	Eisessig	120	2	14,5 ± 0,4	29
DCCI	+	−	CH$_2$Cl$_2$	− 10	48	< 1	< 2
	+	−	CH$_2$Cl$_2$	+ 24	48	< 1	< 2
	−	+	CH$_2$Cl$_2$	− 10	48	< 1	< 2
	−	+	CH$_2$Cl$_2$	+ 24	48	< 1	< 2
Azid	+	−	Äther	− 10	48	< 1	< 2
	−	+	Äther	− 10	48	< 1	< 2
CDI	+	−	THF	+ 24	60	< 1	< 2
	−	+	THF	+ 24	60	0,5	1
Phosphorazo	−	+	Pyridin	100	3	< 1	< 2
Gem. Anhydr. -O-CO$_2$C$_2$H$_5$	+	−	THF	+ 24†	12	< 1	< 2
Woodward	+	−	CH$_3$CN	+ 24	24	< 1	< 2
Patchornik NBS	−	+	DMF	0	7 Min.	< 1	< 2

† Komponenten wurden bei − 35° zusammengegeben nach einer Vorschrift von
E. Schröder (Privatmitteilung).

bzw. keine Racemisierung eintrat. Lediglich bei der Cyanmethylester-Methode, bei der sich durch den langsamen Reaktionsablauf die sterische Hinderung deutlich zeigt, fanden wir eine Racemisierung von 2% und bei der Eisessigmethode mit Thiophenylester (freies L-Valin als zweite Komponente) fanden wir 29% Racemisierung. Bei sterisch wenig gehinderten Aminosäuren hatten wir seinerzeit [6], allerdings auf üblichem Wege, ermittelt, daß keine Racemisierung bei der Synthese mit Benzyloxycarbonyl-aminosäure-thiophenylestern und freien Aminosäuren in Eisessig stattfindet.

Ganz anders ist das Bild, das sich bei den Synthesen von N-TFA-Val.Val. OCH$_3$ ergibt. Von den Peptidsynthesen mit N-TFA-Aminosäurethiophenyl-estern her, insbesondere in Eisessig unter Isolierung der Produkte, wußten wir schon, daß bei den N-TFA-Aminosäuren viel leichter Racemisierung eintritt als bei den Benzyloxycarbonylaminosäuren. Die N-TFA-Aminosäuren ähneln insofern also acylierten Peptiden, was für die Verwendung letzterer zu Peptidsynthesen von großer Bedeutung ist.

Tab. 4 zeigt deutlich, daß von den untersuchten Peptidsynthesen nur zwei, nämlich die Azid-Methode und die Vinylester-Methode keine Racemisierung ergeben. Auch bei der Synthese von N-TFA-L-Val.L-Leu.OC$_2$H$_5$ aus N-TFA-L-Val.OCH=CH$_2$ und L-Leucinäthylester-hydrochlorid + Na-Malonat in Malonester (2 Wochen bei 20°) wurde keine Racemisierung beobachtet. Alle anderen Methoden zeigten in Abhängigkeit von den Reaktionsbedingungen zum Teil sehr starke Racemisierungen.† Von Einfluß sind die Reaktionstemperatur, das Lösungsmittel und die Art und Weise, in welcher L-Valinmethylester eingesetzt wurde, d.h. ob dest. Ester oder Esterhydrochlorid + Triäthylamin verwendet wurde.

Diese Faktoren wurden an der so häufig angewandten Dicyclohexyl-carbodiimid-Methode näher studiert. Tab. 5 zeigt, daß die Racemisierung bei einer Temperatursteigerung von −10° auf +24° durchschnittlich um das 3 bis 5-fache ansteigt. Setzt man dem dest. Ester Triäthylamin (bis 1 Äquiv.) zu, so zeigt sich zunehmende Racemisierung mit steigender Triäthylaminmenge. Aber auch Triäthylammoniumchlorid bewirkt in Abhängigkeit von seiner Konzentration Racemisierung. In Methylenchlorid, in dem es gut löslich ist, findet z.B. bei 24° zu 68% Racemisierung statt, während unter gleichen Bedingungen in Tetrahydrofuran, in dem es wesentlich schwerer löslich ist, nur 8,8% racemisierten. In diesem Zusammenhang konnte festgestellt werden, daß auch andere Salze, wie Triäthylammonium-acetat‡ oder Pyridin-hydrochlorid in Methylenchlorid sowie Lithium-bromid in Tetrahydrofuran beträchtliche Racemisierung hervorriefen. Dem

---

† Die Methode der gemischten Anhydride ist bei N-TFA-Aminosäuren wegen der Azlactonbildung nicht anwendbar. Nicht untersucht wurde bei den N-TFA-Verbindungen die p-Nitrophenylester-Methode und die Phosphorazomethode.

‡ Hierbei entstand auch N-Acetyl-valin-methylester.

TABELLE 4. RACEMISIERUNGSUNTERSUCHUNGEN BEI PEPTIDSYNTHESEN
DARSTELLUNG VON N-TFA-VAL-VAL-OCH$_3$

Methode	Ester dest.	Ester. HCl + N(C$_2$H$_5$)$_3$	Lsgm.	Temp. (°C)	Zeit (h)	Menge an diastereom. Verbindung (%)	Racemisierungsgrad (%)
Akt. Ester							
O-Vinyl	+	−	Malonester.	+ 24	72	< 1	< 2
O-Vinyl	+	−	Cyanessigester	100	2	< 1	< 2
O-CH$_2$.CN	+	−	EtOAc	+ 24	48	kein Peptid	−
O-CH$_2$.CN	+	−	EtOAc	110	2	s. w. Peptid	−
O-CH$_2$.CN	+	−	EtOAc	110	13	8,4 ± 0,4	16,8
O-CH$_2$.CN	−	+	EtOAc	110	8	10,8 ± 0,4	21,6
S-C$_6$H$_5$	freie	Aminosre.	Eisessig	130	2	19,3 ± 0,4	38,6
DCCI	+	−	CH$_2$Cl$_2$	− 10	72	1,2 ± 0,4	2,4
	+	−	CH$_2$Cl$_2$	+ 24	72	3,6 ± 0,4	7,2
	−	+	CH$_2$Cl$_2$	− 10	48	9,2 ± 0,4	18,4
	−	+	CH$_2$Cl$_2$	+ 24	48	21,0 ± 0,4	42,0
Azid†	+	−	EtOAc	− 10	43	< 1	< 2
	−	+	EtOAc	− 10	43	< 1	< 2
CDI	+	−	THF	− 10	19	9,2 ± 0,4	18,4
	+	−	THF	+ 24	23	45,4 ± 0,4	90,8
	−	+	THF	+ 24	22	45,1 ± 0,4	90,2
Woodward	+	−	CH$_3$CN	+ 24	13	34,7 ± 0,4	69,4
Patchornik NBS	−	+	DMF	0	7 Min.	11,7 ± 0,4	23,4

† Wurde über N-TFA-L-Val-NH-NH-CPh$_3$ synthetisiert.   Das Tritylhydrazid wurde aus N-TFA-Val mit DCCI bei Zimmertemperatur dargestellt und durch Umkristallisation gereinigt.

gegenüber bewirkt L-Valinmethylester-hydrochlorid nur eine geringe Zunahme der Racemisierung (von 7,2 auf 13,4%).

Aus Tab. 5, Abschnitt 4, geht ferner hervor, daß mit Dimethylformamid als Lösungsmittel bei + 24° in allen Fällen eine erhebliche Racemisierung auftrat, wobei der gebildete Dicyclohexylharnstoff in Lösung blieb. Lediglich bei tiefer Temperatur und unter Freisetzung von L-Valin-methylester mit nur 0,9 Äquiv. Triäthylamin fand in Methylenchlorid oder Tetrahydrofuran nur geringe Racemisierung statt (etwa 2%).

Da bei der Carbonyl-diimidazol-Methode starke Racemisierung festgestellt worden war, wurde auch bei der Dicyclohexylcarbodiimid-Methode geprüft, wie sich zugesetztes Imidazol oder N-Benzyl-imidazol verhielt. Es zeigte sich in beiden Fällen etwa 80-proz. Racemisierung. Diese Beobachtung kann allgemein für die Synthese von Histidin-haltigen Sequenzen nach der Dicyclohexylcarbodiimid-Methode von Bedeutung sein. Der Zusatz von Wasser zu Tetrahydrofuran hat bei der Dicyclohexyl-carbodiimid-Methode ein starkes Ansteigen der Racemisierung (auf 55%) selbst bei Verwendung von dest. Ester zur Folge.

TABELLE 5. RACEMISIERUNGSUNTERSUCHUNGEN BEI PEPTIDSYNTHESEN
DARSTELLUNG VON N-TFA-VAL-VAL-OCH$_3$ MIT DICYCLOHEXYLCARBODIIMID

Ester dest.	Ester. HCl + $N(C_2H_5)_3$	Lsgm.	Temp. (°C)	Zusätze (Molprozente)	Zeit (h)	Menge an diastereom. Verbindung (%)	Racemisie-rungsgrad (%)
1. TEMPERATUREINFLUSS							
+	−	CH_2Cl_2	− 10	−	72	$1,2 \pm 0,4$	2,4
+	−	CH_2Cl_2	+ 24	−	72	$3,6 \pm 0,4$	7,2
+	−	CH_2Cl_2	− 10	10% TÄA	48	$1,9 \pm 0,4$	3,8
+	−	CH_2Cl_2	+ 24	10% TÄA	41	$11,0 \pm 0,4$	22,0
+	−	CH_2Cl_2	− 10	100% TÄA.HCl	48	$2,6 \pm 0,4$	5,2
+	−	CH_2Cl_2	+ 24	100% TÄA.HCl	41	$34,0 \pm 0,4$	68,0
+	−	THF	− 10	10% TÄA	90	$1,8 \pm 0,4$	3,6
+	−	THF	+ 24	10% TÄA	24	$8,5 \pm 0,4$	17,0
−	+	CH_2Cl_2	− 10	TÄA i. Unters.	48	< 1	< 2
−	+	CH_2Cl_2	+ 24	TÄA i. Unters.	41	$21,8 \pm 0,4$	43,6
2. EINFLUSS VON TERTIÄRER BASE							
+	−	CH_2Cl_2	+ 24	10% TÄA	41	$11,0 \pm 0,4$	22,0
+	−	CH_2Cl_2	+ 24	30% TÄA	47,5	$19,2 \pm 0,4$	38,4
+	−	CH_2Cl_2	+ 24	60% TÄA	47,5	$31,8 \pm 0,4$	63,6
+	−	CH_2Cl_2	+ 24	100% TÄA	70	$44,9 \pm 0,4$	89,8
+	−	CH_2Cl_2	− 10	10% TÄA	48	$1,9 \pm 0,4$	3,8
+	−	THF	− 10	10% TÄA	90	$1,8 \pm 0,4$	3,6
+	−	THF	+ 24	10% TÄA	24	$8,5 \pm 0,4$	17,0
3. EINFLUSS VON SALZEN							
+	−	CH_2Cl_2	+ 24	10% TÄA.HCl	47	$5,3 \pm 0,4$	10,6
+	−	CH_2Cl_2	+ 24	50% TÄA.HCl	47	$17,7 \pm 0,4$	35,4
+	−	CH_2Cl_2	+ 24	100% TÄA.HCl	41	$34,0 \pm 0,4$	68,0
+	−	CH_2Cl_2	− 10	100% TÄA.HCl	48	$2,6 \pm 0,4$	5,2
+	−	THF	− 10	100% TÄA.HCl	90	$2,2 \pm 0,4$	4,4
+	−	THF	+ 24	100% TÄA.HCl	24	$4,4 \pm 0,4$	8,8
+	−	CH_2Cl_2	+ 24	100% TÄA.AcOH	70	$41,5 \pm 0,4$	83,0
+	−	CH_2Cl_2	+ 24	100% Pyrid.HCl	70	$18,3 \pm 0,4$	36,6
+	−	CH_2Cl_2	+ 24	100% Ester.HCl	67	$6,7 \pm 0,4$	13,4
+	−	THF	+ 24	100% LiBr	68	$13,3 \pm 0,4$	26,6
+	−	CH_2Cl_2	+ 24	100% N-TFA-Val 100% H-Val-OCH$_3$	69	$6,2 \pm 0,4$	12,4

TABELLE 5 (Fortsetzung)

Ester dest.	Ester. HCl + $N(C_2H_5)_3$	Lsgm.	Temp. (°C)	Zusätze (Molprozente)	Zeit (h)	Menge an diastereom. Verbindung (%)	Racemisierungsgrad (%)
4. EINFLUSS VON LÖSUNGSMITTELN							
+	−	CH_2Cl_2	− 10	10% TÄA	48	1,9 ± 0,4	3,8
+	−	CH_2Cl_2	− 10	100% TÄA.HCl	48	2,6 ± 0,4	5,2
−	+	CH_2Cl_2	− 10	TÄA i. Unters.	48	< 1	< 2
+	−	THF	− 10	10% TÄA	90	1,8 ± 0,4	3,6
+	−	THF	− 10	100% TÄA,HCl	90	2,2 ± 0,4	4,4
−	+	THF	− 10	TÄA i. Unters.	90	0,9	1,8
+	−	CH_2Cl_2	+ 24	10% TÄA	41	11,0 ± 0,4	22,0
+	−	CH_2Cl_2	+ 24	100% TÄA.HCl	41	34,0 ± 0,4	68,0
−	+	CH_2Cl_2	+ 24	TÄA i. Unters.	41	21,8 ± 0,4	43,6
+	−	THF	+ 24	10% TÄA	24	8,5 ± 0,4	17,0
+	−	THF	+ 24	100% TÄA.HCl	24	4,4 ± 0,4	8,8
−	+	THF	+ 24	TÄA i. Unters.	24	9,5 ± 0,4	19,0
+	−	DMF	+ 24	—	70	26,7 ± 0,4	53,4
+	−	DMF	+ 24	10% TÄA	90	29,7 ± 0,4	59,4
+	−	DMF	+ 24	100% TÄA.HCl	91	31,3 ± 0,4	62,6
−	+	DMF	+ 24	TÄA i. Unters.	91	29,4 ± 0,4	58,8
5. EINFLUSS DER REAKTIONSZEIT							
+	−	CH_2Cl_2	+ 24	100% TÄA.HCl	24	28,0 ± 0,4	56,0
+	−	CH_2Cl_2	+ 24	100% TÄA.HCl	48	28,6 ± 0,4	57,2
+	−	CH_2Cl_2	+ 24	100% TÄA.HCl	96	30,9 ± 0,4	61,8
6. EINFLUSS VON WEITEREN ZUSÄTZEN							
+	−	CH_2Cl_2	+ 24	100% Imidazol	68	41,1 ± 0,4	82,2
+	−	CH_2Cl_2	+ 24	100% N-Benzyl-imidazol	47	38,8 ± 0,4	77,6
+	−	THF/H_2O 1:1	+ 24	—	47	27,5 ± 0,4	55,0
Versuch nach der *Vinylester-Methode*:							
+	−	Malon-ester	+ 24	CO_2 eingeleitet	93	< 1	< 2

Die vorliegenden Ergebnisse zeigen, daß die neue Methode zur Ermittlung der Racemisierung bei Peptidsynthesen eine wertvolle Ergänzung nicht nur der enzymatischen, sondern auch des Young-Testes [15] (Synthese von N-Acetyl-L-Leu.Gly.OC_2H_5), des Anderson-Testes [16] (Synthese von Z.Gly. L-Phe.Gly.OC_2H_5) und des Kenner-Testes [17] (Synthese von Z.Gly.L-

Ala.L-Phe.Gly.OH) darstellt, bei denen die Peptidverknüpfung bei sterisch weniger gehinderten und daher relativ schnell verlaufenden Synthesen vorgenommen wird.

Man darf annehmen, daß bei denjenigen Methoden zur Knüpfung der Peptidbindung, bei denen bei der Synthese von N-TFA-L-Val.L-Val.OCH$_3$ keine Racemisierung gefunden wurde, auch bei der Synthese mit anderen Aminosäuren keine Racemisierung auftritt.   Als nächstes sollen Peptidsynthesen mit racemisierungsempfindlicheren Aminosäuren, wie Phenylalanin und S-Benzyl-cystein untersucht werden, wobei im letzteren Fall mit Raney-Nickel zum Alanin-Derivat zu entschwefeln ist.

Es fragt sich nun, ob die neue Methode auch auf die Untersuchung der Racemisierung bei der Synthese von Tri-oder Oligopeptiden angewandt werden kann.   Dies hängt davon ab, ob die Partialhydrolyse zu Dipeptiden racemisierungsfrei verläuft.·   Im Falle des Tetrapeptid-Derivates Z.Gly.L-Ala.L-Phe.Gly.OH, das umkristallisiert worden war, wurde nach der Partialhydrolyse mit 5N-Chlorwasserstoff im veresterten und N-trifluoracetylierten Dipeptidgemisch—allerdings bei noch nicht über 90-proz. Auflösung—nur N-TFA-L-Ala.L-Phe.OCH$_3$ und kein diastereoisomeres Peptid gefunden. Weitere Untersuchungen sind in dieser Hinsicht noch erforderlich.

Der Deutschen Forschungsgemeinschaft danken wir bestens für eine Sachspende.

REFERENZEN

1. F. Weygand, B. Kolb, A. Prox, M. A. Tilak und I. Tomida, *Hoppe-Seyler's Z. physiol. Chem.* **322**, 38 (1960).
2. R. Kayser, *Chromatographie in der Gasphase*, Bd. II, S. 32, Bibliographisches Institut, Mannheim, 1961.
3. R. Kayser, ebenda Bd. I, S. 53.
4. M. Bodanszky, *Nature* **175**, 685 (1955).
5. R. Schwyzer und Mitarb., *Helv. Chim. Acta* **38**, 69, 80, 83 (1955); F. Weygand und W. Swodenk, *Chem. Ber.* **90**, 639 (1957).
6. F. Weygand und W. Steglich, *Chem. Ber.* **93**, 2983 (1960).
7. F. Weygand und W. Steglich, *Angew. Chem.* **73**, 99 (1961).
8. J. P. Sheehan und G. P. Hess, *J. Amer. Chem. Soc.* **77**, 1067 (1955).
9. T. Curtius, *Ber.* **35**, 3226 (1902); J. I. Harris und T. S. Work, *Biochem. J.* **46**, 582 (1950); M. A. Nyman und R. M. Herbst, *J. Org. Chem.* **15**, 108 (1950).
10. G. W. Anderson und R. Paul, *J. Amer. Chem. Soc.* **80**, 4423 (1958).
11. S. Goldschmidt und H. Lautenschlager, *Liebigs Ann. Chem.* **580**, 68 (1953).
12. T. Wieland und R. Sehring, *Liebigs Ann. Chem.* **569**, 122 (1950); R. A. Boissonnas, *Helv. Chim. Acta* **34**, 874 (1951); J. R. Vaughan, jr., *J. Amer. Chem. Soc.* **73**, 3547 (1951); T. Wieland und H. Bernhard, *Liebigs Ann. Chem.* **572**, 190 (1951).
13. R. B. Woodward, R. A. Olofson und H. Meyer, *J. Amer. Chem. Soc.* **83**, 1010 (1961).
14. Y. Wolman, P. M. Gallop und A. Patchornik, *J. Amer. Chem. Soc.* **83**, 1263 (1961).
15. N. B. North und G. T. Young, *Chem. u. Industry* **1955**, 1597; N. A. Smart, G. T. Young und M. W. Williams, *J. Chem. Soc.* **1960**, 3902.
16. G. W. Anderson und F. M. Callahan, *J. Amer. Chem. Soc.* **80**, 2902 (1958).
17. D. W. Clayton, J A. Farrington, G. W. Kenner und J. M. Turner, *J. Chem. Soc.* **1957**, 1398.

DETECTION OF DIASTEREOISOMERS IN DIPEPTIDES BY PAPER CHROMATOGRAPHY

E. Taschner, A. Chimiak, J. F. Biernat, T. Sokołowska, Cz. Wasielewski and B. Rzeszotarska

Department of General Chemistry, Technical University, Gdańsk, Poland

Methods now used to demonstrate the racemization that occurs during the synthesis of peptides are not always quite satisfactory since they cannot be fully applied to the control of all the chemical operations accomplished in these syntheses. The lack of necessary experimental data due to the short-comings of the actual methods of detection of the racemization hinders an effective search for the elimination of this disturbing phenomenon. In order to solve, at least partially, this problem, we thought that a new tool for the detection of the racemization occurring during the synthesis of peptides was needed.

Having this in mind, we were able to observe that the two diastereoisomers of LD-LD dipeptides can be separated on paper chromatograms (Whatman No. 1 or 3 paper, ascending technique, strip length 30 cm, development with

TABLE 1. DOUBLE R_F VALUES OF DL, DL-DIPEPTIDES

Peptides	R_F	Peptides	R_F
Ala-Pro	0·48 0·41	α-Glu-Abut	0·56 0·44
α-Asp-Ala†	0·21 0·17	α-Glu-Phe	0·82 0·72
α-Asp-Glu†	0·19 0·16	Phe-Pro	0·72 0·65
α-Asp-Phe†	0·43 0·33	Pro-Abut	0·63 0·57
α-Glu-Ala	0·68 0·57	Pro-Phe	0·66 0·58

System: ethyl acetate, pyridine, acetic acid, water (5:5:1:3).
† L, DL-dipeptides.
Abut = α-aminobutyric acid.

TABLE 2. THE R_F VALUES OF DIASTEREOISOMERS OF DIPEPTIDES IN RELATION TO THEIR CONFIGURATION

Dipeptides	Configuration of component amino-acids									
	R_F in S_1					R_F in S_2				
	DL-DL	L-L	D-D	L-D	D-L	DL-DL	L-L	D-D	L-D	D-L
Ala-Ala	do not separ.					0·44 0·37	0·44			
Ala-But	0·53 0·47		0·53		0·47	0·48 0·43		0·48		0·43
Ala-Leu	0·79 0·73	0·79				0·60 0·54	0·60			
Ala-Phe	0·69 0·62	0·69			0·62	0·72 0·55	0·71			0·56
Ala-Val	0·60 0·54	0·60			0·54	0·73 0·50	0·73			0·51
But-Ala	0·58 0·51				0·50	0·68 0·51				0·51
But-But	0·68 0·59				0·51	0·73 0·51				0·51
α-Glu-Asp	0·29 0·23	0·28								
α-Glu-Glu	0·41 0·34	0·40								
Phe-Ala	0·70 0·58	0·70		0·58		0·73 0·60			0·60	
Phe-Val	0·80 0·70	0·80				0·83 0·69	0·82			
Val-Leu	0·80 0·70	0·80				0·83 0·71	0·82			
Val-Phe	0·86 0·78	0·86				0·80 0·71	0·80			
Val-Val	0·83 0·72	0·83				0·80 0·71	0·80			

Solvents: S_1 = Ethyl acetate, pyridine, acetic acid, water (5:5:1:3).
          S_2 = Pyridine, water (4:1).
Paper: Whatman No. 1 (ascending flow), 30 cm length.
Detection: Ninhydrin.

ninhydrin) when the solvent systems acetic acid, ethyl acetate, pyridine, water (1:5:5:3) and pyridine, water (4:1) were used. Also the systems isoamyl alcohol, pyridine, water (7:7:6) or n-butanol, acetic acid, water (4:1:5) gave partial results, but were much less efficient.

All the DL-DL dipeptides obtained exhibit two spots with a difference in their R_F values of 0·05–0·23, so that the two spots are always quite easily distinguishable. Each spot contains one racemic pair, which was proved by the synthesis of the LL, LD, DL and DD diastereoisomers. The LL-DD diastereoisomers correspond to one spot and the LD-DL to the other.

Moreover, as can be seen from Table 2, an interesting regularity can be observed, namely that the LL-DD isomers have always higher R_F values than the corresponding LD-DL diastereoisomers. The observed phenomena allows us to hope that amino-acids or amines with two asymmetric centres could be identified or detected by this or a similar technique.

After these facts were established an important question arose as to the sensitivity of the method for the detection of the second spot (LD-DL). We have found that on Whatman No. 1 or 3 five resp. 1 per cent of the LD diastereoisomer could be detected. To detect still lower amounts of the second diastereoisomer in the reaction mixture the free (or the protected) dipeptides were first crystallized, and the mother liquors submitted to paper chromatography. This procedure enables the detection of 0·5 per cent of the racemate in the reaction product. It is also possible to detect as low as 0·1 per cent of the racemate by running preparative paper chromatography with subsequent ninhydrin analysis of the eluate, corresponding to the lower spot.

Applying the above described method for the estimation of the optical purity of L-amino-acids, we were able to demonstrate that even 0·1 per cent of racemate contained in pure L-amino-acid could be detected, and hence the optical purity of L-amino-acids can be ascertained up to 99·9 per cent.

APPLICATION OF THE "TWO SPOTS" METHOD FOR THE DETECTION OF RACEMIZATION DURING VARIOUS PROCESSES USED IN THE SYNTHESIS OF PEPTIDES

E. Taschner, J. F. Biernat and T. Sokołowska

Department of General Chemistry, Technical University, Gdansk, Poland

Following the finding described in the foregoing communication [1], we firstly examined the degree of racemization in LL-dipeptides caused by the introduction and removal of various protecting groups used in the synthesis of peptides. As model dipeptides the benzyloxycarbonyl-L-alanyl-L-phenylalanine and the benzyloxycarbonyl-L-phenylalanyl-L-valine were used. The groups were introduced or removed by current methods. After the subsequent removal of other protecting groups the free dipeptides were chromatographed on Whatman No. 1 or 3 paper and the amount of the LD diastereoisomer contained in the lower spot, and the amount of the LL diastereoisomer contained in the upper spot, were quantitatively determined (accuracy ± 2 per cent) by the method described by Boissonnas [2].

TABLE 1. Introduction and/or Removal of some Protecting Groups in Model Dipeptides and the Influence of these Processes on the Degree of their Racemization

LL-Dipeptides	Removal of NH$_2$- and -COOH protecting groups	Introduction of ester group	Method	Preparation of the free dipeptide	LD Diastereoisomer† (%)
1. Z-Ala-Phe-OH	Rem. of Z-	—	HBr/AcOH 15 min, 20°	—	Below 0·1
2. Z-Phe-Val-OH	Rem. of Z-	—	HBr/AcOH 15 min, 20°	—	Below 0·1
3. Z-Phe-Ala-OH	Rem. of Z-	—	HBr/AcOH 15 min, 20°	—	Below 0·1
4. Z-Ala-Phe-OBu^t	Rem. of Z- and of OBu^t	—	HBr/AcOH 15 min, 20°	—	Below 0·1

† 0·1 per cent is the limit of the detection of the diastereoisomer.

TABLE 1 (Continued)

LL-Dipeptides	Removal of NH$_2$- and -COOH protecting groups	Intro-duction of ester group	Method	Preparation of the free dipeptide	LD Dia-stereo-isomer† (%)
5. Z-Ala-Phe-OBZL	Rem. of Z- and of OBZL	—	H$_2$/Pd	—	Below 0·1
6. Z-Ala-Phe-OMe	Rem. of -OMe	—	NaOH/Acetone 15 min, 20°	Rem. of Z- as in 1	Below 0·1
7. Z-Phe-Val-OMe	Rem. of -OMe	—	NaOH/Acetone 2 hr, 20°	Rem. of Z- as in 2	Below 0·1
8. Z-Phe-Val-OMe	Rem. of Z- and of -OMe	—	HCl/H$_2$O [3] 30 min, 50°	—	Below 0·1
9. Z-Phe-Val-ONP‡	Rem. of -ONP	—	NaOH/Acetone 1 hr, 20°	Rem. of Z- as in 2	39
10. Z-Phe-Val-ONP	Rem. of Z- and of -ONP	—	HBr/AcOH 5 hr, 20°	—	36
11. Z-Phe-Val-ONP ↓ N$_2$H$_4$ ↓	Left with tert. amine, 4 days, 20° and then rem. of -ONP and -Z	—	HBr/AcOH 5 hr, 20°	—	56
12. Z-Phe-Val-NHNH$_2$	Rem. of -NHNH$_2$	—	NaOBr	Rem. of Z- as in 2	ca. 1
13. Z-Ala-Phe-NHNH$_2$	Rem. of -NHNH$_2$	—	NaOBr	Rem. of Z- as in 1	ca. 0·3
14. Z-Phe-Val-OH	— —	Intr. of -OMe	SOCl$_2$/MeOH [4] 2 days, 20°	Rem. of -OMe as in 7 and of Z- as in 2	Below 0·1
15. Z-Phe-Val-OH	—	Intr. of -OMe	SO$_2$Cl$_2$/MeOH [4] 2 days, 20°	Rem. of Z- and of -OMe as in 8	Below 0·1
16. Z-Phe-Val-OH	—	Intr. of -OEt	AcOEt/TosOH [5] 2 days, 20°	Rem. of -OEt and of -Z as in 7 and 2 resp.	Below 0·1
17. Z-Ala-Phe-OH	—	Intr. of -OBZL	BZL-OH/ SO$_2$Cl$_2$ [6] 5 hr, 100°	Rem. of Z- and of -OBZL as in 5	Below 0·1
18. Z-Ala-Phe-OH	—	Intr. of -ONB	NB-Cl/NEt$_3$ [7] 5 hr, 60°	Rem. of Z- and of -ONB as in 5	ca. 0·2
19. Z-Ala-Phe-OH	—	—	Heating with NEt$_3$ without NB-Cl 5 hr, 60°	Rem. of Z- as in 5	ca. 0·1

† 0·1 per cent is the limit of the detection of the diastereoisomer.
‡ Obtained from Z-Phe-OH and H-Val-ONP.

Introduction of ester groups by various methods does not cause epimerization at all, even in the case of Experiment 19 in Table 1, where the tertiary-amine salt of the benzyloxycarbonyl-dipeptide was heated with the *p*-nitro-benzyl chloride for several hours.

Also no epimerization took place when the benzyloxycarbonyl group was removed by hydrogen bromide in acetic acid or by hydrogenolysis, or when alkyl and benzyl ester groups were removed by solvolysis, hydrogenolysis, or by alkaline or acid hydrolysis.

The *p*-nitrophenylester of benzyloxycarbonylphenylalanylvaline, which was obtained in a way that is known to preserve the optical configuration, showed a quite different behaviour since its alkaline or acid hydrolysis gave a strongly racemized dipeptide. This epimerization was more pronounced, when the benzyloxycarbonyl-dipeptide ester was left for some days in the presence of tertiary amine and then hydrolysed. However, when the nitro-phenyl ester of the above benzyloxycarbonyl-dipeptide was hydrazinolysed and then the benzyloxycarbonyl and the hydrazide groups removed (the last with sodium hypobromite) [8] only slight racemization could be observed. Further experiments are needed to interpret this behaviour.

Our second aim was to examine the degree of epimerization caused by the action of various activating agents on benzyloxycarbonyl-LL-dipeptides, and by the action of nucleophilic agent on such activated dipeptides.

The reaction between the benzyloxycarbonyl-dipeptide and the activating agents leads always to racemization, but it cannot yet be stated at which stage the racemization occurs.

TABLE 2. RACEMIZATION IN THE FORMATION OF ACTIVATED BENZYLOXYCARBONYL-DIPEPTIDES AND IN THEIR REACTION WITH NUCLEOPHILIC AGENTS

LL-Dipeptides	Activation agent	Nucleo-philic partner	Reactions conditions	Preparation of the free dipeptide	LD Dia-stereo-isomer (%)
1. Z-Ala-Phe-OH	Cl.COOEt [9]	—	Dioxan, 3 hr, 20°	Hydrolysis with N-HCl/AcOEt 1 hr and then rem. of Z- by HBr/AcOH†	20
2. Z-Ala-Phe-OH	Cl.COOEt [9]	—	THF, 3 hr, 20°	Hydrolysis with N-HCl/AcOEt 1 hr and then rem. of Z- by HBr/AcOH†	27
3. Z-Ala-Phe-OH	Cl.COOEt [9]	EtOH	THF, 3 hr, 20°	Rem. of -OEt with NaOH/Aceton and then rem. of Z- by HBr/AcOH†	52

† See Table 1.

TABLE 2 (Continued)

LL-Dipeptides	Activation agent	Nucleo-philic partner	Reactions conditions	Preparation of the free dipeptide	LD Dia-stereo-isomer (%)
4. Z-Ala-Phe-OH	POCl₃ [10]	—	Pyridine, 3 hr, 20°	Hydrolysis with N-HCl/AcOEt 1 hr and then rem. of Z- by HBr/AcOH†	54
5. Z-Ala-Phe-OH	POCl₃ [10]	PhOH	Pyridine, 3 hr, 20°	Rem. of -OPh with NaOH/Acetone and then rem. of Z- by HBr/AcOH†	ca. 52
6. Z-Ala-Phe-OH	POCl₃ [10]	BuᵗOH	Pyridine, 3 hr. 20°	Rem. of -Z and of -OBuᵗ with HBr/AcOH	ca. 52
7. Z-Ala-Phe-OH	DCCI [11]	—	THF, 24 hr, 0°	Hydrolysis with N-HCl/AcOEt 1 hr and then rem. of Z- by HBr/AcOH†	30
8. Z-Ala-Phe-OH	DCCI [11]	PhOH	THF, 24 hr 0°	Rem. of -OPh with NaOH/Acetone and then rem. of Z- by HBr/AcOH†	57
9. Z-Phe-Val-OH	DCCI [11]	PhOH	THF, 16 hr 0°	Hydrolysis -OPh with NaOH/Acetone and then rem. of Z- by HBr/AcOH† Rem. of OPh and of Z- with HBr/AcOH 4 hr, 20°	52 54
10. Z-Phe-Val-OH	Benzene-sul-fonylchloride [12]	—	Pyridine, 0·2 hr, −15°	Hydrolysis with N-HCl/AcOEt and then rem. of Z- by HBr/AcOH†	1
11. Z-Phe-Val-OH	Benzene-sul-fonylchloride [12]	—	Pyridine, 18 hr, 20°	Hydrolysis with N-HCl/AcOEt and then rem. of Z- by HBr/AcOH†	49
12. Z-Phe-Val-OH	Benzene-sul-fonylchloride [12]	NBOH	Pyridine, 18 hr, 20°	Rem. of Z- and of -ONB with H₂/Pd	58

† See Table 1.
NBOH = p-nitrobenzyl alcohol.

During the reaction between the activated dipeptide and nucleophilic agents greater racemization (as in the foregoing case) was observed, but here also we cannot state at which stage the racemization occurred.

These studies will be continued.

All the reactions here described were made with *ca.* 0·2 mM of benzyl-oxycarbonyl-dipeptides (LL) which contained less than 0·1 per cent of the LD diastereoisomer. The products of the reaction were obtained by extraction and not by precipitation (to avoid partial separation of the diastereoisomer) and when solid they were never crystallized. All the processes were conducted under the usual conditions, applying methods that habitually give fair yields.

REFERENCES

1. This volume, p. 109.
2. R. A. BOISSONNAS, *Helv. Chim. Acta* **33,** 1975 (1950).
3. B. RINIKER and R. SCHWYZER, *ibid.* **44,** 677 (1961).
4. E. TASCHNER and Cz. WASIELEWSKI, *Liebig's Ann. Chem.* **640,** 136 (1962).
5. *Idem, ibid.* **640,** 139 (1962).
6. *Idem, ibid.* **640,** 142 (1962).
7. H. SCHWARZ and K. ARAKAWA, *J. Amer. Chem. Soc.* **81,** 5691 (1959).
8. M. BRENNER and W. HOFER, *Helv. Chim. Acta,* **44,** 1794 (1961).
9. J. R. VAUGHAN, Jr. and R. L. OSATO, *J. Amer. Chem. Soc.* **74,** 676 (1952).
10. E. TASCHNER, J. F. BIERNAT, B. RZESZOTARSKA and Cz. WASIELEWSKI, *Liebig's Ann. Chem.* **646,** 123 (1961).
11. J. C. SHEEHAN and G. P. HESS, *J. Amer. Chem. Soc.* **77,** 1067 (1955).
12. G. BLOTNY, J. F. BIERNAT and E. TASCHNER, *Liebig's Ann. Chem.,* in the press.

FURTHER STUDIES ON RACEMIZATION DURING PEPTIDE SYNTHESIS

M. W. Williams and G. T. Young

The Dyson Perrins Laboratory, Oxford, England

The condensation of benzoyl-L-leucine with glycine ethyl ester offers certain advantages over the analogous reaction with acetyl-L-leucine [1, 2], as a model for the evaluation of the racemization caused by various methods of coupling. In our experience so far, the crude product has always been crystalline and, in nearly every case, of analytical purity, and therefore racemization may be estimated directly from the optical rotation. To confirm the presence of racemate, the benzoyl-leucylglycine ethyl ester is saponified to benzoyl-leucylglycine; control experiments have shown that careful fractional crystallization can yield racemic or nearly racemic benzoyl-peptide from mixtures containing 2 per cent or more of racemate.

The results obtained so far are summarized in Table 1. As expected, racemization is often greater in this reaction than when using the acetyl analogue, but still no racemate could be found in the product of the acid azide route, nor in that from the cyanomethyl ester, or from the p-nitrophenyl ester in the absence of chloride ion. The effect of solvent on the optical activity of the peptide formed by the use of N-ethyl-5-phenyl-isoxazolium-3'-sulphonate [3] is very marked. The effect of the presence of chloride ion (i.e. condition B) is again notable, and we shall refer to this again below.

We have taken advantage of the favourable properties of benzoyl-L-leucine p-nitrophenyl ester to try to settle the vexed question of the mechanism by which racemization occurs, in this particular case. The addition of tertiary amine to a solution of the p-nitrophenyl ester in chloroform sets up the following equilibrium (A); the azlactone is detected by the infrared carbonyl absorption at $1832\,\mathrm{cm}^{-1}$:

(A) $\mathrm{Ph.CO.NH.CH.CO_2.C_6H_4.NO_2 + NR_3}$ $\rightleftharpoons$ (azlactone equilibrium)

$$\mathrm{Ph.CO.NH.CH.CO_2.C_6H_4.NO_2 + NR_3} \rightleftharpoons \underset{\mathrm{DL}}{\mathrm{Ph.C{=}N / O \backslash CO \quad CH.CH_2.CHMe_2}} + \overset{+}{\mathrm{NHR_3}} + \overset{-}{\mathrm{O.C_6H_4.NO_2}}$$

Ph.C=N \
| \ CH.CH₂.CHMe₂ + ⁺NHR₃ \
O \
\ CO   DL   + ⁻O.C₆H₄.NO₂ \
| NH₂.CH₂.CO₂Et \
DL-Peptide

Ph.CO.NH.CH.CO₂.C₆H₄.NO₂ + NR₃ \
| CH₂.CHMe₂ \
L \
| NH₂.CH₂.CO₂Et \
Ph.CO.NH.CH.CO.NH.CH₂.CO₂Et \
| CH₂.CHMe₂ \
L-peptide

TABLE 1

Method	Conditions[a]	Solvent	Yield[b] (%)	L-Isomer[b, c] (%)	Racemate isolated
Acid azide	A	Ether	80	94	None
	C		71	91	,,
Cyanomethyl ester	A; D	Ethyl acetate	85	91	,,
	A; E		72	97	,,
p-Nitrophenyl ester	A		95	100	,,
	B(NMP)		89	80	DL-acid
	A	Chloroform	86	96	None
	B(NMP)		84	75	DL-acid
Dicyclohexylcarbo-di-imide	A	Dichloro-methane	79	53	DL-ester
	B(N Et₃)		70	16	,,
	A; 0°		77	53	—
Et₄ pyrophosphite	A; "standard"	Et₂ phosphite	74	50	—
	B(NEP)		75	25	DL-ester
	A	Chloroform	83	88	DL-acid
	B(NEP)		82	43	—
	A; Amide		97	48	DL-ester
	B(NEt₃)		79	27	,,
Carbonic mixed anhydride	A	Tetrahydro-furan	87	20	,,
Phosphorazo	—	Pyridine	59	2	,,
Phenylisoxazolium	A	Acetonitrile	76	96	None
	B(NEt₃)		78	89	DL-acid
	A	Nitromethane	84	64	DL-ester
	B(NEt₃)		81	70	,,

^a Conditions: A, Distilled glycine ethyl ester used. B, Ester hydrochloride with an equivalent of the named tertiary amine (NMP = N-methylpiperidine; NEP = N-ethyl-piperidine). C, 1 equivalent of N-methylpiperidine added to the azide. D, Cyanomethyl ester prepared at reflux temperature. E, Cyanomethyl ester prepared at 0°.

^b Averaged results.

^c Excluding L-isomer present as racemate.

The rate of fall in optical rotation caused by the addition of triethanolamine to the ester closely parallels the fall in intensity of the ultraviolet absorption at 270 mμ, due to the p-nitrophenyl ester grouping. When the reaction of the p-nitrophenyl ester with glycine ethyl ester in the presence of N-methyl piperidine was stopped before completion, no racemate could be isolated from the recovered p-nitrophenyl ester, whereas the peptide formed contained some 20 per cent of racemate; in addition a considerable quantity of azlactone (which yields DL-peptide) was recovered. Further, when benzoyl-L-leucine p-nitrophenyl ester was treated with triethylamine before coupling with gly-cine ester, racemic peptide resulted, whereas under the same conditions p-nitrobenzoyl-L-proline p-nitrophenyl ester gave fully active product. There is therefore no evidence that direct exchange of α-hydrogen in the ester makes any important contribution to racemization, and we believe that, in this case, the main route to racemic peptide is through the azlactone.

We mentioned above that in our latest model reaction we have again observed the harmful effect of replacing free amino-ester by the hydrochloride with an equivalent of tertiary amine. When a solution of benzoyl-leucine p-nitrophenyl ester in chloroform is heated with tertiary amine hydrochlorides, the typical infrared carbonyl absorption of the azlactone develops. That this is due to the action of chloride ion is shown by the fact that tetraethylammonium chloride is equally effective, whereas tertiary amine (and quaternary ammonium) perchlorates cause no such absorption. We believe that this " chloride effect " is due to the basicity of the chloride ion in organic solvents, or possibly to its nucleophilic attack on the active ester to yield acid chloride (and hence azlactone), or to both these causes. We have evidence that the latter can occur, since when p-nitrophenyl phenylacetate was heated with tetraethylammonium chloride the presence of some p-nitrophenoxide anion was shown by the ultraviolet absorption at 420 mμ. But it seems likely that the major factor is the basicity of chloride anion, which we have measured with respect to the equilibrium [4]:

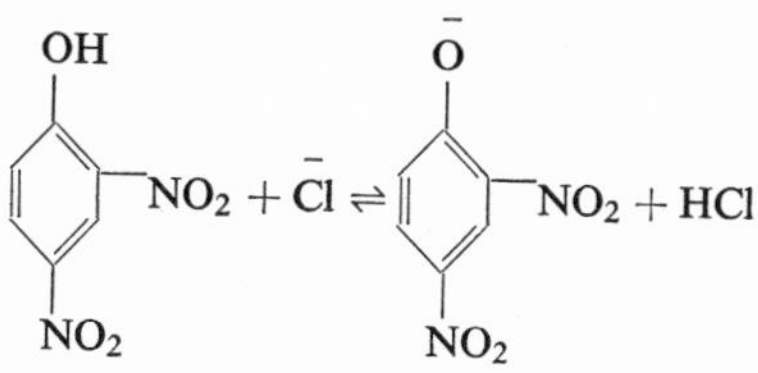

For chloroform solutions we find chloride has log $K = 1 \cdot 2$, compared with 0·8 for $\overset{+}{N}H_2.CH_2.CO_2Et$. We are now examining the basicity of a variety of anions in solvents commonly used for coupling.

It will have been noted in Table 1 that even in the presence of tertiary amine, the acid azide method still failed to yield racemate. When benzoyl-leucyl azide in ether was allowed to stand at 0° in the presence of N-methyl-piperidine, no absorption at 1832 cm^{-1} developed, and the same negative result was obtained when benzoyl-leucine cyanomethyl ester and the tertiary amine were heated in chloroform. Apparently the activation of these acid derivatives is insufficient to allow attack by the amide oxygen, even in the presence of tertiary amine. It would now be of interest to determine the relative rates of attack on these activated carboxyl compounds by nucleophilic oxygen and nitrogen in other cases.

REFERENCES

1. G. T. YOUNG, Proc. Symposium on Methods of Peptide Synthesis, Prague, 1958, Collection Czechoslov. Chem. Commun. 24, Special Issue, p. 39 (1959).
2. N. A. SMART, G. T. YOUNG, and M. W. WILLIAMS, J. Chem. Soc. 1960, 3902.
3. R. B. WOODWARD, R. A. OLOFSON, and H. MAYER, J. Amer. Chem. Soc. 83, 1010 (1961).
4. PEARSON and VOGELSONG, J. Amer. Chem. Soc. 80, 1038 (1958).

NEW WORK ON INSERTION REACTIONS

Institut für Organische Chemie, Universität Basel, Switzerland

THE characteristic features of insertion reactions, i.e. the insertion of amino-cyl residues into amide bonds, are:

(1) a relatively small change of bond energies, and
(2) a strong dependence of reaction rate on probability factors.

Minor alterations in a molecule susceptible to a reaction of the insertion type may therefore exert a profound influence on its reactive behaviour. This state of affairs is borne out by the following observations.

A. BASE CATALYSED INSERTIONS

A discussion of their mechanism has been presented elsewhere [1]; it seems, however, appropriate in the present context to recall the first two of the several consecutive transformations supposed to occur in the molecule. The basic catalyst abstracts a proton from the amide bond to be disrupted. An anionic species is thus formed. This species now may undergo a series of internal chemical changes ultimately resulting in the formation of the ionized insertion product. The overall rate of these changes depends—other factors being equal—on the concentration of the primary anionic species, or in other words, on the basicity of the reaction medium. The first one of the said internal changes involves interaction of the negatively charged amide nitrogen with the carbonyl group of the residue to be inserted, leading to formation of a cyclic anionic intermediate. This interaction evidently depends on the probability of internal collision of the respective parts of the molecule, and the ensuing transformation is considered to represent the rate-determining step of the insertion reaction.

In earlier experiments it was observed that insertion reactions using salicylic acid as the " inserting machine " required much less vigorous catalysis (weaker base) than insertion reactions in the aliphatic series with β-hydroxy-acids, glycolic acid or α-amino-acids as " inserting machines ". This difference was explained as a result of a more favourable steric situation in salicylic acid derivatives. Stronger acidity of the amide group in the latter may play an additional role.

It has now been found that insertion in the aliphatic series does not only require more vigorous catalysis, but is much more sensitive to steric hindrance.

In the aliphatic series it is, for instance, difficult to run consecutive insertions [2], and the sequence isomerization observed with dipeptide amides [3]
does not occur in tripeptide amides [1]. The situation is particularly well
illustrated by the model experiments shown below; yields refer to material
isolated in the crystalline state.

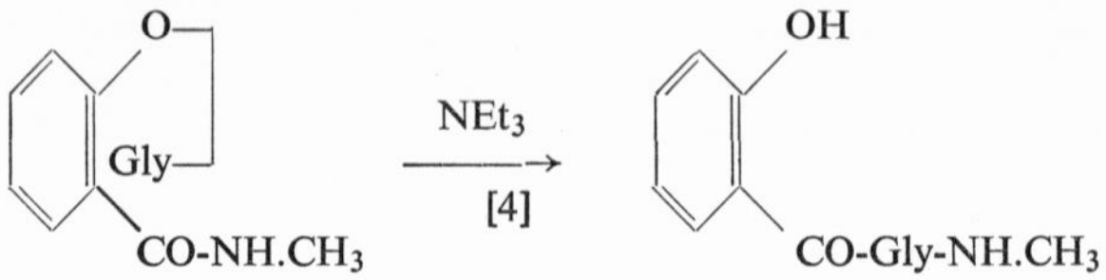

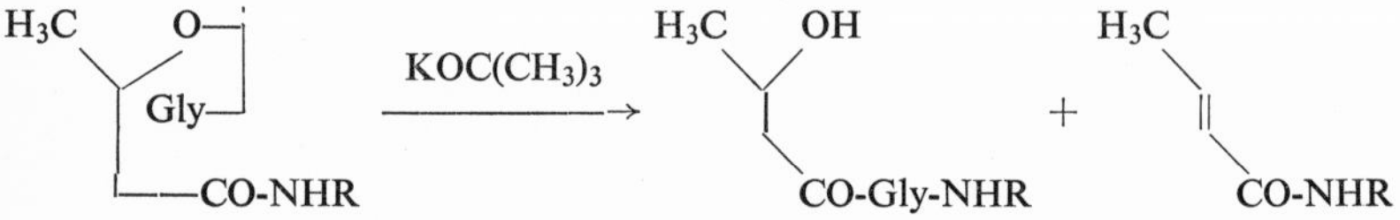

Compound†	R	Reference	Yield (%)	
(II)	CH₃	[5]	10	12
(III)	H	[6]	70	
(IV)	CH₂.CO.NH₂	[5]	6	10
(V)	CH₂.CO.NH.CH₃	[5]	9	18
(VI)	CH₂.CO.N(CH₃)₂	[5]	very small	25

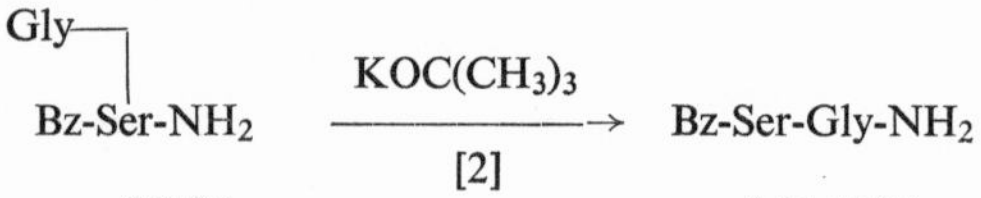

Comment

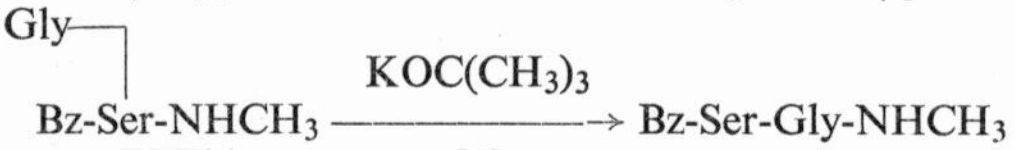

No reaction of II occurs under conditions which promote the conversion I. The difference
is due to different driving force (phenyl ester in I and steric compression of reactive centre
as revealed by molecular models and u.v.-spectra) and a different probability of reaction
(preferred conformation of II is unfavourable to necessary interaction of reactive centres).
Note the difference between III and II, and between VII and VIII! III and VII may be
more acidic than their N-methyl derivatives; more important, however, is probably the
additional steric interference which the anions of II and VIII have to overcome in order
to arrive at a conformation favourable to cyclization. It must account for the decrease
in reaction rate which is reflected by the decrease in yield.
In IV and V the inductive effect of R on the ionization of -CO.NH- is opposite to the
inductive effect of R in II. The yield of insertion product is nevertheless about the same.

† The formulae are drawn according to recommendations on Nomenclature as published in this volume (Section V).

Gly- = NH₂.CH₂.CO-   -Gly- = -NH.CH₂.CO-

One may conclude, on the assumption of about equal steric hindrance in the three compounds, that the acidity of the peptide bond involved is indeed not very critical.

No explanation can be offered for the surprising effect of $N(CH_3)_2$ in VI.

Slowing down the rate of the insertion quite naturally favours side reactions: Abstraction of a proton from the α-carbon instead of the amide nitrogen of O-glycyl-β-hydroxyacid amides induces β-elimination with formation of glycine and derivatives of crotonic acid. This reaction type is practically always observed. It is less subject to steric hindrance by substituents R on the amide nitrogen. The required general conformation is the same for both insertion and elimination, but in the case of elimination the repulsion between -CO.NHR and -O.OCCH₂.NH₂ may remain less since there is no need to reach the high energy level of the transition state leading to the insertion product (cf. Fig. 1).

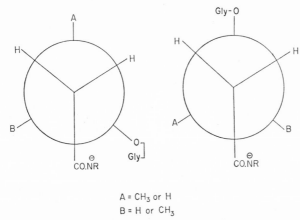

A = CH₃ or H
B = H or CH₃

" Gauche " position of large substituents is required for insertion and β-elimination.

" Anti " position of large substituents is energetically favoured.

FIG. 1.† Conformations about the αC-βC bond in open chain anions of O-Glycyl-β-hydroxyacid amides.

In view of such experimental evidence one might get the impression that reactions of the insertion type were of no practical importance in the chemistry of real peptides. This conclusion is thought to be misleading. Steric factors can be checked by other steric factors as is shown, for example, in the case of the salicylic acid derivatives. It is felt that the occurrence of insertions in peptides is merely a question of conformation. A suitable neighbouring group at a favourable position in one peptide moiety may be all that is required to activate the other peptide moiety. Unfortunately, as long as we have no means to picture peptide conformations we must in our endeavour to construct insertion-active peptides rely on trial and error.

I want to report here on one approach which was partly successful and indicates the feasibility of the general idea. Insertion yields from III and II are significantly increased if a hydrogen atom in the methyl group of the hydroxybutyric acid is substituted by a benzoylamino group (cf. IX and X).

† See footnote on page 124.

The benzoylamino group might exert an influence because of its space filling properties, its electrostatic effect or its hydrogen bonding capacity. An electrostatic effect of the charge deficiency on the nitrogen atom is probably ruled out by the further observation that the carnitin derivative XI rearranges less readily than IX; these latter experiments were run for two minutes in 55 per cent potassium hydroxide at $-20°C$ and gave yields of 7 and 78 per cent respectively [7].

Compound†	R	X	Reference	Yield (%)
(IX)	H	$C_6H_5.CO.NH$	[7]	85; 78 (in KOH)
(X)	CH_3	$C_6H_5.CO.NH$	[7]	23
(XI)	H	$(CH_3)_3N^+$	[7]	7 (in KOH)

B. ACID CATALYSED INSERTION

The acid catalysed insertion discussed below constitutes in the mechanistic sense a case of simple N,N'-acyl migration. In an operative sense, however, it is comparable to the insertion reactions. A classification among the latter is therefore thought to be justified.

The reaction XII $\rightleftarrows$ XIII has been described elsewhere [8, 9, 10]. It is mentioned in this context because it provides an excellent example on the influence of the surrounding medium on the reactivity of a dissolved substance. Materials of the type XII and XIII in water or neutral organic solvents show by themselves no tendency to rearrangement.

Acyl-NH.NH-OCCHR.NH$_2$ Acyl-NH.CHR.CO-NH.NH$_2$
(XII)   (XIII)

Nevertheless, at least XII is inherently unstable. Its apparent stability is best explained on the assumptions

(1) that only one conformer of XII can convert to XIII, and
(2) that this specific conformer exists in water or neutral organic solvents at a concentration too small to allow for an observable reaction rate.

Any means to trap or freeze the respective conformer would then enhance the reaction rate. As a matter of fact, this conception accounts for the peculiar reaction medium necessary for the actual conversion XII → XIII [8, 9]: The presence of a material such as acetic acid which can act as a bifunctional catalyst is vital, and a certain degree of dilution by a solvent which is not a hydrogen-bond donor is optimal!

† See footnote page 124.

Presumably, acetic acid and similar materials form with an amino-diacyl-hydrazine some sort of complex XIIa which now has the capacity of rearrangement, lacking in XII. It is indeed tempting to assume that this new property of XIIa is due to a change in conformation. The effect of the diluent, on the other hand, is seen in a reduction of protonation of the amino group of XIIa. The diluent should not be a hydrogen-bond donor in order to avoid competition with the mutual donating functions of the catalyst and of XII [8].

The bicarbonate ion bears a certain similarity to CH_3COOH. Indeed, it weakly catalyses in water the rearrangement XII → XIII. Carbonate is more effective. The transfer of a proton from XII to the carbonate ion would yield a complex of bicarbonate ion with anionic XII. The reverse reaction, XIII → XII, cannot be observed in the presence of bicarbonate or carbonate.

Actually, the conversion XIII → XII [10] only occurs in the presence of appreciable amounts of acid. This fact is due either to fulfilment of a specific requirement for proton catalysis or to an equilibrium shift caused by protonation of formed XII or to both effects. In 0·05 N hydrochloric acid the formation of XII from XIII is virtually complete [10]. In glacial or in N acetic acid, on the other hand, an equilibrium between XII and XIII tends to be established [8]. It is not clear whether the difference between the hydrochloric and acetic acid-induced processes is only a function of different acidity or as well a function of different reactivities. The completeness of the transformation XIII → XII in the presence of hydrochloric acid may actually be due to a mechanistic block of the back reaction (absence of a suitable catalyst such as acetic acid) and not to more complete protonation than in, for example, glacial acetic acid. This concept is not at variance with the principle of microscopic reversibility. Between appropriate conformers, the reaction XII ⇄ XIII is indeed thought to be reversible. If, however, the concentration of the appropriate conformer on one side of the system (XII) always remains practically zero because of an instantaneous change to some preferred conformation, then the overall process corresponds to an irreversible transformation of XIII into XII. At any rate it seems to be borne out by experiment that a reactive conformation is less easily acquired in the case of XII than in the case of XIII.

The driving force responsible for a practically complete conversion of XII or XIIa to XIII is probably provided by charge repulsion on the hydrazine nitrogen atoms [8, 9]; owing to energy release in complex formation it might be somewhat smaller in the case of XIIa. Protonation of the amino group of XII will, on the other hand, release so much energy that the process is now at least partly driven in the opposite direction [10]. A more refined picture would of course have to consider a number of additional solvation phenomena.

M. BRENNER

REFERENCES

1. M. BRENNER, *J. Cellular Comp. Physiol.* **54**, Suppl. 1 221 (1959).
2. M. BRENNER, J. P. ZIMMERMANN, J. WEHRMÜLLER, P. QUITT, A. HARTMANN. W. SCHNEIDER and I. BEGLINGER, *Helv. Chim. Acta* **40**, 1497 (1957).
3. SUSANNE SCHMIDT, Thesis, Basel, 1960. M. BRENNER, M. A. STEVENS and E. WALTON, Abstract of Papers, American Chemical Society, New York, Sept. 1960, p. 85 P.
4. W. SCHNEIDER, Thesis, Basel, 1958.
5. H. MOSER, Thesis, Basel, 1962.
6. A. HARTMANN, Thesis, Basel, 1957.
7. J. PLESS, Thesis, Basel, 1960.
8. W. HOFER, Thesis, Basel, 1962.
9. M. BRENNER and W. HOFER, *Helv. Chim. Acta* **54**, 1794 (1961).
10. A. N. KURTZ and C. NIEMANN, *J. Amer. Chem. Soc.* **83**, 3309 (1961).

DISCUSSION ON METHODS OF COUPLING

E. TASCHNER:

Siemion and Nowak [1] observed that acetyl, benzoyl or formyl-L-amino-acids whose carboxyl groups were activated with ethyl chloroformate or dicyclohexylcarbodi-imide gave the corresponding azlactones with high optical rotation that vanished after some time. Based on this observation, a mechanism of racemization could tentatively be proposed that could account for the peculiar behaviour of the azide group.

In the reaction of the N-protected peptide with an ester of an amino-acid the end product is obtained in two different ways. One way is a direct coupling of the components leading to a compound which has retained its optical configuration. Simultaneously, intramolecular cyclization could occur giving the azlactone which instantaneously reacts further with the amino group of the ester of the amino-acid giving a partially or totally racemized product. However, when the carboxyl group is activated by the azide or cyanomethyl ester no such azlactonization can occur since, as it is known, these groups do not react with alcohols or phenols to give the corresponding esters.

This hypothesis permits the explanation of the exceptional and singular behaviour of the cyanomethyl ester and especially of the azide group in not promoting racemization when used for the coupling of peptide bonds.

REFERENCE

1. SIEMION and NOWAK, *Roczniki Chem.* **35,** 153, 979 (1961).

J. S. MORLEY:

The oxidative coupling of benzyloxycarbonylamino-acid hydrazides with glycine p-nitrobenzyl ester hydrobromide by Patchornik's N-bromosuccinimide procedure [1] was unsatisfactory in our hands. However, 60–70 per cent yields of the pure dipeptides were obtained using free glycine p-nitrobenzyl ester in tetrahydrofuran at $-20°$. A number of alternative oxidizing agents were examined and mercuric trifluoracetate found the most satisfactory. Limited yields arose from (a) competition of the amino-acid ester with hydrazide in the oxidation, and (b) the ability of unoxidized hydrazide to compete with amino-acid ester in the coupling reaction (leading to diacylhydrazides as by-products). We have examined the oxidative coupling of benzyloxycarbonyl- and phenylazobenzyl-oxycarbonyl-glycine protected hydrazides with glycine p-nitrobenzyl ester, using hydrazine protecting groups that might be expected to depart as cations in the oxidation:

$$
\begin{array}{ll}
& -2H \\
\text{Z-Gly-NHNHX} \xrightarrow{\hspace{1cm}} \text{Z-Gly-N}_2^+ + \text{X}^+ \\
\text{(PZ)} \qquad\qquad -2e \qquad | \\
\text{I} \qquad\qquad\qquad\qquad\quad \downarrow \qquad \text{Gly-ONB} \\
\qquad\qquad \text{N}_2 + \text{Z-Gly}^+\text{-} \xrightarrow{\hspace{1cm}} \text{Z-Gly-Gly-ONB}
\end{array}
$$

Many of the protected hydrazides (e.g. X = BOC, But, 2-trichloro-1-hydroxyethyl, and the hydrazone from alloxan) were in fact capable of oxidative coupling. Diacyl-hydrazide formation was avoided, but the yield of pure dipeptide never exceeded 45 per cent even in the most favourable case (X = But).

The t-butyl hydrazides (I; X = Bu^t) were readily prepared from benzyloxycarbonyl- and phenylazobenzyloxycarbonyl-glycine and t-butylhydrazine by the mixed anhydride procedure, and were split to benzyloxycarbonyl- and phenylazobenzyloxycarbonyl-glycylhydrazide under acidic conditions, though less readily than the corresponding t-butyloxycarbonylhydrazides (I; X = t-butyloxycarbonyl). Such selective protection of the hydrazide group may be of value in peptide synthesis.

REFERENCE

1. G. WOLMAN P. M. GALLOP, and A. PATCHORNIK, *J. Amer. Chem. Soc.* **83,** 1263 (1961).

SECTION III

SYNTHESIS: SPECIAL PROBLEMS WITH UNCOMMON AMINO-ACIDS; ABNORMAL PEPTIDES

SYNTHESIS OF PEPTIDES WITH SOME "UNNATURAL" AMINO-ACIDS

J. Rudinger

Institute of Organic Chemistry and Biochemistry,
Czechoslovak Academy of Science, Na wicistr 2, Praha 6

For the purposes of this review the " unnatural " amino-acids will be defined as those which do not commonly occur in proteins. A definition excluding all amino-acids found in nature would leave little to discuss; there seems to be no amino-acid structure, however improbable, which nature could not produce.†

Since the earliest days of the art and mystery of peptide synthesis‡ there has been an interest in the synthesis of peptides containing non-protein amino-acids. The motivation—an interest in the effect of particular structural changes on the physical, chemical, and biological properties of peptides— is still valid today. The first aspect is illustrated in the synthesis of numerous poly(amino-acids) derived from " unnatural " building stones [2], the second for instance in work on rates of acid hydrolysis, and the third in studies on enzyme specifities which have continued from the days of Abderhalden and Max Bergmann in unbroken line. In the exploration of structure-activity relationships of biologically active peptides which is now being increasingly carried out the use of " non-protein " amino-acids is likely to play an important part because the structural modifications required to achieve precisely defined, arbitrary changes in the overall structure or topochemistry of a peptide molecule will often demand the incorporation of " unnatural " amino-acids.

A further stimulus to peptide syntheses with non-protein amino-acids has been provided precisely by the fact that they are not unnatural but that many amino-acids of the most diverse structure do occur in nature in peptide bonding, for instance in the peptide antibiotics or in the particularly wide-spread γ-glutamyl combination [3-6].

Since this Symposium is concerned chiefly with synthetic aspects the " unnatural " amino-acids will be classified chemically, according to the special or additional problems they may present in peptide synthesis.

† The symbols used follow the lines proposed in the Nomenclature Report presented to the Symposium (p. 259–69); they will be defined in the text as required.
‡ The historical aspects of the subject are admirably treated in the monograph of Greenstein and Winitz [1].

α-AMINO α-CARBOXYLIC ACIDS

Amino-acids Containing No Additional Functional Groups

Among the isomers and homologues of the protein constituents without additional functional groups those unbranched at the α position conform to the most conventional structural type; these include *allo*isoleucine (*a*Ile), α-aminobutyric acid (Abu), norvaline (Nva), norleucine (Nle), and tertiary leucine or pseudoleucine (tLeu). All these amino-acids are available in their optically active forms, most conveniently by the enzymic methods developed by Greenstein's school. It is worth noting that pseudoleucine is not resolved by the action of renal acylase I on the chloroacetyl derivative but is amenable to the method based on the action of amidase [7]. Alkyl and benzyl esters as well as benzyloxycarbonyl derivatives of most of these amino-acids are available (Table 1), and some *N,N*-dibenzyl derivatives have also been

TABLE 1. INTERMEDIATES FOR THE SYNTHESIS OF PEPTIDES OF L-α-AMINOBUTYRIC ACID, L-NORVALINE, L-NORLEUCINE, L-*allo*ISOLEUCINE AND L-PSEUDOLEUCINE

	X-OMe . HCl		X·OEt . HCl		X-OBZL . TosOH	
	M.p.	Ref.	M.p.	Ref.	M.p.	Ref.
Abu			? [a]	15	117°	21
Nva	107–108°	20	? [b]	15		
Nle	135–137°	20	? [c]	23	127°	21
*a*Ile	118–120°	20	89–90°	25	162–164° [d]	26

	Z-X		TFA-X		BZL$_2$X	
	M.p.	Ref.	M.p.	Ref.	M.p.	Ref.
Abu	78–79°	17, 24	55–57°	22	133–134°	8
Nva	86°	18	64–67°	22	118–119°	8
Nle	58°	24	71–73°	22		
*a*Ile	65°	16				
tLeu	oil	7				

[a] $[\alpha]_D + 6\cdot1°$ (c 2, 5N-HCl).   [b] $[\alpha]_D + 9\cdot5°$ (c 2, 5N-HCl).
[c] $[\alpha]_D - 7\cdot25°$ (c 12, water).   [d] D-Isomer.

resolved [8] though only the corresponding racemates have actually been used in peptide synthesis [9]. The glycyl peptides have been prepared by amination of the chloroacetyl derivatives [10–14], and a number of other simple peptides chiefly by the benzyloxycarbonyl–acid chloride or benzyloxycarbonyl–mixed anhydride combinations [15, 16]. Recent examples include syntheses of ophthalmic acid by Waley [17], a series of chymotrypsin substrates of the types X-Tyr-OEt, X-Tyr-NH$_2$, and Gly-X-Tyr-NH$_2$ by

Izumiya and Yamashita [18, 19], and of oxytocin analogues containing *allo*-isoleucine, norleucine, and norvaline in place of isoleucine carried out by Dr. Nesvadba in cooperation with our laboratory [20]. No problem that could fairly be called novel or specific seems to have been encountered in this work though there may be differences in solubility or crystallinity of some practical import—for instance, Z-*a*Ile is crystalline, while Z-Ile is not [16]. Amide derivatives of pseudoleucine appear to be exceptionally resistant to acid hydrolysis [7].

A second structural type within this group of amino-acids is characterized by the presence of a quaternary α-carbon. The best-known compound of this type, α-aminoisobutyric acid (α-methylalanine; Aib), has been figuring in synthetic peptides ever since Abderhalden's days [27]. Some derivatives are listed in Table 2. Two recent systematic studies review earlier work and

TABLE 2.   INTERMEDIATES FOR THE SYNTHESIS OF PEPTIDES OF α-AMINOISOBUTYRIC, 1-AMINOCYCLOPENTANECARBOXYLIC AND 1-AMINOCYCLOHEXANECARBOXYLIC ACID

	X-OMe . HCl		X-OE . HCl		X-OBZL . Tos-OH		X-OBZL . HCl	
	M.p.	Ref.	M.p.	Ref.	M.p.	Ref.	M.p.	Ref.
Aib	186–187°	40, 41	155–157°	41	154°	21	170–171°	39
Acp	207–208°	35	228°	35	193–195°	36	162°	36
Ach					167–169°	36	211°	36

	⌐CO-X⌐		Z-X		PHT-X		TFA-X	
	M.p.	Ref.	M.p.	Ref.	M.p.	Ref.	M.p.	Ref.
Aib	95–97°	32, 42	78°	28–30, 43	152–153°	44	170–172°	29
Acp	128°	36	92–93°	36	163°	35		
Ach	112°	36	154–156°	36				

	Tos-X		FOR-X	
	M.p.	Ref.	M.p.	Ref.
Aib	150–151°	29, 45	145–147°	29

give a good picture of the specific problems encountered—due, as would be expected, to steric hindrance. Faust and Lange in Halle investigated conventional methods [28], Kenner's group at Liverpool contributed some unconventional ones [29]. One point of apparent disagreement in the literature is the stability of the chloride, Z-Aib-Cl. Bergmann and his co-workers [30] had used this intermediate but the Liverpool group found it to cyclize to the *N*-carboxyanhydride extremely readily, presumably owing to the operation of the Thorpe-Ingold effect; the *N*-carboxyanhydride has, incidentally, found use in the preparation of oligopeptides [31] as well as polypeptides [32, 33]. The Halle chemists record that Z-Aib-Cl can be prepared and used provided the temperature is kept at about $-30°$.

Both recent papers [28, 29] agree that steric hindrance is more serious when α-aminoisobutyric acid is reacting at the amino group than when it is reacting at the carboxyl group; examples are provided by the yields listed in Table 3. It should be kept in mind that this effect might be connected at

TABLE 3. YIELDS OF SOME PEPTIDE SYNTHESES WITH
α-AMINOISOBUTYRIC ACID [a]

Product	Yield (%)	Product	Yield (%)	Product	Yield (%)
Z-Aib|Gly	80	Z-Aib-Gly|Aib	11–12	Tos-Aib|Gly	71
Z-Gly|Aib	6–12	Z-Aib-Gly-Aib|Gly	78–82	Tos-Gly|Aib	0
Z-Aib|Aib	9	Z-Aib-Gly-Aib-Gly|Aib	5–6	Tos-Aib|Aib	0

[a] The benzyloxycarbonyl peptides were prepared by mixed carbonic anhydride coupling in aqueous alkaline tetrahydrofuran [28], the tosyl derivatives by coupling the tosylamino-acid chloride with the amino-acid in aqueous acetone buffered with magnesium oxide [29]. The vertical line denotes the site of the peptide bond formed.

least in part with the availability of side-reaction paths, as when tosylamino-acid chlorides are used [29]). Faust and Lange did obtain the dipeptide, Z-Aib-Aib-OH, in about 10 per cent yield by the mixed anhydride procedure but found Wieland's phosphorus oxychloride method, with benzyl esters as the amine components, the most useful; they prepared sequences up to the hexapeptide of alternating glycine and α-aminoisobutyric acid residues. The English chemists found that pivaloyl chloride, introduced by Zaoral [34] as an activating reagent for tosylamino acids and asparagine derivatives, gave remarkably good results with Z-Aib, affording a crystalline mixed anhydride which coupled in practically quantitative yield [29]. However, their favourite technique was the use of oxazolidone intermediates. In one variant of this approach (1), 3,3-dimethyl-5-trifluoromethyloxazolid-2-one was added to methyl α-aminoisobutyrate, the trifluoroacetyl group removed and the chain further extended at the amino end. In a second variant (2), with the benzyloxycarbonyl or tosyl protecting group, the peptide chain was extended at the carboxyl end; a dipeptide was also coupled with a tripeptide in this way. Protected sequences consisting of Aib residues only, up to the pentapeptide, were prepared [29].

$$CF_3.C:N.C(Me_2).CO + H.(Aib)_n.OMe \longrightarrow TFA.(Aib)_{n+1}.OMe \longrightarrow$$
$$\underset{O\rule{3cm}{0.4pt}}{|}$$

$$\longrightarrow H.(Aib)_{n+1}.OMe \longrightarrow etc. \qquad (1)$$

$$R.NH.\overset{Me}{\underset{O\rule{1cm}{0.4pt}}{\underset{|}{C}}}\overset{Me}{\underset{}{C}}:N.\overset{Me}{\underset{}{C}}.\overset{Me}{\underset{}{C}}O \xrightarrow{\text{(Aib)}_n\text{OMe}} R.(NH.\overset{Me}{C}.\overset{Me}{C}O)_{n+2}.OMe \longrightarrow$$

$$\longrightarrow R.(NH.\overset{Me}{C}.\overset{Me}{C}O)_{n+2}.OH \longrightarrow R.(NH.\overset{Me}{C}.\overset{Me}{C}O)_n.NH.\overset{Me}{C}.\overset{Me}{C}:N.\overset{Me}{C}.\overset{Me}{C}O \longrightarrow$$

$$\longrightarrow \text{etc.} \qquad (2)$$

Two amino-acids of the same structural type which have recently become of interest are 1-aminocyclohexanecarboxylic acid (Ach) and 1-aminocyclopentanecarboxylic acid (Acp), particularly the latter which has carcinostatic properties. Connors and Ross [35] prepared several peptides (Table 4) using the phthaloyl protecting group and acid chloride or carbodiimide coupling

TABLE 4. PEPTIDES OF 1-AMINOCYCLOPENTANECARBOXYLIC AND
1-AMINOCYCLOHEXANECARBOXYLIC ACID

Peptide	Method [a]	Ref.	Peptide	Method [a]	Ref.
Gly-Acp	A	35	Acp-Gly	A	35
	B	36		D	36
Ala-Acp [b]	C	37	Acp-DL-Phe	D	36
DL-Phe-Acp	A	35	Gly-Acp-DL-Phe	B	36
	D	36	Gly-Ach	B	36
His-Acp	D	37	DL-Phe-Ach	D	36
DL-Met-Acp	E	37	Ach-DL-Phe	D	36
Acp-Acp	C	37	Gly-Ach-DL-Phe	B	36

[a] A through phthaloyldipeptide ethyl esters, chloride synthesis; B by amination of chloroacetyl derivatives; C through benzyloxycarbonylpeptide methyl esters, mixed carbonic anhydride synthesis; D through benzyloxycarbonylpeptide benzyl ester, carbodiimide synthesis; E through benzyloxycarbonylpeptide methyl ester, carbodiimide synthesis.
[b] Analogously Val-Acp, Leu-Acp, Arg-Acp and Phe-Acp.

procedures. An interesting and somewhat unexpected feature of this work is the behaviour of the phthaloyldipeptide esters on treatment with hydrazine under mild conditions: in the case of PHT-Acp-Gly-OEt the phthaloyl group is attacked first whereas in the case of PHT-Gly-Acp-OEt the same treatment followed by mild acid hydrolysis leads only to removal of the ester group. The same peptides, and the corresponding derivatives of aminocyclohexanecarboxylic acid, have been prepared by Tailleur and Berlinguet [36] through the benzyloxycarbonyl benzyl esters or, where appropriate, amination of chloroacetyl derivatives. Finally, Shankman with his coworkers [37] has prepared a range of dipeptides X-Acp (cf. Table 4) using the benzyloxycarbonyl protecting group and chloroformate or carbodiimide reagents. 3,3-Tetramethylenecyclopentane-2,5-dioxopiperazine (Gly-Acp anhydride) on acid hydrolysis affords about 58 per cent of Gly-Acp and 42 per cent of Acp-Gly [38]; this suggests that here, at any rate, the amide bonds involving the amino and carboxyl groups of the hindered amino acid are about equally reactive. The good yield in which Z-Acp-Acp-OMe is obtained by conventional procedures [37] indicates, not unexpectedly, that steric hindrance with this amino-acid is a less serious problem than in the case of α-aminoisobutyric acid.

All the amino-acids of this type described so far share with glycine the distinction of possessing no centre of asymmetry and therefore not causing any racemization headaches. Isovaline (Ival), though it is asymmetric, also lacks the α-hydrogen essential to racemization. An interesting exploitation of this asymmetry for steric induction [46] involves conversion of the optically active chloroacetylisovaline to a dioxopiperazine, condensation with benzaldehyde, and hydrogenation: after hydrolysis, the phenylalanine formed was found to contain an excess of the L-antipode (3).

Glycyl-L- and -D-isovaline have been prepared by amination of the chloroacetyl derivatives [14]; another asymmetric amino-acid with quaternary α-carbon, α-isopropylalanine, has not been resolved but the glycyl peptide of the DL-form has been obtained through the phthaloyl peptide ester [35].

The homologues of proline, pipecolinic and azetidinecarboxylic acids, both occur in nature but no peptides seem to have been prepared from them. With Dr. Vereš [47] we have obtained a derivative of an aziridinecarboxylic acid peptide (4) using the tritylaziridinecarboxylic acid which had served as the intermediate in a cycloserine synthesis developed at our Institute [48]; but we have not examined the possibility of removing the protecting group.

$$CH_2\!-\!CH.CO.NH.CH_2.CO.OR$$

$$\underset{\underset{TRI}{|}}{N}$$

$$R = Et\ or\ H \qquad\qquad (4)$$

Of the homologues of phenylalanine, phenylglycine (α-aminophenylacetic acid) has occasionally figured in peptide syntheses, generally as the racemate [31, 49–51].   Glycyl-β-(p-tolyl)alanine and its benzyloxycarbonyl derivative [52] have served in enzymic and microbiological studies [53, 54].

Isomers and Homologues of Polyfunctional Protein Constituents†

Of the homologous diamino-monocarboxylic acids, both α,β-diamino-propionic acid and α,γ-diaminobutyric acid occur in peptide antibiotics and a number of peptide derivatives have been prepared from them.   An important special feature of diaminopropionic acid chemistry is presented by the copper complex which appears to involve the β-amino group [55] and cannot serve for the selective protection of the α-amino group and preparation of N^β-substituted derivatives.   However, the other standard routes to such derivatives [56]—selective acylation of the free amino-acid on N^β [57] and elimination of an N^α-benzyloxycarbonyl group by way of the N-carboxy-anhydride [58]—are both feasible; various glycine peptides have been prepared in the L-series [59] and from the racemic acid [60, 61].   The N^α-tosyl derivatives of the optically active diaminopropionic acids are available by Hofmann degradation from the corresponding tosylasparagines [62, 63]; but somewhat unexpectedly, this reaction may be attended by some racemization, as also is the removal of the N^α-tosyl group from certain N^β-substituted compounds such as willardiine [64] and mimosine [65].   This danger will have to be kept in mind if such derivatives are to be used in peptide syntheses; another likely complication is reaction of an N^β-substituent with the α-amino group (see below).

α,γ-Diaminobutyric acid (Dab) has been the subject of a good deal of synthetic work, particularly in our laboratories at Prague [66–71], by Vogler and his colleagues at Basel [72–78], and by Kurihara and Suzuki in Japan [79, 80].   The list of optically active protected intermediates available for peptide syntheses (Table 5) might be envied by many a "natural" amino-acid. Furthermore, diaminobutyric acid illustrates some general points encountered in the chemistry of amino-acids with functional groups in the γ position. Thus, N^γ-acyl derivatives, particularly the N^γ-tosyl derivatives, tend to cyclize under carboxyl-activating conditions [66–68, 81], so much so that the

† The synthesis of peptides from amino-acids carrying functional or potentially functional substituents in the α position (e.g. α-hydroxy-α-amino-acids and their derivatives) has been reviewed by Shemyakin at the first Symposium of this series [266]; further advances were reported by Antonov [267].

TABLE 5. DERIVATIVES OF L-α,γ-DIAMINOBUTYRIC ACID SUITABLE FOR USE IN PEPTIDE SYNTHESIS[a]

Dab(Y)

Y	Ref.
Z	66, 80, 88
Tos[b]	68, 90b
BZS	90a
PHT	89
BTC	89
POC	89

X-Dab

X	Ref.
Tos	62, 70, 84

X-Dab(Y)

X	Y	Ref.
Z	Z	81
Tos	Tos	90[b], 68
Z	Tos[b]	68
Tos	Z	88, 68
BOC	Z	85
BOC	Tos	68
FOR	Z[c]	74
Tos	POC	89
Tos	PHT	89
PHT	PHT	80

X-Dab(Y)-R

X	Y	R	Ref.
—	—	OEt[a]	81
—	Z	OMe[a]	72, 80
—	Z	OEt[a]	66
—	Tos	OMe[e]	74
Tos	—	OMe[a]	70, 84
Z	Z	OMe	80
Z	Tos	OMe	68, 84
Tos	Z	OMe	84
O:C:	Z	N_2H_3	66
O:C:	Tos[b]	N_2H_3	68

Y⌐ X-Dab-

X	Y	Ref.
—	Z[d]	67
—	Tos	68
Z	Z	81
Tos	Tos	67
Z	Tos[b]	67
BOC	Tos	68
BOC	Z	85
O:C:	Z	67
O:C:	Tos	68

X-Ala(β-CN)

X	Ref.
Z	69, 70
Tos	70
POC	89
TRI	91

Y⌐ -CO-Dab⌐

Y	Ref.
Z	66, 67

[a] The less familiar protecting-group symbols are: BZS benzenesulphonyl, POC cyclopentyloxycarbonyl, BTC butylthiocarbonyl.
[b] Also in the D-series [76].
[c] Also in the D-series [73].
[d] Hydrochloride.
[e] Sulphate.

only method of carboxyl activation which gives reasonable yields of peptide with only limited amounts of cyclization product is azide coupling in weakly acid solution [67, 68]. On the other hand, the N-acyl-lactams are useful carboxyl-activated intermediates and can undergo aminolysis reactions with peptide bond formation [66–68]; this type of synthesis (5) has been discussed in some detail elsewhere [82].

$$
\begin{array}{ccc}
\begin{array}{l}
CH_2\!-\!CH.NH.Z \\
\mid \quad\quad \mid \\
CH_2 \quad CO.Y \\
\quad \backslash \quad / \\
\quad\quad NH \\
\quad\quad \mid \\
\quad\quad X
\end{array}
&
\begin{array}{l}
CH_2\!-\!CH.NH.Z \\
\mid \quad\quad \mid \\
CH_2 \quad CO \\
\quad \backslash \;\; / \\
\quad\quad N \\
\quad\quad \mid \\
\quad\quad X
\end{array}
&
\begin{array}{l}
\quad\quad\quad R \\
\quad\quad\quad \mid \\
Z.NH.CH.CO.NH.CH.COOR' \\
\quad\quad \mid \\
\quad\quad CH_2.CH_2.NH.X
\end{array}
\end{array}
$$

$$ \longrightarrow \quad\quad \longrightarrow \quad\quad \text{(5a)} $$

$$ X = Z \text{ or Tos} $$

$$
\begin{array}{ccc}
\begin{array}{l}
CH_2\!-\!CH.NH_2 \\
\mid \quad\quad \mid \\
CH_2 \quad CO \\
\quad \backslash \;\; / \\
\quad\quad N \\
\quad\quad \mid \\
\quad\quad Tos
\end{array}
&
\begin{array}{l}
CH_2\!-\!CH.NH.CO.R \\
\mid \quad\quad \mid \\
CH_2 \quad CO \\
\quad \backslash \;\; / \\
\quad\quad N \\
\quad\quad \mid \\
\quad\quad Tos
\end{array}
&
\begin{array}{l}
R.CO.NH.CH.CO.NHR' \\
\quad\quad \mid \\
\quad\quad CH_2.CH_2.NH.Tos
\end{array}
\end{array}
$$

$$ \longrightarrow \quad\quad \longrightarrow \quad\quad \text{(5b)} $$

$$ R.CO = \text{protected aminoacyl}; \quad NH_2.R' = \text{amino-ester} $$

In free peptides of diaminobutyric acid, again, the γ-amino group is favourably placed for intramolecular aminolysis of the peptide bond—a reaction which was predicted by Le Quesne and Young [83] from analogy with γ-glutamyl peptides and experimentally confirmed by Barrass and Elmore [84] and by Poduška [85] ((6), X = NH).

$$
\begin{array}{ccc}
\begin{array}{c}
\quad CH_2 \\
\;\; / \quad\quad \backslash \\
CH_2 \quad XH \\
\mid \\
\sim NH.CH\!-\!\!-\!C\!-\!\!-\!NH\sim \\
\quad\quad\quad\quad \parallel \\
\quad\quad\quad\quad O
\end{array}
& \longrightarrow &
\begin{array}{c}
\quad CH_2 \\
\;\; / \quad\quad \backslash \\
CH_2 \quad X \\
\mid \quad\quad \mid \\
\sim NH.CH\!-\!\!-\!CO + NH_2\sim
\end{array}
\end{array}
$$

$$ \text{(6)} $$

$$ X = NH \text{ or } O $$

Another general principle illustrated in the synthesis of diaminobutyric acid peptides is the possibility of introducing functional groups into the side-chain of amino-acids already bound in peptide form. We have shown that suitably protected peptides of asparagine can be dehydrated to the nitriles and these can be reduced to diaminobutyric acid peptides, in some cases with simultaneous removal of the α-amino protecting group [69]; an indication of this type of transition (7) was also encountered in the oxytocin studies of the Cornell group [86].

$$\underset{\substack{| \\ CO.NH_2}}{\underset{\substack{| \\ CH_2}}{\sim NH.CH.CO \sim}} \longrightarrow \underset{\substack{| \\ CN}}{\underset{\substack{| \\ CH_2}}{\sim NH.CH.CO \sim}} \longrightarrow \underset{\substack{| \\ CH_2.NH_2}}{\underset{\substack{| \\ CH_2}}{\sim NH.CH.CO \sim}} \qquad (7)$$

No peptides containing the lower homologues of arginine have been recorded; a cyclization reaction (8) proceeding with the elimination of ammonia and formation of cyclic guanidine derivatives [62] may be expected to complicate the synthesis of derivatives and peptides of these amino-acids. Presumably such peptides would best be prepared by conversion of the ω-amino groups of diaminopropionic and diaminobutyric acid peptides to guanidine groups, in the same way in which peptides of "homoarginine" (ε-guanidinonorleucine) have been prepared from lysine peptides [87].

$$\underset{\substack{\backslash \\ C=NH \\ | \\ NH_2}}{\underset{\substack{| \\ NH}}{CH_2(CH_2)_nCH.CO.OH}} \quad \underset{\longrightarrow}{\overset{-NH_3}{}} \quad \underset{\substack{\backslash \\ C \\ | \\ NH_2}}{\underset{\substack{| \\ NH}}{CH_2(CH_2)_nCH.CO.OH}} \qquad (8)$$

$n = 0$ or 1; the position of the double bond in the cyclized product is uncertain.

Several peptides of aminomalonic acid (Amal) were synthesized by Schneider [59] using the benzyloxycarbonyl protecting group. In Gly-Amal, Ala-Amal, and Ala-Amal(NH_2)$_2$ the aminomalonic acid residue is not asymmetric but Amal-Gly and Amal(NH_2)-Gly, prepared through the benzyloxycarbonyl monoester, are racemates. Protected peptides of the type Z-X-Amal(OEt)$_2$ have been recorded [92] and the N-carboxyanhydride obtained from the methoxycarbonyl monoethyl ester has been polymerized [93]. Interesting possibilities for the synthesis of optically active derivatives and perhaps peptides are opened up by the finding that acyl-aminomalonic acid diesters may undergo asymmetric hydrolysis in the presence of chymotrypsin [94].

A comparison of α-aminoadipic acid (Aad) with glutamic acid reveals differences as well as similarities. Like glutamic acid, α-aminoadipic acid can be selectively esterified at the ω-carboxyl group and the δ-ethyl ester served as the starting point for the first synthesis of an α-aminoadipic acid peptide, the δ-glycine derivative, by Abraham and Newton [95]. As was reported at the Moscow symposium [96], tosyl-α-aminoadipic acid can be cyclized to a lactam analogous to tosylpyroglutamic acid but with a six-membered ring, and this lactamcarboxylic acid and its chloride can be used in the same way as tosylpyroglutamic acid for the synthesis of α- and δ-peptides [97] (9).

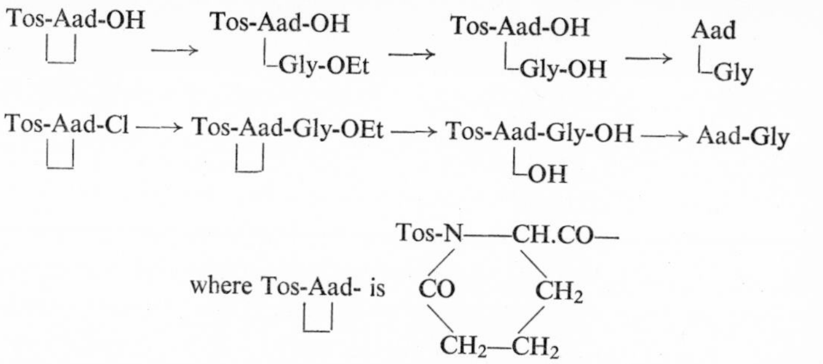

(9)

On the other hand, those specific properties of glutamic acid which follow from the possibility of six-membered ring formation with the participation of both carboxyl groups are not found in aminoadipic acid derivatives since here the corresponding ring would have to be seven-membered. In consequence acylaminoadipic acids do not form cyclic anhydrides and this type of intermediate, which has played such an important part in glutamic acid chemistry [56], is not available. Conversely, a point in favour: the imide formation and peptide shifts which plague those of us who work with glutamic acid [98] are absent. That is for instance why we were, with Dr. D. Morris [99], able to use the oxazolone intermediate obtained from tosylaminoadipic acid and formaldehyde in analogy to the glutamic acid series [100] for the synthesis of the possible natural penicillin precursor [101], δ-(α-aminoadipyl)cysteinylvaline (10); in the corresponding derivatives of glutamic acid hydrolysis of the oxazolone ring is attended by cyclization and transpeptidation.

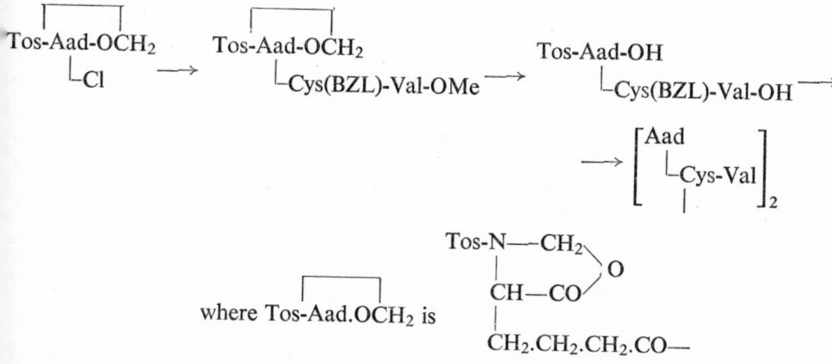

(10)

An oxytocin analogue with α-aminoadipic acid in place of tyrosine would be of interest since it would have an acidic hydroxyl group at about the same distance from the peptide backbone as the phenolic hydroxyl is in the natural hormone. In the synthesis of such an analogue [102] we used the δ-monomethyl ester and converted it by a series of reactions (11) to a crystalline protected dipeptide activated ester which was then condensed with the carboxyl-terminal heptapeptide moiety of the oxytocin molecule—a procedur based on the general principle proposed by Goodman and Stueben [103].

Aad   Z-Aad[a]   Z-Aad-ONP   Aad-ONP[b]   Tos-Cys-Aad-ONP
$\lfloor$OMe $\longrightarrow$ $\lfloor$OMe $\longrightarrow$ $\lfloor$OMe $\longrightarrow$ $\lfloor$OMe $\longrightarrow$ $\lfloor$BZL $\lfloor$OMe (11

[a] Crystalline dicyclohexylamine salt.   [b] Crystalline hydrobromide.

The homologues of serine and cysteine are of two kinds: Those in whicl the hydroxyl or sulphydryl group remains in the β-position and those ii which it does not. Even amino-acids of the first group show some difference from the parent " natural " amino-acids.† For instance, Wieland and hii coworkers [104] have prepared peptides of β-hydroxyleucine, Leu(β-OH)-Al and Ala-Leu(β-OH), through the benzyloxycarbonyl derivatives by the mixec carbonic anhydride method. They showed that derivatives of hydroxy leucine and hydroxyvaline show a decreased tendency to dehydration ii alkaline solution as compared with serine or even threonine, but an increase tendency to C-C bond fission in a reaction of the dealdolization type. Whe the peptide Leu(β-OH)-Ala was hydrolysed with baryta one of the product was, in fact, Gly-Ala, formed by loss of isobutyr-aldehyde from the intac peptide.

Penicillamine, which may be symbolized by Cys(β-Me$_2$), has been th subject of a great deal of research but surprisingly few straightforwar peptides of this amino-acid have been prepared. In work connected witl penicillin it was usually the aim to introduce amino substituents containin a potential aldehyde group or equivalent, and the resulting derivatives ar too complicated to be dealt with here. The standard protected intermediate are available largely from the wartime work on penicillin [105]. Peptid derivatives prepared by standard methods include hippuryl- [105] and phen aceturyl-DL-penicillamine [105–7], phenylacetyl-D- and -L-seryl [108] an -α-DL-glutamyl-D-penicillamine [109], and glycyl-S-benzyl-DL-penicillamin [105]. F. E. King and his coworkers have used the N-phthaloyl-S-benzy derivative [110] and also intermediates of the thiazolidine type [111 for the synthesis of several peptides. The most interesting feature of penicil lamine chemistry, suspected by Süs [106] and established by Knunyants Kil'disheva and Pervova [112] is the ease with which N-acylpenicillamine (formyl, acetyl, phenacetyl, but not benzoyl) form β-thiolactones whe treated with chloroformate in the presence of base; the same ring-closur has also been effected with carbodiimide [113]‡. The β-thiolactones readil undergo aminolysis in non-aqueous or aqueous media, offering a route t penicillamine peptides [116]. In such peptides with carboxyl-termina

† Arold and his coworkers [268] have found appreciable differences in the behaviour threonine and *allo*threonine derivatives. Thus Z-aThr-N$_3$ shows an increased tendency t rearrangement, being unstable even at − 10°.

‡ The thiolactones of tosyl, benzyloxycarbonyl, and phthaloylcysteine have been pr pared by the action of aluminium halides on the acyl-S-benzylcysteine chlorides [114, 115

penicillamine a thiolactone ring can again be closed and the process continued (12). Incidentally, it is worth keeping in mind that the elimination of hydrogen sulphide or mercaptan from penicillamine or its S-substituted derivatives under alkaline conditions proceeds even more readily than from the corresponding derivatives of cysteine.

$$
\begin{array}{c}
\text{Cys}(\beta\text{-Me}_2) \\
\text{Ac-Cys}(\beta\text{-Me}_2) \overline{\rule{0pt}{1em}}\!\!\!\rule[-1.5ex]{0.4pt}{3ex} \xrightarrow{\hspace{3em}} \text{Ac-Cys}(\beta\text{-Me}_2)\text{-Cys}(\beta\text{-Me}_2)\text{-OH} \longrightarrow
\end{array}
$$

$$
\xrightarrow[\text{NEt}_3]{\text{Cl.CO.OBu}^i} \quad \text{Ac-Cys}(\beta\text{-Me}_2)\text{-Cys}(\beta\text{-Me}_2)\overline{} \xrightarrow[]{\text{Cys}(\beta\text{-Me}_2)\text{-OMe}}
$$
$$
\underset{\text{-}i\text{BOC}}{\big\lfloor}
$$

$$
\longrightarrow \text{Ac-Cys}(\beta\text{-Me}_2)\text{-Cys}(\beta\text{-Me}_2)\text{-Cys}(\beta\text{-Me}_2)\text{-OMe} \qquad (12)\dagger
$$
$$
\underset{\text{-}i\text{BOC}}{\big\lfloor}
$$

† DL-Penicillamine was used throughout.

For the homologues of serine and cysteine with the functional group on the γ carbon, lactone or thiolactone formation is again characteristic. The thiolactones of N-benzoyl- and N-acetylhomocysteine undergo aminolysis with peptide formation when kept alkaline in glycine or glycylglycine buffers [117]; the temperature coefficients of aminolysis and hydrolysis differ and the reactions were run at 0° to favour aminolysis. Little use has been made of such thiolactones for the synthesis of homocysteine peptides. The use of S-benzylated intermediates seems more popular, as in the preparation of several DL-homocysteine peptides including an analogue of glutathione [118, 119]. S-Benzylhomocysteinylglycine was the unexpected product of the decarbobenzoxylation of Z-Met-Gly-OH with hydrogen bromide in nitromethane [120] but the same decarbobenzoxylation–benzylation was later put to use intentionally for the preparation of S-benzylhomocysteinyl-glycine ethyl ester [119].

In contrast, the γ-aminobutyrolactones have been popular synthetic intermediates. An early application was in the preparation of the amino analogue of pantothenic acid by aminolysis of α-benzyloxycarbonylamino-β,β-dimethyl-γ-butyrolactone with β-alanine as the sodium salt [121, 122] or ethyl ester [123] (13); only the first approach was carried to completion.

$$
\begin{array}{l}
\text{Z.NH.CH} \!\!-\!\!\!-\!\! \text{CO} \\
\quad\ \ |\qquad\quad | \\
\text{Me}_2\text{C}\quad\ \ \text{O} \ \ + \text{NH}_2.\text{CH}_2.\text{CH}_2.\text{CO.OR} \longrightarrow \text{Z.NH.CH.CO.NH.CH}_2.\text{CH}_2.\text{CO.OR} \\
\quad\ \ \diagdown\ \ \diagup \qquad\qquad\qquad\qquad\qquad\qquad\qquad\ \ | \\
\qquad \text{CH}_2 \qquad\qquad\qquad\qquad\qquad\qquad \text{Me}_2\dot{\text{C}}.\text{CH}_2.\text{OH} \\
\qquad\qquad\qquad \text{R} = \text{Et or Na} \qquad\qquad\qquad\qquad\qquad (13)
\end{array}
$$

Sheradsky, Knobler and Frankel [124] have systematically investigated the use of (racemic) benzyloxycarbonylaminobutyrolactone, and aminoacylated aminobutyrolactones, in the synthesis of peptides (including poly-mers) of homoserine [Abu(γ-OH)] by a general scheme (14) analogous to that discussed in connection with peptides of diaminobutyric acid or penicillamine. By two aminolytic reactions aminobutyrolactone gives bis-β-hydroxyethyl-dioxopiperazine; this can be converted to the dichloro compound which, in its optically active form, is a versatile intermediate in the synthesis, e.g. of cystathionine [125].

$$\underset{\substack{| \\ CH_2 \quad O \\ \diagdown \quad \diagup \\ CH_2}}{Z.NH.CH\text{———}CO} \quad \xrightarrow[\text{EtOH or Pr}^i\text{OH}]{NH_2.CHR.CO.ONa} \quad \underset{\substack{| \\ CH_2.CH_2.OH}}{Z.NH.CH.CO.NH.CHR.CO.ONa} \quad (14a)\dagger$$

$$\underset{\substack{\gamma| \\ O\text{——}}}{Z\text{-Gly} + Abu\text{┐}} \quad \xrightarrow[\text{NEt}_3]{Cl.CO.OEt} \quad \underset{\substack{\gamma| \\ O\text{——}}}{Z\text{-Gly-Abu┐}} \quad \xrightarrow{Ala\text{-ONa}} \quad Z\text{-Gly-Abu}(\gamma\text{-OH})\text{-Ala-OH}$$
$$(14b)\dagger$$

† Derivatives of DL-homoserine were used throughout.

In this connection it will be convenient to discuss *allo*hydroxyproline and the hydroxylysines. On the proline ring lactone formation is, of course, possible only with the hydroxyl and carboxyl groups *cis*, as they are in the *allo* stereoisomer. Unlike hydroxyproline, *allo*hydroxyproline (as the benzyl-oxycarbonyl derivative) undergoes lactone ring closure on carboxyl activation and Patchett and Witkop [126] have shown that the lactone can be once more utilized in peptide synthesis: L- and D-*allo*hydroxyprolylglycine have been prepared by this route. In the hydroxylysine series both isomers (studied again as the N,N'-dibenzyloxycarbonyl derivatives) readily pass into the lactones; so readily, in fact, that even the azide cyclizes rather than react with an amine. Zahn and Zürn [127] have prepared *allo*hydroxylysylglycine amide and *allo*hydroxylysylalanine amide from the appropriate bisbenzyloxy-carbonyl lactone. The behaviour of these two compounds on acid hydrolysis also provided evidence for the participation of the hydroxyl group (cf. eqn. (6), X = O), the peptide bond being hydrolysed as readily as the carboxyl-terminal amide group which in normal peptide amides is considerably more reactive. Here, then, we have the reverse of the lactone aminolysis reaction. The same type of effect has also been invoked by Wieland to explain the selective fission of the cyclopeptide ring in phalloidin at the carboxyl group of dihydroxyleucine.

The use of lactones as intermediates in peptide synthesis can presumably be extended to other γ- and δ-hydroxy amino-acids. Thus we have found that L-α-tosylamino-δ-valerolactone and the lactone of N-tosyl-γ-hydroxy-glutamic acid readily undergo aminolysis [91].

The hydroxy derivatives of the aromatic amino-acids (excepting, of course, tyrosine) have received relatively little attention as constituents of peptides.

The glycyl derivatives of DL-*o*- and *m*-tyrosine have been obtained by amination of the chloroacetylamino-acids [128]. A protected peptide ester of 3,4-dihydroxyphenylalanine (Dopa) has been prepared by coupling phthaloylglycine chloride with the methyl ester, the use of benzyloxycarbonyl derivatives having failed [129]. An interesting route to such peptides is the hydroxylation of the corresponding tyrosine peptides: The action of mushroom polyphenol oxidase, or of ascorbic acid and ferrous ions, on glycyl- and leucyltyrosine is said to give the Dopa peptides [130]. Analogously, the action of the ascorbic acid–ferrous ion reagent on glycylphenylalanine gives a mixture containing the appropriate peptides of *o*-, *m*-, and *p*-tyrosine, 2,3-dihydroxyphenylalanine, and Dopa [130]. The identification of these products was carried out by amino-acid analysis after chromatographic separation. A peptide of phenylserine, Arg-Phe(β-OH), has been prepared by conventional procedures [131].

Special problems are presented by amino-acids containing two complete α-amino-acid groupings such as diaminopimelic acid (Dapi), diaminosuberic acid (Dasu), lanthionine (Lan), and cystathionine. They have a partial analogy in the chemistry of cystine, but whereas the possibility of disulphide exchange looms important in work with cystine, both in a negative and a positive sense—that is, as a side reaction vitiating the peptide chemist's intentions and as one possible route to unsymmetrical derivatives and peptides—similar considerations would not seem to apply to the amino-acids listed above. The stability of their derivatives is, indeed, satisfactory for most purposes; but in the positive sense, the possibility of obtaining unsymmetrically substituted derivatives by combination of two monoamino-monocarboxylic units exists and has been utilized, as in the synthesis of mono-N-carboxyanhydride derivatives of lanthionine in the polymer work of Frankel and Gertner [132] and in the elegant synthesis, by Arnstein and Clubb [133], of heterodetically cyclic peptides of β,β-dimethyllanthionine as possible penicillin precursors (15). The chief drawback in this approach is the lack of steric specificity in the alkylation step, which in every case makes use of aminoacrylic acid derivatives. Syntheses of the symmetrical peptides, Gly$_2$: Lan and Lan: Gly$_2$, have been described [134] but an attempt to obtain a monobenzyloxycarbonyl derivative from lanthionine failed [132].

$$\begin{array}{ccccc}
\text{NH}_2 & & \text{NH}_2 & & \text{CO.OH} \\
| & & | & & | \\
\text{Me}_2\text{C.CH.CO.OH} & & \text{Me}_2\text{C.CH.CO.OH} & & \text{Me}_2\text{C . CH . NH} \\
| & \longrightarrow & | & \xrightarrow[\text{2. HNO}_2]{\text{1. N}_2\text{H}_4} & | \qquad | \\
\text{SH} & & \text{S} & & \text{S} \qquad | \\
& & | & & | \qquad | \\
\text{CH}_2\text{:CH.CO.OMe} & & \text{CH}_2\text{.CH.CO.OMe} & & \text{CH}_2\text{.CH.CO} \\
| & & | & & | \\
\text{X.NH} & & \text{X.NH} & & \text{X.NH}
\end{array} \quad (15)$$

X = Ac, PhCH$_2$.CO, or Z

11–2

Several (sterically inhomogeneous) symmetrical peptides of α,α'-diamino-suberic acid of the type X_2:Dasu have been prepared by the classical amina-tion method [135]. In the diaminopimelic acid series, the elegant enzymic hydrolysis studies of the Greenstein group with E. Work [136, 137] have been extended by Bricas and his colleagues [138] to the synthesis of unsym-metrical peptides. Unfortunately this approach is by its very nature confined to the *meso* diastereomer. The synthesis from two differently substituted units would at first sight seem to be inapplicable here; but since the synthesis of L,L-diaminosuberic acid from (protected) L-glutamic acid has been described [139] this approach appears to hold some promise after all. Work with this group of amino-acids should provide some very interesting chemis-try, and stereochemistry, yet.

Amino-acids Containing Groups Not Found in Protein Constituents

Derivatives of aliphatic amino-acids. The simplest group which is not found in the constituent amino-acids of proteins is the double bound. The so-called " dehydro " acids, i.e. derivatives of α-aminoacrylic acid, have been exten-sively studied but since their chemistry, and that of their peptides, is exhaustively reviewed in the monograph of Greenstein and Winitz [140] it would serve no useful purpose to deal with them here. Examples of other unsaturated amino-acids which have figured in peptide syntheses are β-methy-lenecyclopropanealanine (" hypoglycin A ") whose γ-glutamyl derivative, hypoglycin B, was prepared by Jöhl and Stoll [141] without particular diffi-culty by a mixed anhydride synthesis with TFA-Glu-OEt; and 2-aminopent-4-enoic acid (C-allylglycine) which has been converted to the N-carboxy-anhydride and polymer [142] with a view to introducing side-chain sub-stituents such as halogen into the finished polymer. The recent use of the cis- and trans-isomers of 2,6-diaminohex-4-enoic acid (" dehydrolysine ") [143] and sterically constrained cyclic analogues of lysine [144] for exploring the geometry of a bacterial metabolic site suggests that suitable peptides of these compounds might similarly be used to derive information about the active centres of the appropriate proteolytic enzymes. The glycyl peptide of 2-amino-trans-4-hexenoic acid, a methionine isoester, has in fact been prepared [145].

With halogenated aliphatic acids, difficulties are to be anticipated when the halogen is in the β-position (dehydrohalogenation) or in the γ- and (to a lesser extent) the δ-position. Thus even the fluorine in γ-fluoro-α-amino-butyric acid [146] and in γ-fluoroglutamic acid [147] is eliminated rather readily with lactone formation. Halogen anions being good leaving groups, halogen substituents in such positions should also favour peptide bond fission by engaging the carbonyl oxygen (16), as in the specific fission of peptides at the carboxyl group of tyrosine, tryptophan, and methionine [148–150].

$$
\begin{array}{ccc}
\underset{|}{X} & & \underset{|}{R} \\
\mathrm{CHR} & & \mathrm{CH} \\
\diagup & & \diagup \quad \diagdown \\
\mathrm{CH_2 \quad O} & \longrightarrow & \mathrm{CH_2 \quad O} \\
| \qquad \| & & | \qquad | \\
\sim\mathrm{NH.CH\!-\!\!-\!\!C.NH}\sim & & \sim\mathrm{NH.CH\!-\!\!-\!\!C\!=\!O + NH_2}\sim
\end{array}
\qquad (16)
$$

Ether and thioether derivatives of serine and cysteine, in as far as they have served as protected intermediates, are more suitably discussed elsewhere. In certain cases substituents on oxygen or sulphur are conveniently introduced at the protected peptide stage. Thus the extensive natural family of γ-glutamyl-S-alkyl- or -carboxyalkylcysteines [151, 152] should be accessible from a common intermediate such as tosyl-γ-glutamyl-S-benzylcysteine by reduction and alkylation in situ. We have, in fact, prepared the simplest member of this family, γ-glutamyl-S-methylcysteine, by this route [91]. On the other hand, because of the difficulty of removing S-benzyl groups from higher polypeptides Frankel and his coworkers have preferred to use S-alkylcysteines [153] and S-alkylhomocysteines [154] in the preparation of the appropriate polymers. Certain interesting derivatives of the ether and thioether class which are isosters of lysine will be dealt with in later contributions to this Symposium (pp. 171, 177; see also [155]). A particularly complex structure which can be regarded as a thioether is present in phalloidin and related toxins: formally, it consists of a cysteine residue linked through sulphur to the indole β-position of tryptophan. Wieland and his co-workers [156] have accomplished the synthesis of peptides containing this structure by reaction of a tryptophan-containing sequence (e.g. Ala-Hypro-Try-Ile-OMe) with the sulphenyl chloride derived from the cysteine moiety (Z-Ala-Thr-Cys).

Peptides containing carbonyl groups would seem to present formidable problems. However, Kögl's synthesis [157] of " glutamal " and " aspartal " peptides, e.g. Gly-Glu(H)-Gly, using thioacetal formation to protect the carbonyl group, and the use of a diethylketal for the same purpose in a synthesis involving reduction with sodium in liquid ammonia [158] indicate that these problems can be successfully solved.

Nitrile groups have been introduced into peptides either starting from derivatives of the appropriate amino-acids (" anhydro " glutamine or asparagine; Abu(γ-CN) or Ala(β-CN), respectively), or by dehydrating the side chain amide groups in peptides [69, 70]. Zaoral and Arnold [159] have shown that dehydration and peptide bond synthesis can be carried out in a single operation; the involuntary formation of " anhydro " derivatives has been recorded during work on the $Glu(NH_2)$-$Asp(NH_2)$-Cys sequence of the posterior pituitary hormones [86, 160]. No free cyano-peptides have yet been prepared; the problem is essentially that of protecting-groups removable without destruction of the nitrile. The trityl [91] and t-butyloxy-carbonyl groups might make this feasible, and even benzyloxycarbonyl can be removed without reduction of the cyano group, with sodium in dry liquid ammonia [161]. A polymer of γ-cyano-α-aminobutyric acid has been prepared through ill-defined intermediates [162].

Citrulline, although it has trouble-making potentialities by virtue of the α,δ-relation of the carboxyl and imino groups, appears to have offered no special problems. Izumiya and Shitô [163] have used the benzyloxycarbonyl derivative in the synthesis of a number of dipeptides by the carbodiimide method, and Bodanszky and his coworkers [164] have recently prepared the p-nitrophenyl ester and synthesized citrulline analogues of vasopressin and bradykinin.

The γ-aminoxy substituent of canaline has been protected by the benzyl-oxycarbonyl group during the preparation of a polycanaline [165], though the removal of the protecting group was not carried out. The problem of the N-hydroxyamino acids which is becoming topical with the detection of N^δ-hydroxyornithine in albomycin and related antibiotics [166, 167] is presumably being tackled, but no peptide syntheses with such amino-acids have been described so far (see also p. 156).

Ring-substituted derivatives and analogues of the aromatic amino-acids. The simple halogenated phenylalanines are well known. The benzyloxycarbonyl-glycyl-*o*, *m*, and *p*-fluorophenylalanines and the *p*-chloro derivative have been studied as carboxypeptidase substrates [54] but no detailed account of their synthesis seems to have been given. p-Bromophenylalanine has been resolved [168] and a hypertensin analogue containing this amino-acid has been reported [169]; it will be interesting to hear if any difficulties were encountered, e.g. in hydrogenations during its synthesis. I should like to take this opportunity to confess that our attempted synthesis of a hormone analogue containing p-fluorophenylalanine, Phe(p-F)^2-oxytocin [170], failed in the last stage since the fluorine was, somewhat unexpectedly, reduced off with sodium in liquid ammonia. This confirms the findings of Bodanszky and J. T. Sheehan [171] in model experiments with p-fluorophenylalanine itself.

Halogenated tyrosine peptides have figured in degradations—e.g. the β-sulphoalanyl-dibromotyrosine of the oxytocin structural work [172, 173]. The dibromo derivatives of Cys(O_3H)-Tyr and Tyr-Cys(O_3H) were obtained from these peptides by bromination [174]. Peptides of diiodotyrosine and thyroxine have been prepared through the halogenoacyl derivatives [175, 176], by acylation with benzyloxycarbonylglutamic anhydride [177], or by iodi-nating the appropriate tyrosine peptides [177, 178], including polytyro-sine [179]; more careful analysis [178] has shown the products obtained by iodination to be inhomogeneous. Trifluoroacetylated derivatives of the iodinated amino-acids have been used in work outside the peptide field [180,

181].† An interesting reaction in which the formation of thyroxine from the diiodotyrosine side-chain takes place on mere standing in alkaline solution has also been applied to acetyl-diiodotyrosyl-glutamic acid [183] and constitutes a synthesis of a thyroxine peptide.

p-Nitrophenylalanine has been obtained optically active by nitration of phenylalanine [184] or by resolution [185] but the polymer has been prepared from the racemic N-carboxyanhydride [186]. Poly-p-aminophenylalanine was made by reduction of this poly-p-nitrophenylalanine [186] or by synthesis from the N,N'-dibenzyloxycarbonyl derivative [187]. p-Dimethylaminophenylalanyl-alanine (mixture of diastereomers) has been obtained through phthaloylated intermediates [188] and converted into the N-oxide (17).

$$\text{PHT-Phe}(p\text{-NMe}_2) + \text{Ala-OEt} \xrightarrow{\text{DCCI}} \text{PHT-Phe}(p\text{-NMe}_2)\text{-Ala-OEt} \longrightarrow$$

$$\xrightarrow[\text{2. Ph.N}_2\text{H}_3]{\text{1. HCl}} \text{Phe}(p\text{-NMe}_2)\text{-Ala} \xrightarrow[\text{EDTA}]{\text{H}_2\text{WO}_4/\text{H}_2\text{O}_2} \text{Phe}(p\text{-N(O)Me}_2)\text{-Ala} \quad (17)$$

Azo substituents can be introduced into polytyrosine by coupling with the appropriate diazonium salts [189]; on the other hand, poly-p-aminophenyl-alanine has been diazotized and coupled with phenols, including protein-bound tyrosine [189]; this reaction forms the basis for the preparation of " insoluble " enzymes [190].

A nitrotyrosine peptide was obtained, unintentionally, by Schnabel and Zahn [191] as the result of an azide synthesis with Z-Tyr-N$_2$H$_3$ in which excess nitrite had been used; more conventionally, glycylnitrotyrosine was made [128] by amination of the chloroacetyl derivative.

The most important group of peptides in this class are those derived from p-bis-2-chloroethylaminophenylalanine,‡ a nitrogen mustard also called melphalan (L-form [184, 185]) or merphalan (DL-form) by the Chester Beatty research group (Bergel, Stock, and others) and sarcolysin by Soviet workers associated with Knunyants and with Berlin; it is to these groups that most of the work is due. The motivation was a search for derivatives with improved therapeutic properties and it seems that certain peptides of Phe(M) have in fact fulfilled this expectation [192, 193].

In 1955 and 1958, the Soviet workers [194, 195] described nine protected peptides of the general formula FOR-DL-Phe(M)-X-OEt including one where X was also a mustard-type derivative, S-2-chloroethylcysteine [195]; dicyclo-hexylcarbodiimide was used as the reagent. Bergel and Stock [196] in 1957 prepared four benzoylated peptide esters, Bz-DL-Phe(M)-X-OEt, by the

† For derivatives of thyronine of potential use in peptide synthesis see ref. 182.
‡ The ad hoc symbol Phe(M) may be conveniently used for this amino acid, M signifying the mutagenic bis-2-chloroethylamino grouping in the para position.

azlactone route, the double bond of the dehydrophenylalanine derivative initially formed being reduced by hydrogenation over a combination of catalysts or chemically with zinc and acetic acid. Peptide derivatives with inverted sequence, Z-X-Phe(M)-OEt and Ac-X-Phe(M)-OEt, where in the first case X is an amino-acid or short peptide residue and in the second case Phe, Phe(p-NO$_2$), or Phe(p-NH$_2$), were prepared [197] from optically active starting materials by the azide or mixed carbonic anhydride procedures, though in individual cases the combination of an N-acetyl substituent with anhydride activation makes the optical purity of the products uncertain.†
All stereoisomers of the sequences, Ac-Phe(M)-Val-OMe and Ac-Phe(M)-Phe-OMe, have been prepared by the carbodiimide procedure [198]; again, the method of synthesis itself does not guarantee full optical purity. It is interesting to note that there are considerable differences in the carcinolytic activities of the individual stereoisomers. Alekseeva and Pushkareva [199] have been able to separate the diastereomeric racemates of Ac-DL-Phe(M)-DL-Glu(OEt)-OEt by crystallization.

Initially, the formyl protecting group was used [197, 199, 200] as an amino protecting group removable (solvolytically) without damage to the bis-2-chloroethylamine grouping; in a particularly favourable case [Z-Val-Phe(M)-OEt] the benzyloxycarbonyl and ethyl ester group could be removed by aqueous hydrogen chloride without fission of the peptide bond [197]. Benzyl ester [200] and benzyloxycarbonyl groups [197, 201] can, however, be split by catalytic hydrogenation even in presence of the nitrogen mustard grouping and the derivatives Z-DL-Phe(M) and DL-Phe(M)-OBZL, prepared by conventional procedures, were introduced [201]. The development of these methods has paved the way to the synthesis of higher peptides such as Z-Val-Phe(M)-Gly-OEt [197] and Val-DL-Phe(M)-Val [201], both through formylated dipeptide intermediates. At the Fourth Symposium in Moscow a further series of peptides was reported [202], including some containing p-bis-2-chloropropylaminophenylalanine and the bis-ethyleneimide of phenyl-alanine-p-phosphonic acid as the mutagenic groups; details have not yet been published.

This work is encouraging to the peptide chemist in showing that the introduction of a biologically active grouping into a peptide carrier can, indeed, modify the properties of this grouping in a useful way.

Numerous analogues of the aromatic amino-acids with a varied assortment of homocyclic and heterocyclic substituents in the β-position of the alanine side-chain have been prepared in recent years but only a few of them have been introduced into peptides. The dipeptides, Gly-DL-Ala(β-R) with R = 1-naphthyl, 2-naphthyl, and 2- or 3-thienyl have been prepared through

---

† Recently, this work has been revised with the possibility of racemization in mind and optically homogeneous products have been obtained [269]; additional peptides have also been prepared [270].

the benzyloxycarbonyl derivatives, as has the peptide DL-Ala(β-R)-Gly with R = 2-thienyl [52]. The removal of the protecting group from the thienylalanine peptides was effected by phosphonium iodide since catalytic hydrogenation had failed [52]. Both antipodes of glycyl-β-2-thienyl-alanine have been prepared [203a] as well as some additional peptides of the racemate [203b]; the well-known resemblance between thiophene and benzene should make thienylalanine analogues of biologically active phenyl-alanine peptides particularly interesting.

Of the alanine analogues carrying nitrogenous rings only the saturated β-4-piperidylalanine appears to have been introduced into a peptide [204]. The possibility should be kept in mind of building heterocyclic structures into the side-chains of finished peptides, e.g. by making use of the nitrile (" anhydro ") derivatives of glutamine and asparagine.

β-AMINO-ACIDS

Of the β-amino-acids, β-alanine has received by far the greatest attention. Numerous peptides have been prepared for enzyme specificity studies [205–7] and a considerable amount of work has been done in connection with syntheses of carnosine, its derivatives and analogues [207–11]. The benzyloxy-carbonyl [205–8, 211–14] and phthaloyl [209, 210] protecting groups have been used in conjunction with the chloride [205, 208–10, 212], azide [206–9, 214], and mixed anhydride [211, 213] methods of coupling. A series of peptides, Z-(β-Ala)$_n$-OEt with n = 2–6, has been prepared using N-acyl-pyrazoles as carboxyl-activated intermediates [215]. By treating a number of amino-acids, including several " unnatural " ones, with β-alanine adenyl-ate Kalyankar and Meister [216] obtained the appropriate β-alanyl peptides, required as standards in enzymic studies; the products were characterized by chromatography only. β-Amino-acids other than β-alanine have received much less attention. Peptides of β-phenyl-β-alanine have been prepared by amination of the β-bromoacylamino acids [212]. Birkofer's studies on β-amino-acids have been extended to the synthesis of peptides containing optically inactive β-Abu, β-Leu, β-Met, and β-Lys by standard procedures; in the synthesis of a β-aminopimelic acid peptide, the lactam-chloride served as intermediate [213].

Attempts to obtain an N-carboxyanhydride from β-alanine have failed so far though N-arylated derivatives of this type have been prepared [217]. Syntheses of poly-β-alanine were based on the use of the acid chloride hydrochloride [218] or thiophenyl ester [219].

Two rather unusual methods for the formation of peptide bonds are available in the case of β-amino-acid peptides. One is exemplified by the Beckmann rearrangement of cyclohexane-1,4-dione dioxime [220, 221] which affords cyclo-β-alanyl-β-alanine. The second method, which is of rather

more general interest, is an elegant variant of the Arndt-Eistert synthesis
developed by Fleš and Markovac-Prpić [222, 223] and illustrated in equation (18) by the synthesis of L-β-aminobutyryl-L-methionine.† The advantage
of this procedure is that it leads directly to optically active peptides.

$$
\begin{array}{cc}
\text{CH}_3 & \text{CH}_2.\text{CH}_2.\text{SMe} \\
| & | \\
\text{PHT.N.CH.CO.CHN}_2 + \text{NH}_2.\text{CH.CO.OEt} & \xrightarrow[\text{dioxan}]{\text{Ag}_2\text{O}}
\end{array}
$$

$$
\begin{array}{cc}
& \text{CH}_3 \qquad\qquad \text{CH}_2.\text{CH}_2.\text{SMe} \\
& | \qquad\qquad\qquad | \\
\longrightarrow & \text{PHT.N.CH.CH}_2.\text{CO.NH.CH.CO.OEt} \qquad (18)
\end{array}
$$

Peptides of γ-aminobutyric acid (γ-Abu), δ-aminovaleric acid (δ-Nva),
and ε-aminocaproic acid (ε-Nle) have been prepared chiefly because of their
relevance to the chemistry of the polyamides. Although they do present
points of chemical and also of biochemical interest (e.g. γ-Abu-His occurs in
brain tissue [224], and Gly-δ-Nva, being an isoster of Gly-Gly-Gly, is a
substrate for tripeptidase [225]) it is not possible to deal with them within
the scope of this review.

COMPOUNDS WITH MODIFIED PEPTIDE BONDS

Peptides Substituted on the Amide Bond

Among compounds containing a modified peptide bond the peptides of
methylamino acids are the most familiar. Numerous peptides of sarcosine
were prepared in the " classical " period both by the Fischer amination
procedure [226–8] and through benzyloxycarbonyl-protected intermediates [229, 230]. Several N-methylleucine (MeLeu) peptides were also
prepared, generally by amination or methylamination of halogenacyl
derivatives (e.g. Gly-DL-MeLeu and DL-Leu-Gly-DL-MeLeu [228]). Recently
interest in peptides of the methylamino-acids has revived, largely because
of their natural occurrence. Methylation of the peptide bond also appeared
one possible way of making analogues of biologically active peptides resistant
to enzymic inactivation [231]; in pursuance of this idea analogues of oxytocin
containing N-methyltyrosine (MeTyr) and N-methylcysteine (MeCys) have
been prepared, i.e. MeTyr^2-oxytocin [170, 232] and MeCys^1-oxytocin [170].

The special properties of methylamino-acids relevant to peptide synthesis
can be characterized as decreased crystallinity (with increased solubility);
increased steric hindrance; and a marked tendency of dipeptides to cyclization. The first property, which is presumably largely due to decreased

---

† Where there is no danger of confusion it appears convenient, and permissible, to
extend the α-amino acid convention for denoting absolute configuration to the related
β-amino acids.

hydrogen bonding, is notorious; it is illustrated for the case of N-methyl-tyrosine in Table 6. A striking example of decreased reactivity presumably due to steric hindrance is provided by Russell's finding [233] that N-methyl-leucine methyl ester is not acylated by benzyloxycarbonylvaline p-nitrophenyl ester under standard conditions. The increased tendency of dipeptides substituted on the peptide nitrogen to cyclization is not, as is sometimes assumed,

TABLE 6.   COMPARISON OF MELTING-POINTS OF SOME PEPTIDE DERIVATIVES OF TYROSINE AND N-METHYLTYROSINE

Structure	X = Tyr		X = MeTyr	
	M.p.[a]	Ref.	M.p.	Ref.
Z-Cys(BZL)-X-OMe	89°	247	Oil	232
Z-Cys(BZL)-X-OH	198–200°	248	70° [b]	232
Z-Cys(BZL)-X-Ile-OMe	159–160°	249	Oil	232
Z-Cys(BZL)-X-Ile-OH	185–186°	249	185–190°	232
Z-Cys(BZL)-X-Y [c]	245–248°	250	140°	232
Tos-Cys(BZL)-X-OR	116–118° [d]	246	Oil [e]	170
Tos-Cys(BZL)-X-N$_2$H$_3$	201°	246	128–131°	170
Tos-Cys(BZL)-X-Y . H$_2$O[c]	241–243°	170	127–130°	170

[a] The highest melting-point recorded in the literature is given.
[b] Non-crystalline.
[c] Y = Ile-Glu(NH$_2$)-Asp(NH$_2$)-Cys(BZL)-Pro-Leu-Gly-NH$_2$.
[d] R = Et.
[e] R = Me.

confined to derivatives of proline. Thus treatment of α-bromopropionyl- or α-bromoisovalerylsarcosine with methylamine affords the corresponding dioxopiperazines rather than the peptides [227] and sarcosylsarcosine is thought to be in equilibrium with N,N'-dioxopiperazine even in acid solution [226]. The formation of the α-hydroxyisocaproyl amides by amination of α-bromoisocaproylsarcosine [228] and α-bromoisocaproyl-N-phenylglycine [235] presumably takes the course shown in equation (19) [229], where the intramolecular cyclization reaction successfully competes with intermolecular amination.

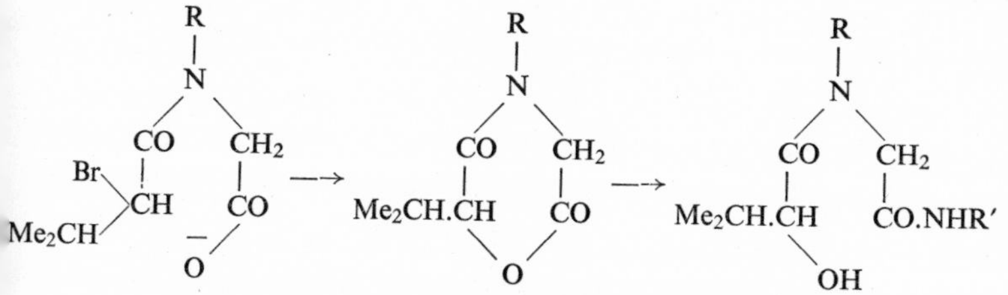

$$\text{(19)}$$

R = Ph,   R′ = H [234],   R = R′ = Me [228]

A more recent example of the same tendency is provided by the formation of N-methyl-N'-tosyldioxopiperazine as a byproduct in the treatment of tosylglycylsarcosine with hydrogen bromide in acetic acid; no corresponding product is formed from tosylglycylglycine under analogous conditions [235].

Among compounds carrying an acyl group on a peptide-bond nitrogen the N-acyldioxopiperazines are the best known; however, these compounds are considered to be outside the scope of this review. An acyclic peptide of this type, N-acetyl-(N-acetylglycyl)glycine ethyl ester (20a), was obtained by Bergmann, du Vigneaud, and Zervas [236] by the base-catalysed alcoholysis of N,N'-diacetyldioxopiperazine. Analogous derivatives carrying benzyl-oxycarbonyl (20c–e) or tosyl groups (20b) have been isolated as byproducts from peptide syntheses with the appropriate protected glycines [237–40].

$$X.CH_2.CO.\overset{\displaystyle X}{\overset{\displaystyle |}{N}}.CH_2.CO.Y \tag{20}$$

a. X = Ac,   Y = OEt [236] c. X = Z,   Y = OH [237]
b. X = Tos, Y = OH [240] d. X = Z,   Y = Gly.OEt [238]
                e. X = Z,   Y = Glu(OEt).OEt [239]

The N-acylpeptide structure can also be discerned in the imides which result by cyclization from peptides of glutamic or aspartic acid (21a) [for summary see ref. 98] or the pyroglutamic acid derivatives formed by another mode of cyclization (21b) from α-glutamyl peptides [241].

$$\sim NH.CH.CO.NH\sim \qquad \sim NH.CH{-\!\!-}CO \qquad\qquad \sim NH.CH.COOH$$
$$\underset{(CH_2)_n.COOH}{|} \longrightarrow \qquad \underset{(CH_2)_n{-\!\!-}CO}{|} \bigg\rangle N\sim \ \longleftarrow\ \underset{(CH_2)_n.CO.NH\sim}{|} \tag{21a}$$
$$n = 1 \text{ or } 2$$

$$\sim NH.CHR.CO.NH.CH.CO.NH\sim \qquad \sim NH.CHR.CO.N{-\!\!-\!\!-}CH.CO.NH\sim$$
$$\underset{CH_2}{|} \qquad\qquad \longrightarrow \qquad \underset{CO}{|} \quad \underset{CH_2}{|} \tag{21b}$$
$$\underset{CH_2.COOH}{|} \qquad\qquad\qquad\qquad CH_2$$

N-Acylated peptides with aminoacyl as the substituent have also been postulated as intermediates in rearrangement reactions [242, 243] but no systematic study of this whole group of derivatives has yet been made.

N-Hydroxypeptides formally result from N-aminoacylation of α-hydroxy-amino acids. The only representatives of this type so far appear to be the dioxopiperazine derivatives prepared [244] by the action of ammonia and of hydroxylamine on the appropriate N-halogenoacylhydroxyamino acid esters. Being hydroxamic acids such peptides would be expected to show interesting complex-forming properties.

N-Aminopeptides should similarly arise by N^{α}-substitution in α-hydrazino acids. Though simple representatives of this type have yet to be made, compounds carrying (blocked) aminoacyl substituents on both nitrogens of the hydrazine grouping have been prepared and will be described in a contribution to this Symposium (p. 181) [245].

Compounds with Modified Carbonyl Groups

Modifications of the peptide bond can be envisaged in which the amide bond is replaced by a thioamide, iminoether, or amidine linkage. No iminoether derivatives of this type have been described, and the only amide analogues reported have been derivatives of dioxopiperazine [251, 252] whose amidine structure yet remains to be conclusively established. However, true thioamide analogues of peptides have recently been prepared by Ried and von der Emden [253] by reaction of protected amino-acid thionesters (obtained from the nitriles through the imidates) with amino-acids (22). The benzyloxycarbonyl protecting group can be removed with hydrogen bromide. Silver or mercury(II) ions convert the thiopeptide to true peptide derivatives.

$$X.NH.CH_2.CN \rightarrow X.NH.CH_2.C(:NH).OR \rightarrow X.NH.CH_2.CS.OR \rightarrow$$
$$\rightarrow X.NH.CH_2.CS.NH.CH_2.CO.OH \qquad (22)$$
$$X = Tos\ or\ Z$$

Cyclol-type structures, which are orthoester derivatives, should also be counted in this class. The chemistry of these interesting and controversial compounds has been discussed at the Moscow Symposium [254] and is the subject of further reports at this meeting (p. 221) so that it need not be reviewed here.

HETEROPEPTIDES

The same is true of the depsipeptides; in fact, regular participants at these Symposia have been in an excellent position to follow the development of this subject from Shemyakin's review in 1959 [255] through subsequent reports [256–8] to the most recent results to be reported here. Again, O-aminoacyl derivatives of the hydroxy amino-acids (" O-peptides ") and their reactions have been extensively discussed at these Symposia [243, 259–61] (for a recent review of depsipeptide chemistry see ref. 262).

A further class of heteropeptides, those involving α-hydrazino acids, is also dealt with in a separate communication at this meeting [245, 263]. Analogous derivatives of aminoxyacetic acid have also been mentioned [264] but only N^{ω}-aminoacyl derivatives of canaline have been described in more detail [264].

Sulphamide Analogues

No true sulphamide analogues of peptides, i.e. compounds containing the structure $\sim$NH.CHR.SO$_2$.NH.CHR'.CO$\sim$, have yet been recorded, though several approaches in this direction have been made. Moses and Frankel [265], who have investigated the problem in some detail, obtained on the one hand aminoacyl derivatives of α-aminoalkylsulphonic acid, e.g. NH$_2$.CH$_2$.CO.NH.CHR.SO$_3$H (R = H or CH$_3$) and on the other (protected) tauryl peptides such as PHT.N.CH$_2$.CH$_2$.SO$_2$.NH.CH$_2$.CO.OEt or the corresponding benzyloxycarbonyl derivative. In spite of the difficulties discussed by these authors [265] true peptide analogues of the sulphamide type should be capable of existence.

CONCLUSION

The growing importance of the synthetic approach to biochemical problems relating to peptides and even proteins (structure–activity relationships, metabolic studies, topochemical problems, etc.), and the mounting synthetic attack on the structures of a number of naturally occurring peptide derivatives (e.g. the actinomycins) will increasingly bring the " unnatural " amino-acids within the purview of the chemist engaged in peptide synthesis. The recent developments in synthetic methods have made the introduction of quite complex and structurally unorthodox amino-acids into peptide bonding feasible and it is to be anticipated that the demands of further work along these lines will in turn stimulate the development and testing of additional synthetic methods in our fields.

ACKNOWLEDGEMENTS

My thanks are due to Dr K. Poduška and Dr K. Jošt for assistance in the compilation of the Tables.

REFERENCES

1. J. P. GREENSTEIN and M. WINITZ, *Chemistry of the Amino Acids*, Vol. 2. Wiley, New York 1961.
2. C. H. BAMFORD, A. ELLIOTT and W. E. HANBY, *Synthetic Polypeptides*. Academic Press, New York 1956.
3. E. BRICAS and C. FROMAGEOT, *Adv. Protein. Chem.* **8**, 4 (1953).
4. P. EDMAN, *Ann. Rev. Biochem.* **28**, 69 (1958); R. SCHWYZER, *Ann. Rev. Biochem.* **29**, 183 (1960).
5. G. BISERTE and M. DAUTREVAUX, *Expos. Ann. Biochim. Med.* **23**, 107 (1961).
6. M. M. SHEMYAKIN, A. S. KHOKHLOV, M. N. KOLOSOV, L. D. BERGEL'SON and V. K. ANTONOV, *Khimia Antibiotikov*, Vol. 2, Akad. Nauk S.S.S.R. Moscow 1961.
7. N. IZUMIYA, S.-C. J. FU, S. M. BIRNBAUM and J. P. GREENSTEIN, *J. Biol. Chem.* **205**, 221 (1953).

8. L. VELLUZ, G. AMIARD and R. HEYMÈS, *Bull. Soc. Chim. France* **1955**, 201.
9. L. VELLUZ, J. ANATOL and G. AMIARD, *Bull. Soc. Chim. France* **1954**, 1449.
10. E. ABDERHALDEN, HSING LANG CHANG and E. WURM, *Z. physiol. Chem.* **72**, 24 (1911).
11. E. ABDERHALDEN, C. FROEHLICH and D. FUCHS, *Z. physiol. Chem.* **86**, 454 (1913).
12. E. ABDERHALDEN and H. KÜRTEN, *Fermentforsch.* **4**, 327 (1921).
13. K. R. RAO, S. M. BIRNBAUM, R. B. KINGSLEY and J. P. GREENSTEIN, *J. Biol. Chem.* **198**, 507 (1952).
14. D. S. ROBINSON, S. M. BIRNBAUM and J. P. GREENSTEIN, *J. Biol. Chem.* **202**, 1 (1953).
15. J. S.-C. FU, S. M. BIRNBAUM and J. P. GREENSTEIN, *J. Amer. Chem. Soc.* **76**, 6054 (1954).
16. M. WINITZ, L. BLOCH-FRANKENTHAL, N. IZUMYIA, S. M. BIRNBAUM, C. G. BAKER and J. P. GREENSTEIN, *J. Amer. Chem. Soc.* **78**, 2423 (1956).
17. S. G. WALEY, *Biochem. J.* **68**, 189 (1958).
18. N. IZUMIYA and T. YAMASHITA, *J. Biochem.* **46**, 19, 337 (1959).
19. T. YAMASHITA, *J. Biochem.* **48**, 846 (1960).
20. H. NESVADBA, J. HONZL and J. RUDINGER, *Coll. Czechoslov. Chem. Commun.*, in press.
21. N. IZUMIYA and S. MAKISUMI, *J. Chem. Soc. Japan, Pure Chem. Sect.* **78**, 662 (1957).
22. W. S. FONES and M. LEE, *J. Biol. Chem.* **210**, 227 (1954).
23. C. S. MARVEL and W. A. NOYES, *J. Amer. Chem. Soc.* **42**, 2259 (1920).
24. N. IZUMIYA, H. UCHIO and T. YAMASHITA, *J. Chem. Soc. Japan, Pure Chem. Sect.* **79**, 420 (1958).
25. E. L. SMITH and D. H. SPACKMANN, *J. Biol. Chem.* **212**, 271 (1955).
26. L. ZERVAS, M. WINITZ and J. P. GREENSTEIN, *J. Org. Chem.* **22**, 1515 (1957).
27. E. ABDERHALDEN and F. GEBELEIN, *Z. physiol. Chem.* **152**, 125 (1926).
28. G. FAUST and H. LANGE, *J. prakt. Chem.* [4], **11**, 153 (1960).
29. M. T. LEPŁAWY, D. S. JONES, G. W. KENNER and R. C. SHEPPARD, *Tetrahedron* **11**, 39 (1960).
30. M. BERGMANN, L. ZERVAS, J. S. FRUTON, F. SCHNEIDER and H. SCHLEICH, *J. Biol. Chem.* **109**, 325 (1935).
31. W. LANGENBECK and P. KRESSE, *J. prakt. Chem.* [4], **2**, 261 (1955).
32. W. E. HANBY, S. G. WALEY and J. WATSON, *J. Chem. Soc.* **1950**, 3009.
33. D. COLEMAN and A. C. FARTHING, *J. Chem. Soc.* **1950**, 3218.
34. M. ZAORAL, *Angew. Chem.* **71**, 743 (1959); *Coll. Czechoslov. Chem. Commun.* **27**, 1273 (1962).
35. T. A. CONNORS and W. C. J. ROSS, *J. Chem. Soc.* **1960**, 2119.
36. P. TAILLEUR and L. BERLINGUET, *Can. J. Chem.* **39**, 1309 (1961).
37. S. SHANKMAN, S. HIGA, F. LEW and M. E. ROBERTS, *Coll. Czechoslov. Chem. Commun.* **27**, 2249 (1962); *J. Med. Pharm. Chem.* **5**, 42 (1962).
38. P. TAILLEUR and L. BERLINGUET, *J. Org. Chem.* **27**, 653 (1962).
39. G. FAUST and M. KLEPEL, *J. prakt. Chem.* [4], **11**, 133 (1960).
40. A. P. N. FRANCHIMONT and H. FRIEDMANN, *Rec. Trav. Chim.* **27**, 192 (1908).
41. A. L. BARKER and G. S. SKINNER, *J. Amer. Chem. Soc.* **46**, 403 (1924).
42. A. C. FARTHING, *J. Chem. Soc.* **1950**, 3213.
43. N. IZUMIYA and J. S. FRUTON, *J. Biol. Chem.* **218**, 59 (1956).
44. J. H. BILLMAN and W. F. HARTING, *J. Amer. Chem. Soc.* **70**, 1473 (1948).
45. F. FICHTER and M. SCHMID, *Helv. Chim. Acta* **3**, 704 (1920).
46. S. AKABORI, T. IKENAKA and K. MATSUMOTO, *Proc. Japan. Acad.* **27**, 7 (1951); *Chem. Abstr.* **47**, 3795 (1953).
47. K. VEREŠ and J. RUDINGER, unpublished results.
48. J. SMRT, J. BERÁNEK, J. SICHER and F. ŠORM, *Coll. Czechoslov. Chem. Commun.* **22**, 262 (1957).
49. S. GOLDSCHMIDT and M. WICK, *Ann.* **575**, 217 (1952).
50. F. C. McKAY and N. F. ALBERTSON, *J. Amer. Chem. Soc.* **79**, 4686 (1957).
51. S. GOLDSCHMIDT and F. OBERMEIER, *Ann.* **588**, 24 (1954).
52. F. W. DUNN and K. DITTMER, *J. Biol. Chem.* **188**, 263 (1951).
53. F. W. DUNN and E. L. SMITH, *J. Biol. Chem.* **187**, 385 (1950).

54. E. L. SMITH, R. LUMRY and W. J. POLGLASE, *J. Phys. Colloid Chem.* **55,** 125 (1951
55. A. ALBERT, *Biochem. J.* **50,** 690 (1952).
56. J. RUDINGER, *Coll. Czechoslov. Chem. Commun.* **24,** Special Issue, 95 (1959).
57. A. KJAER, *Acta Chem. Scand.* **3,** 1087 (1949).
58. F. SCHNEIDER, *Ann.* **529,** 1 (1937).
59. F. SCHNEIDER, *Biochem. Z.* **291,** 328 (1937).
60. Y. MYIANOKI, *J. Biochem.* **13,** 389 (1931); *Chem. Zentr.* **1933,** II, 2686.
61. K. PODUŠKA, J. RUDINGER and F. ŠORM, *Coll. Czechoslov. Chem. Commun.* **20,** 117
   (1955).
62. J. RUDINGER, K. PODUŠKA and M. ZAORAL, *Coll. Czechoslov. Chem. Commun.* **2**
   2022 (1960).
63. A. KJAER and E. VESTERAGER, *Acta Chem. Scand.* **14,** 961 (1960).
64. A. KJAER, A. KNUDSEN, and P. OLESEN LARSEN, *Acta Chem. Scand.* **15,** 1193 (1961)
65. I. D. SPENSER and A. D. NOTATION, *Can. J. Chem.* **40,** 1374 (1962).
66. M. ZAORAL, J. RUDINGER and F. ŠORM, *Coll. Czechoslov. Chem. Commun.* **18,** 53
   (1953).
67. K. PODUŠKA and J. RUDINGER, *Coll. Czechoslov. Chem. Commun.* **22,** 1283 (1957).
68. K. PODUŠKA and J. RUDINGER, *Coll. Czechoslov. Chem. Commun.* **24,** 3449 (1959).
69. M. ZAORAL and J. RUDINGER, *Proc. Chem. Soc. (London)* **1957,** 176.
70. M. ZAORAL and J. RUDINGER, *Coll. Czechoslov. Chem. Commun.* **24,** 1993 (1959).
71. M. ZAORAL, *Coll. Czechoslov. Chem. Commun.* **24,** 1314 (1959).
72. K. VOGLER and P. LANZ, *Helv. Chim. Acta* **43,** 270 (1960).
73. K. VOGLER and L. H. CHOPARD-DIT-JEAN, *Helv. Chim. Acta* **43,** 279 (1960).
74. K. VOGLER, P. LANZ, W. LERGIER and R. O. STUDER, *Helv. Chim. Acta* **43,** 57
   (1960).
75. K. VOGLER, R. O. STUDER, W. LERGIER and P. LANZ, *Helv. Chim. Acta* **43,** 175
   (1960).
76. R. O. STUDER, K. VOGLER and W. LERGIER, *Helv. Chim. Acta* **44,** 131 (1961).
77. R. O. STUDER and K. VOGLER, *Helv. Chim. Acta* **45,** 819 (1962).
78. K. VOGLER, R. O. STUDER, P. LANZ, W. LERGIER and E. BÖHNI, *Experientia* **17,** 22
   (1961).
79. K. SUZUKI, *Ann. Rep. Tohôku Coll. Pharm.* **2,** 22 (1955).
80. T. KURIHARA and K. SUZUKI, *J. Pharm. Soc. Japan* **75,** 1269 (1955).
81. S. WILKINSON, *J. Chem. Soc.* **1951,** 104.
82. J. RUDINGER, *Record Chem. Progress* **23,** 3 (1962).
83. W. J. LE QUESNE and G. T. YOUNG, *J. Chem. Soc.* **1952,** 594.
84. B. C. BARRASS and D. T. ELMORE, *J. Chem. Soc.* **1957,** 4830.
85. K. PODUŠKA, unpublished results.
86. C. RESSLER, *J. Amer. Chem. Soc.* **78,** 5956 (1956).
87. J. E. FOLK and J. A. GLADNER, *J. Biol. Chem.* **231,** 379 (1958).
88. B. C. BARRASS and D. T. ELMORE, *J. Chem. Soc.* **1957,** 4830.
89. M. ZAORAL, unpublished results.
90. (a) A. C. KURTZ, *J. Biol. Chem.* **122,** 477 (1938).
   (b) H. N. CHRISTENSEN and T. R. RIGGS, *J. Biol. Chem.* **220,** 265 (1956).
91. J. RUDINGER, unpublished results.
92. H. E. ZAUGG, M. FREIFELDER, H. J. GLENN, B. W. HORROM, G. R. STONE an
   M. R. VERNSTEN, *J. Amer. Chem. Soc.* **78,** 2626 (1956).
93. M. FRANKEL, M. HARNIK, Y. LEVIN and Y. KNOBLER, *J. Amer. Chem. Soc.* **75,** 7
   (1953); M. FRANKEL, M. HARNIK and Y. LEVIN, *Experientia* **8,** 98 (1952).
94. S. G. COHEN and L. ALTSCHUL, *Nature* **183,** 1678 (1959); S. G. COHEN and L. H. KLE
   J. Amer. Chem. Soc. **82,** 6038 (1960).
95. E. P. ABRAHAM and G. G. F. NEWTON, *Biochem. J.* **58,** 266 (1954).
96. J. RUDINGER, *Coll. Czechoslov. Chem. Commun.* **27,** 2246 (1962).
97. J. RUDINGER and V. GUT, *Coll. Czechoslov. Chem. Commun.,* in press.
98. K. MEDZIHRADSZKY, *Coll. Czechoslov. Chem. Commun.* **24,** Special Issue, 107 (1959
99. D. MORRIS, V. GUT and J. RUDINGER, unpublished results.
100. F. MICHEEL and H. HANEKE, *Chem. Ber.* **92,** 309 (1959).

101. H. R. V. ARNSTEIN and D. MORRIS, *Biochem. J.* **76**, 357 (1960).
102. O. L. MNDZHOYAN and J. RUDINGER, unpublished results.
103. M. GOODMAN and K. C. STUEBEN, *J. Amer. Chem. Soc.* **81**, 3980 (1959).
104. T. WIELAND, H. CORDS and E. KECK, *Chem. Ber.* **87**, 1312 (1954).
105. H. M. CROOKS, in H. T. Clarke *et al.*, *Chemistry of Penicillin*, p. 455, Princeton University Press 1949.
106. O. SÜS, *Ann.* **561**, 31 (1949).
107. I. L. KNUNYANTS and V. V. SHOKINA, *Izv. Akad. Nauk SSSR, Otd. Khim. Nauk* **1955**, 462.
108. W. BAKER and W. D. OLLIS, *J. Chem. Soc.* **1951**, 556.
109. W. BAKER and P. G. JONES, *J. Chem. Soc.* **1951**, 1143.
110. F. E. KING, J. W. CLARK-LEWIS and W. A. SWINDIN, *J. Chem. Soc.* **1959**, 2259.
111. F. E. KING, J. W. CLARK-LEWIS, G. R. SMITH and R. WADE, *J. Chem. Soc.* **1959**, 2264.
112. I. L. KNUNYANTS, O. V. KIL'DISHEVA and E. YA PERVOVA, *Izv. Akad. Nauk SSSR, Otd. Khim. Nauk* **1955**, 689.
113. J. C. SHEEHAN, *Ann. New York Acad. Sci.* **88**, 665 (1960).
114. D. FLEŠ, A. MARKOVAC-PRPIC and V. TOMAŠIC, *J. Amer. Chem. Soc.* **80**, 4654 (1958).
115. D. FLEŠ, A. MARKOVAC-PRPIĆ, V. TOMAŠIC and M. MILOHNOJA, *Croatica Chim. Acta* **30**, 167 (1958).
116. I. L. KNUNYANTS, O. V. KIL'DISHEVA and E. YA. PERVOVA, *Izv. Akad. Nauk SSSR, Otd. Khim. Nauk* **1955**, 696.
117. R. BENESCH and R. E. BENESCH, *J. Amer. Chem. Soc.* **78**, 1597 (1956).
118. E. C. HERRICK and C. W. TODD, U.S. Patents 2,723,972 and 2,727,973; *Chem. Abstr.* **50**, 4214, 4215 (1956).
119. O. GAWRON and F. DRAUS, *J. Org. Chem.* **24**, 1392 (1959).
120. N. F. ALBERTSON and F. C. MCKAY, *J. Amer. Chem. Soc.* **75**, 5323 (1953).
121. T. WIELAND, *Chem. Ber.* **81**, 323 (1948).
122. E. M. LANSFORD and W. SHIVE, *J. Biol. Chem.* **194**, 329 (1952).
123. F. W. HOLLY, R. A. BARNES, F. R. KONIUSZY and K. FOLKERS, *J. Amer. Chem. Soc.* **70**, 3088 (1948).
124. T. SHERADSKY, Y. KNOBLER and M. FRANKEL, *J. Org. Chem.* **26**, 2710 (1961).
125. S. WEISS and J. A. STEKOL, *J. Amer. Chem. Soc.* **73**, 2497 (1951).
126. A. A. PATCHETT and B. WITKOP, *J. Amer. Chem. Soc.* **79**, 185 (1957).
127. H. ZAHN and L. ZÜRN, *Ann.* **613**, 76 (1958).
128. E. ABDERHALDEN and W. SCHAIRER, *Fermentforsch.* **12**, 295 (1931).
129. J. J. O'NEILL, F. P. VEITCH and T. WAGNER-JAUREGG, *J. Org. Chem.* **21**, 363 (1956).
130. S. LISSITZKI, M. ROQUES and M.-T. BENEVENT, *Compt. Rend. Soc. Biol.* **151**, 351 (1957).
131. C. BERSE and L. PICHET, *J. Org. Chem.* **21**, 808 (1956).
132. M. FRANKEL and D. GERTNER, *Bull. Res. Council Israel* **9A**, 65, 66 (1960); *J. Chem. Soc.* **1961**, 459.
133. H. R. V. ARNSTEIN and M. E. CLUBB, *Biochem. J.* **68**, 528 (1958).
134. H. ZAHN and H. KESSLER, *Makromol. Chem.* **27**, 218 (1958).
135. E. ABDERHALDEN and W. ZEISSET, *Fermentforsch.* **9**, 336 (1928).
136. E. WORK, S. M. BIRNBAUM, M. WINITZ and J. P. GREENSTEIN, *J. Amer. Chem. Soc.* **77**, 1916 (1955).
137. R. WADE, S. M. BIRNBAUM, M. WINITZ, R. J. KOEGEL and J. P. GREENSTEIN, *J. Amer. Chem. Soc.* **79**, 648 (1957).
138. E. BRICAS, C. NICOT and J. VAN HEIJENOORT, *Coll. Czechoslov. Chem. Commun.* **27**, 2240 (1962); *Comp. Rend.* **254**, 1685 (1962).
139. K. MORI, *J. Chem. Soc. Japan, Pure Chem. Sect.* **82**, 1375 (1961).
140. See ref. 1, pp. 838–860.
141. A. JÖHL and W. G. STOLL, *Helv. Chim. Acta* **42**, 716 (1959).
142. K. SCHLÖGL and H. FABITSCHOWITZ, *Monatsh.* **85**, 1060 (1954).
143. A. L. DAVIS, C. G. SKINNER and W. SHIVE, *J. Amer. Chem. Soc.* **83**, 2279 (1961).
144. A. L. DAVIS, C. G. SKINNER and W. SHIVE, *Arch. Biochem. Biophys.* **87**, 88 (1960).
145. C. G. SKINNER, J. EDELSON and W. SHIVE, *J. Amer. Chem. Soc.* **83**, 2281 (1961).

P

146. M. S. RAASCH, *J. Org. Chem.* **23**, 1567 (1958).
147. M. HUDLICKÝ, *Coll. Czechoslov. Chem. Commun.* **26**, 1414 (1961); M. HUDLICKÝ, unpublished results.
148. E. J. COREY and L. F. HAEFELE, *J. Amer. Chem. Soc.* **81**, 2225 (1959); G. L. SCHMIR, L. A. COHEN and B. WITKOP, *J. Amer. Chem. Soc.* **81**, 2228 (1959).
149. A. PATCHORNIK, W. B. LAWSON and B. WITKOP, *J. Amer. Chem. Soc.* **80**, 4748 (1958).
150. W. B. LAWSON, E. GROSS, C. M. FOLTZ and B. WITKOP, *J. Amer. Chem. Soc.* **83**, 1509 (1961).
151. A. I. VIRTANEN and I. MATTILA, *Suomen Kem.* **34B**, 73 (1961); A. I. VIRTANEN and E. J. MATIKALLA, *Suomen Kem.* **34B**, 53 (1961); A. I. VIRTANEN, M. HATANAKA, and M. BERLIN, *Suomen Kem.* **35B**, 52 (1962).
152. H. RINDERKNECHT, D. THOMAS and S. ASLIN, *Helv. Chim. Acta* **41**, 1 (1958); R. M. ZACHARIUS, C. J. MORRIS and J. F. THOMPSON, *Arch. Biochem. Biophys.* **73**, 281 (1958).
153. M. FRANKEL, D. GERTNER; H. JACOBSON and A. ZILKHA, *J. Chem. Soc.* **1960**, 1390.
154. M. FRANKEL and D. GERTNER, *J. Chem. Soc.* **1961**, 463.
155. T. SHIOTA, J. MAURON and J. E. FOLK, *Biochim. Biophys. Acta* **53**, 360 (1961).
156. T. WIELAND, K. FRETER and E. GROSS, *Ann.* **626**, 154 (1959).
157. F. KÖGL and W. SCHOPMAN, *Rec. Trav. Chim.* **75**, 29 (1956).
158. H. ADKINS and B. D. TIFFANY, *J. Amer. Chem. Soc.* **79**, 4544 (1957).
159. M. ZAORAL and Z. ARNOLD, *Coll. Czechoslov. Chem. Commun.* **27**, 2252 (1962).
160. D. T. GISH, P. G. KATSOYANNIS, G. P. HESS and R. J. STEDMAN, *J. Amer. Chem. Soc.* **78**, 5954 (1956) ; P. G. KATSOYANNIS, D. T. GISH, G. P. HESS and V. du VIGNEAUD, *J. Amer. Chem. Soc.* **80**, 2558 (1958).
161. C. RESSLER and H. RATZKIN, *J. Org. Chem.* **26**, 3355 (1961).
162. F. WESSELY, K. SCHLÖGL and G. KORGER, *Monatsh.* **83**, 678 (1952).
163. N. IZUMIYA and M. SHITÔ, *J. Chem. Soc. Japan, Pure Chem. Sect.* **79**, 975 (1958).
164. M. BODANSZKY, M. A. ONDETTI, B. RUBIN, J. J. FIALA, J. FRIED, J. T. SHEEHAN and C. A. BIRKHEIMER, *Nature* **194**, 485 (1962).
165. Y. KNOBLER and M. FRANKEL, *J. Chem. Soc.* **1958**, 1632.
166. T. EMERY and J. B. NEILANDS, *J. Amer. Chem. Soc.* **83**, 1626 (1961).
167. J. TURKOVÁ, O. MIKEŠ and F. ŠORM, *Coll. Czechoslov. Chem. Commun.* **27**, 591 (1962).
168. R. SCHWYZER and E. SURBECK-WEGMANN, *Helv. Chim. Acta* **43**, 1073 (1960).
169. R. SCHWYZER, *Helv. Chim. Acta* **44**, 667 (1961).
170. K. JOŠT, J. RUDINGER and F. ŠORM, *Coll. Czechoslov. Chem. Commun.* **26**, 2496 (1961).
171. M. BODANSZKY, private communication.
172. J. M. MUELLER, J. G. PIERCE and V. du VIGNEAUD, *J. Biol. Chem.* **204**, 857 (1953).
173. C. RESSLER, S. TRIPPETT and V. du VIGNEAUD, *J. Biol. Chem.* **204**, 861 (1953).
174. C. W. ROBERTS and V. du VIGNEAUD, *J. Biol. Chem.* **204**, 871 (1953).
175. J. N. ASHLEY and C. R. HARINGTON, *Biochem. J.* **22**, 1436 (1928).
176. E. ABDERHALDEN and E. SCHWAB, *Fermentforsch.* **11**, 164 (1930).
177. J. S. FRUTON and M. BERGMANN, *J. Biol. Chem.* **127**, 627 (1939).
178. C. BECKERS, M. J. SPIRO and J. B. STANBURY, *Endocrinol.* **66**, 669 (1960).
179. K. SCHLÖGL, F. WESSELY and E. WAWERSICH, *Monatsh.* **84**, 705 (1953).
180. S. TAUROG, S. ABRAHAM and I. L. CHAIKOFF, *J. Amer. Chem. Soc.* **75**, 3473 (1953).
181. R. BENNETT, H. BURGER and C. L. GEMMILL, *J. Med. Pharm. Chem.* **2**, 483 (1960).
182. C. R. HARINGTON and R. V. PITT RIVERS, *J. Chem. Soc.* **1940**, 1101.
183. R. V. PITT RIVERS, *Biochem. J.* **43**, 223 (1948).
184. F. BERGEL and J. A. STOCK, *J. Chem. Soc.* **1954**, 2409.
185. F. BERGEL, V. C. E. BURNOP and J. A. STOCK, *J. Chem. Soc.* **1955**, 1223.
186. K. SCHLÖGL, F. WESSELY and G. KORGER, *Monatsh.* **83**, 845 (1952).
187. M. SELA and E. KATCHALSKI, *J. Amer. Chem. Soc.* **76**, 129 (1954).
188. B. L. MOL'DAVER and Z. V. PUSHKAREVA, *Zh. Obshch. Khim.* **31**, 3793 (1961).
189. M. SELA and E. KATCHALSKI, *J. Amer. Chem. Soc.* **77**, 3662 (1955).

190. A. BAR-ELI and E. KATCHALSKI, *Bull. Res. Council Israel* **9A**, 101 (1960); *Nature* **188**, 856 (1960).
191. E. SCHNABEL and H. ZAHN, *Monatsh.* **88**, 646 (1957).
192. L. F. LARIONOV and Z. P. SOF'INA, *Dokl. Akad. Nauk SSSR* **114**, 1070 (1957).
193. L. A. ELSON, A. HADDOW, F. BERGEL and J. A. STOCK, *Biochem. Pharmacol.* **11**, 1079 (1962).
194. I. L. KNUNYANTS, O. V. KIL'DISHEVA and N. E. GOLUBEVA, *Izv. Akad. Nauk SSSR, Otd. Khim. Nauk* **1956**, 1418.
195. N. E. GOLUBEVA, O. V. KIL'DISHEVA and I. L. KNUNYANTS, *Dokl. Akad. Nauk SSSR* **119**, 83 (1958).
196. F. BERGEL and J. A. STOCK, *J. Chem. Soc.* **1958**, 4563.
197. F. BERGEL and J. A. STOCK, *J. Chem. Soc.* **1960**, 3658.
198. E. N. SHKODINSKAYA, O. S. VASINA, A. YA. BERLIN, Z. P. SOF'INA and L. F. LARINOV, *Zh. Obshch. Khim.* **32**, 324 (1952); *Coll. Czechoslov. Chem. Commun.* **27**, 2254 (1962).
199. L. V. ALEKSEEVA and Z. V. PUSHKAREVA, *Zh. Obshch. Khim.* **31**, 2918 (1961).
200. I. L. KNUNYANTS, K. I. KARPAVICHUS and O. V. KIL'DISHEVA, *Izv. Akad. Nauk SSSR, Otd. Khim. Nauk* **1961**, 1297.
201. I. L. KNUNYANTS, K. I. KARPAVICHUS and O. V. KIL'DISHEVA, *Izv. Akad. Nauk SSSR, Otd. Khim. Nauk* **1962**, 1024.
202. I. L. KNUNYANTS, N. E. GOLUBEVA, K. I. KARPAVICHUS and O. V. KIL'DISHEVA, *Coll. Czechoslov. Chem. Commun.* **27**, 2253 (1962); *Zh. Vsesoyuz. Khim. Obshchestva im. Mendeleyeva* **4**, 238 (1962).
203. (a) F. W. DUNN, *J. Org. Chem.* **21**, 1525 (1956).
    (b) F. W. DUNN, J. M. RAVEL and W. SHIVE, *J. Biol Chem.* **219**, 809 (1956).
204. J. I. HARRIS and T. S. WORK, *Biochem. J.* **46**, 190 (1950).
205. H. T. HANSON and E. L. SMITH, *J. Biol. Chem.* **175**, 833 (1948).
206. E. ADAMS, N. C. DAVIS and E. L. SMITH, *J. Biol. Chem.* **199**, 845 (1952).
207. N. C. DAVIS, *J. Biol. Chem.* **223**, 935 (1956).
208. R. H. SIFFERD and V. du VIGNEAUD, *J. Biol. Chem.* **108**, 753 (1935).
209. H. KROLL and H. HOBERMAN, *J. Amer. Chem. Soc.* **75**, 2511 (1953).
210. R. A. TURNER, *J. Amer. Chem. Soc.* **75**, 2388 (1953).
211. F. W. DUNN, *J. Biol. Chem.* **227**, 575 (1957).
212. E. DYER and E. BALLARD, *J. Amer. Chem. Soc.* **59**, 1697 (1937).
213. L. BIRKOFER and I. HARTWIG, *Chem. Ber.* **89**, 1608 (1956).
214. M. A. NYMAN and R. M. HERBST, *J. Org. Chem.* **15**, 108 (1950).
215. W. RIED and K. MARQUARD, *Ann.* **642**, 141 (1961).
216. G. D. KALYANKAR and A. MEISTER, *J. Biol. Chem.* **234**, 3210 (1958).
217. L. BIRKOFER and R. MODIC, *Ann.* **604**, 56 (1957).
218. M. FRANKEL, Y. LIWSCHITZ and A. ZILKHA, *J. Amer. Chem. Soc.* **76**, 2814 (1954).
219. T. WIELAND and K. FRETER, *Chem. Ber.* **87**, 1099 (1954).
220. I. L. KNUNYANTS and B. F. FABRICHNYI, *Dokl. Akad. Nauk SSSR* **68**, 701 (1949).
221. M. ROTHE, *Chem. Ber.* **95**, 783 (1962).
222. D. FLEŠ and A. MARKOVAC-PRPIĆ, *Croatica Chim. Acta* **28**, 73 (1956).
223. D. FLEŠ and A. MARKOVAC-PRPIĆ, *Croatica Chim. Acta* **29**, 79 (1957).
224. J. J. PISANO, J. D. WILSON, L. COHEN, D. ABRAHAM and S. UDENFRIEND, *J. Biol. Chem.* **236**, 499 (1961).
225. N. C. DAVIS and E. L. SMITH, *J. Biol. Chem.* **214**, 209 (1955).
226. P. A. LEVENE, H. S. SIMMS and M. H. PFALTZ, *J. Biol. Chem.* **61**, 445 (1924).
227. P. A. LEVENE, H. S. SIMMS and M. H. PFALTZ, *J. Biol. Chem.* **70**, 253 (1926).
228. E. ABDERHALDEN, E. SCHWAB and J. G. VALDECASAS, *Fermentforsch.* **13**, 396 (1932).
229. M. BERGMANN, L. ZERVAS, H. SCHLEICH and F. LEINERT, *Z. physiol. Chem.* **212**, 72 (1932).
230. M. BERGMANN, L. ZERVAS and J. S. FRUTON, *J. Biol. Chem.* **111**, 225 (1935).
231. M. ZAORAL, K. JOŠT, J. RUDINGER and F. ŠORM, XVIIth International Congress of Pure and Applied Chemistry, Munich, September 1959.
232. R. L. HUGUENIN and R. A. BOISSONNAS, *Helv. Chim. Acta* **44**, 213 (1961).
233. D. W. RUSSELL, private communication.

234. E. Fischer and W. Glund, *Ann.* **369**, 247 (1909).
235. J. Rudinger and V. Gut, unpublished results.
236. M. Bergmann, V. du Vigneaud and L. Zervas, *Ber.* **62**, 1909 (1929).
237. T. Wieland and B. Heinke, *Ann.* **599**, 70 (1956).
238. K. D. Kopple and R. J. Renick, *J. Org. Chem.* **23**, 1565 (1958).
239. P. Schellenberg and J. Ullrich, *Chem. Ber.* **92**, 1276 (1958).
240. M. Zaoral and J. Rudinger, *Coll. Czechoslov. Chem. Commun.* **26**, 2316 (1961).
241. A. R. Battersby and J. C. Robinson, *J. Chem. Soc.* **1956**, 2076.
242. T. Wieland, E. Bokelman, L. Bauer, H. U. Lang and H. Lau, *Ann.* **583**, 129 (1953).
243. M. M. Botvinik, A. P. Andreeva and L. M. Koksharova, *Coll. Czechoslov. Chem. Commun.* **27**, 2244 (1962).
244. A. H. Cook and C. A. Slater, *J. Chem. Soc.* **1956**, 4130.
245. H. Niedrich and W. Knobloch, *Z. prakt. Chem.* [4], **17**, 263 (1962).
246. J. Honzl and J. Rudinger, *Coll. Czechoslov. Chem. Commun.* **20**, 1190 (1955).
247. R. A. Boissonnas, S. Guttmann, P.-A. Jaquenoud and J.-P. Waller, *Helv. Chim. Acta* **38**, 1491 (1955).
248. C. R. Harington and R. V. Pitt Rivers, *Biochem. J.* **38**, 417 (1944).
249. C. Ressler and V. du Vigneaud, *J. Amer. Chem. Soc.* **79**, 4511 (1957).
250. M. Bodanszky and V. du Vigneaud, *J. Amer. Chem. Soc.* **81**, 5688 (1959).
251. N. I. Gavrilov and L. N. Akimova, *Zh. Obshch. Khim.* **17**, 2101 (1947); **21**, 289 (1951).
252. N. I. Gavrilov, L. N. Akimova and M. S. Khludova, *Coll. Czechoslov. Chem. Commun.* **27**, 2250 (1962).
253. W. Ried and W. von der Emden, *Ann.* **642**, 128 (1961).
254. A. Hofmann, A. J. Frey, H. Ott and J. Rutschmann, *Coll. Czechoslov. Chem. Commun.* **27**, 2245 (1962).
255. M. M. Schemjakin, *Angew. Chem.* **72**, 342 (1960).
256. H. Gibian and K. Lübke, *Chimia* **14**, 380 (1960); *Ann.* **644**, 130 (1961).
257. R. Schwyzer and J. P. Carrión, *Helv. Chim. Acta* **43**, 2101 (1960).
258. M. M. Shemyakin, *Coll. Czechoslov. Chem. Commun.* **27**, 2252 (1962).
259. M. M. Botwinik, *Coll. Czechoslov. Chem. Commun.* **24**, Special Issue, 54 (1959).
260. M. Brenner, *Coll. Czechoslov. Chem. Commun.* **24**, Special Issue, 120 (1959).
261. J. Pless and H. Moser, *Chimia* **14**, 377 (1960).
262. M. M. Shemyakin, *Uspekhi Khim.* **31**, 269 (1962).
263. W. Knobloch and H. Niedrich, *J. prakt. Chem.* [4], **17**, 273 (1962).
264. M. Frankel, Y. Knobler and G. Zvilichowsky, *Tetrahedron Letters* **1960**, No. 18, 28.
265. M. Frankel and P. Moses, *Tetrahedron* **9**, 289 (1960).
266. M. M. Schemyakin, *Coll. Czechoslov. Chem. Commun.* **24**, Special Issue, 143 (1959).
267. W. K. Antonov, G. A. Ravdel and M. M. Chemiakine, *Chimia* **14**, 374 (1960).
268. H. Arold, private communication.
269. F. Bergel, J. M. Johnson and R. Wade, *J. Chem. Soc.* **1962**, 3802.
270. J. M. Johnson and J. A. Stock, *J. Chem. Soc.* **1962**, 3806.

SYNTHESIS OF OPTICALLY ACTIVE
N-METHYLATED AMINO-ACIDS

P. QUITT

F. Hoffmann-La Roche & Co. Limited, Basle, Switzerland

INTRODUCTION

Among the unusual amino-acids found in natural products the N-mono-methylated derivatives are of some interest, since they are present in a series of antibiotics that were discovered and elucidated during the last few years. *Enniatins* A and B contain N-methylisoleucine and N-methylvaline respectively, and were isolated 14 years ago from a strain of fungi, by Plattner and Nager [1]. Very recently, synthetic work was done on this problem by Shemyakin and coworkers [2]. The *Actinomycins*—investigated and synthesized by Brockmann [3]—also contain methylvaline in addition to sarcosine. *Etamycin*, described by Sheehan and coworkers [4] in 1957, contains L-phenyl-sarcosine, L-N-β-dimethyl-leucine and sarcosine. N-Methylphenylalanine was found by Vanderhaeghe and Parmentier [5] in *Staphylomycin*, whereas the structural analogue *Ostreogrycin B* has N-methylphenylalanine replaced by its p-dimethylamino derivative, as was shown by Todd and coworkers [6]. Finally, the depsipeptide *Sporidesmolide I* studied by Russell [7] contains N-methyl-leucine.

It therefore appears that N-methylated amino-acids play an important role as constituents of peptide or depsipeptide antibiotics, and the synthesis of such—or related—compounds may be of interest. However, there were still no simple and generally applicable syntheses for optically active N-mono-methylated amino-acids. Substitution reactions on α-halogenated fatty acids with methylamine not only require the preparation of optically active starting materials, they also produce partially racemized compounds. It is also far more convenient to start from the nowadays commercially available optically active amino-acids than to resolve racemic products obtained by total synthesis. So far, only two generally applicable syntheses of this type have been in use, the first being Emil Fischer's [8] classical method of methylating the N-tosylated amino-acids. Although monomethylation can be achieved in most cases by this method, it certainly does not proceed without racemization. Besides, the isolation of the endproduct from the reaction mixture after detosylation is often rather troublesome. A second method uses the principle of reductive alkylation by means of aldehydes, as described

165

by Bowman [9]. This generally leads to monoalkylation except in the case of formaldehyde, where dimethylation is inevitable. The yield of the mono-methylated compounds rarely exceeds 20 per cent and the necessary separa-tion from starting material and dimethylated product is not too simple. Izumiya and coworkers [10], who furnished most of the data available concerning N-methylamino-acids, synthesized their compounds either by total synthesis via α-halo-acids or by Fischer's method.

SCHEME OF SYNTHESIS

Our scheme of synthesis also uses the principle of reductive methylation, but only to introduce a benzyl group for temporary protection as outlined in Table 1. The sequence of reactions is as follows: an aqueous solution of

TABLE 1. GENERAL SCHEME OF SYNTHESIS

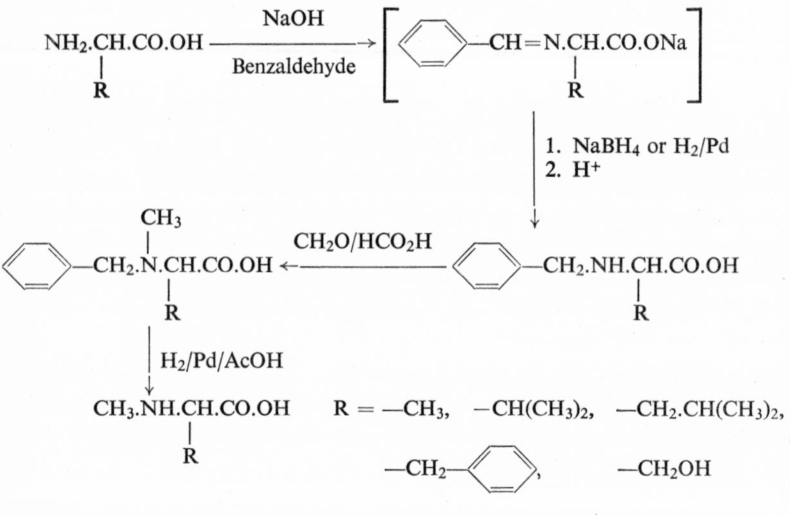

the sodium salt of an amino-acid is treated with benzaldehyde, thus forming a Schiff base that is subsequently reduced by means of either sodium boro-hydride or hydrogen and palladized charcoal. Both procedures give good yields, the sodium borohydride method being faster and more suitable for small-scale laboratory purposes. The monobenzyl amino-acids are quite insoluble at their isoelectric point and precipitate readily on neutralization. The crude products are often pure enough to be used in the second step. This step follows the methylation procedure of Leuckart and Wallach, using formaldehyde in formic acid at a temperature of 100°C. The benzyl-methyl-amino-acids that are mostly obtained in a crystalline state are sub-sequently hydrogenolysed to yield the optically active N-monomethylated amino-acids. If basic amino-acids serve as starting materials the amino group which is not to be methylated has to be protected. The reaction sequences for lysine and arginine are put down in Table 2. The N^ε-tosyl derivative

TABLE 2. SYNTHESIS OF BASIC METHYLAMINO-ACIDS

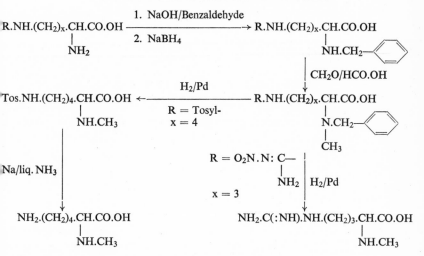

preferably used in the case of lysine is treated in the same manner as outlined before, finally leading to N^ε-tosyl-N^α-methyl-L-lysine which either may be employed in further synthetic steps or may be detosylated by means of sodium in liquid ammonia. Attempts to remove both the benzyl and the tosyl groups at once by this method failed due to the stability of the *N*-benzyl group. The tosyl group may of course be replaced by another protecting agent that is sufficiently stable under the reaction conditions involved. *N*-Methyl-L-arginine can be prepared essentially in the same way, starting from nitroarginine. The last step involves simultaneous hydrogenolysis of the two protecting groups. Some of the data are compiled in Table 3. The first column gives the overall yield which is highest in the case of methyl-valine and methylphenylalanine. The figure given in brackets for the lysine derivative refers to the N^ε-tosyl compound. The isolation of the detosylated product does not proceed too well. However, the N^ε-protected derivative might in most cases be the desired product. The next four columns give the optical rotations of the starting materials, of the intermediates and the endproducts. A series of *N*-methylamino-acids have already been described in the literature, although the values reported do not always agree. The rotations are usually measured in 6-normal hydrochloric acid unless otherwise stated. The rotation of methylalanine in water is in accordance with the one given by Izumiya [10], and −11° was found by Ley and Temme [11] for the antipode in hydrochloric acid. L- Methylvaline isolated from enniatin B by Plattner and Nager [1] exhibited a rotation of +30°, while we had found a

P. QUITT

TABLE 3. AMINO-ACIDS AND THEIR N-ALKYLATED DERIVATIVES

Amino-acid; Yield of N-methyl derivative	$[\alpha]_D$ (c 1)				References
	Amino-acid	N-Benzyl-amino-acid	N-Benzyl-N-methyl-amino-acid	N-Methyl-amino-acid	
Alanine; 35%	+13·5°	+3·9°	−5·7°	+11·5° +5·2°‡	−11·0° (Antipode) +5·6° Izumiya [10]
Valine; 75%	+28·8°	+20·2°	+27·3°	+33·1°	+30·0° Plattner, Nager [1]
Leucine; 54%	+15·1°	+13·0°	+14·3°	+31·8° +22·3°‡	+31·3° Izumiya [10] +21·0° Russell [7]
Phenylalanine; 64%	−7·1°	+26·9°†	+20·0°†	+26·6° +49·3°§	+25·5° Vanderhaeghe [5] +49·6° Fischer [12]
Serine; 48%	+19·3°	+5·1°	— (oil)	+8·0°	No reference
	Nε-tosyl-derivative				
Lysine; (69%), 48%	+14·4°	+15·3°†	+11·7°† +16·8°	+30·6°	+24·7° Izumiya [10]
	G-nitro-derivative				
Arginine; 53%	+18·8°	+21·4°	—(oil) —	+32·9°	+29·5° Izumiya [10]

† Taken in 6N-hydrochloric acid/acetic acid 1:1.
‡ Taken in water (c 2).
§ Taken in N-sodium hydroxide.

somewhat higher value for the synthetic compound. In the case of L-methyl-leucine both values agree well. The same is true for L-methylphenylalanine. Here, the second value of 49·6° was taken in normal sodium hydroxide solution as indicated by Fischer [8]. The value of 49·3° we found confirms this. Kanao [12] erroneously gives normal hydrochloric acid as the solvent. No data on the rotation of L-methylserine could be found in the literature, while the values for N^α-methyl-lysine and N^α-methylarginine were somewhat higher than the ones reported by Izumiya [10].

THE QUESTION OF RACEMIZATION

The question whether or not racemization takes place during the formation of the Schiff base had already been studied before. Gulland and Mead [13] and later Taguchi and Ishida [14] had treated amino-acids in alkaline solution with different aldehydes and had found that the Schiff bases from aliphatic aldehydes as well as from benzaldehyde were not racemized even if they were boiled for several hours. Since in our case the first reaction step is performed at a temperature around 10 to 20°, no racemization was to be expected. The crude product obtained by reductive benzylation of L-valine with benzaldehyde and hydrogen, in the presence of palladium on charcoal, exhibited a rotation of 20·2° in 6-normal hydrochloric acid. Different fractions of a crystallization showed no significant deviation from this value. Hydrogenolysis of the crude product furnished L-valine with the specific rotation of +27·1° compared with 27·9° found for the starting material. This difference can be considered insignificant. As to the next two steps that involve methylation and hydrogenolysis, the problem of racemization was studied in the case of *N*-methylphenylalanine. When several fractions were carefully crystallized the values observed ranged between 26·7 and 25·9° in 6-normal hydrochloric acid. These differences do not indicate any significant amount of racemized material.

Since all the reaction steps are simple to perform and since the end products are easily isolated due to the absence of inorganic salts, this synthesis opens a very convenient path to *N*-monomethylated amino-acids and thus to peptide analogues containing such amino-acids. The chemical and biological behaviour of such peptide analogues may be quite interesting.

REFERENCES

1. Pl. A. PLATTNER and U. NAGER, *Helv. Chim. Acta* **31**, 665, 2192 (1948).
2. M. M. SHEMYAKIN, Yu. A. OVCHINNIKOV, A. A. KIRYUSHKIN and V. I. IVANOV, *Tetrahedron Letters* **7**, 301 (1962).
3. H. BROCKMANN, *Angew. Chem.* **72**, 939 (1960); *Ann. N.Y. Acad. Sci.* **89**, 323 (1960).
4. J. C. SHEEHAN, H. G. ZACHAU and W. B. LAWSON, *J. Amer. Chem. Soc.* **79**, 3933 (1957); *ibid.* **80**, 3349 (1958).
5. H. VANDERHAEGHE and G. PERMENTIER, *J. Amer. Chem. Soc.* **82**, 4414 (1960).
6. F. W. EASTWOOD, B. K. SNELL and A. TODD, *J. Chem. Soc.* **1960**, 2286.
7. D. W. RUSSELL, *Biochim. Biophys. Acta* **45**, 411 (1960).
8. E. FISCHER and W. LIPSCHITZ, *Ber.* **48**, 360 (1915).
9. R. BOWMAN, *J. Chem. Soc.* **1950**, 1346; R. BOWMAN and H. H. STROUD, *ibid.* 1342.
10. N. IZUMIYA, A. NAGAMATSU and S. OTA, *Kyushu Mem. Med. Sci.* **4**, 1 (1953).
11. H. LEY and Th. TEMME, *Ber.* **59**, 2712 (1926).
12. S. KANAO, *J. Pharm. Soc. Japan* (*Yakugaku Zasshi*) **66**, 21 (1946).
13. J. M. GULLAND and Th. H. MEAD, *J. Chem. Soc.* **1935**, 210.
14. T. TAGUCHI and T. ISHIDA, *Pharm. Bull.* (*Tokyo*) **5**, 181 (1957).

PEPTIDSYNTHESE MIT
S-(β-AMINOÄTHYL)-L-CYSTEIN

P. Hermann und C. A. Gründig

Physiologisch-chemisches Institut der Martin-Luther-Universität, Halle

Man kennt eine Reihe von Vorgängen, die als begrenzte, enzymatische Proteolyse aufzufassen sind. Dazu gehören Aktivierungsprozesse (z. B. beim Trypsinogen) und Inaktivierungsreaktionen (wie z. B. die der Oxytocinase). Bestimmte, meistens mehrfunktionelle Aminosäuren im Peptidverband sind Angriffspunkte der enzymatischen Wirkung.

Wir glaubten, daß man bei den Möglichkeiten der Synthese von Proteohormon-Analogen eine Aminosäure einsetzen sollte, deren generelle Teilnahme bei der enzymatischen Proteolyse durch Lindley [1] und Folk u. Mitarb. [2] qualitativ bereits erwiesen war: S-(β-Aminoäthyl)-L-cystein. Wir benennen sie wegen ihrer Analogie zum Lysin und ihres gleichwertigen Verhaltens bei proteolytischen Prozessen Thialysin.

Mit geeigneten Substraten für die Peptidasen Trypsin und Carboxypeptidase B wollten wir quantitative Unterschiede in der Hydrolyse Lysin- und Thialysin-haltiger Peptidderivate ermitteln. Beim Vorliegen von Inaktivierungsprozessen, die durch Enzyme vom Typ des Trypsins oder der Carboxypeptidase B bewirkt werden, sollte dann bei biologisch wirksamen Thialysin-Analogen von Lysin-haltigen Proteohormonen eine veränderte Inaktivierungsgeschwindigkeit (eventuell eine protrahierte Wirkung) erreichbar sein.

Die N^α-Hippuryl-Aminosäuren als Substrate für Carboxypeptidase B und die N^α-Hippuryl-Aminosäuremethylester und -amide als Substrate für Trypsin wurden auf folgendem Wege erhalten. Die Umsetzung der N^ε-Benzyloxycarbonyl-Aminosäuremethylester mit Hippursäure erfolgte nach der Anhydridmethode. Zur weiteren Herstellung der Amide wurde mit Ammoniak in Methanol behandelt, zur Herstellung der Hippuryl-Aminosäuren mit wässrig-methanolischer Natronlauge verseift. Die Abspaltung der Benzyloxycarbonyl-Gruppe erfolgte in allen Fällen mit Bromwasserstoff in Eisessig. Die Hippuryl-Aminosäurehydrobromide wurden durch Ionenaustauschchromatographie in die freien Hippuryl-Aminosäuren übergeführt. Ester und Amide wurden als Hydrobromide isoliert. Von allen Substraten war nur das Hippuryl-lysinmethylesterhydrobromid nicht kristallin. Da es zersetzlich war, wurde es in wässriger Lösung mit einem stark basischen Austauscher

171

in der Acetatform in das beständige, als glasartiger Sirup isolierte Ester-acetat umgewandelt.

Zur Analytik der Hippurylverbindungen nutzten wir die UV-Absorption des Hippurylrestes ($\varepsilon_{263m\mu} = 943$). Bei dieser Wellenlänge sind bekanntlich auch Benzyloxycarbonyl- und Tosyl-Gruppen und Phenylalanin bestimmbar. Die Substrate und Zwischenprodukte waren in verschiedenen Lösungs-mittelgemischen papierchromatographisch einheitlich; dabei hatten die Thialysin- gegenüber den Lysinverbindungen einen nur wenig geringeren R_F-Wert.

Die enzymatische Hydrolyse der Estersubstrate wurde mit dem pH-Stat verfolgt, die Hydrolyse der anderen Substrate wurde durch quantitative Papierchromatographie ermittelt. Bei allen Substraten konnten wir 100% Hydrolyse erzielen, ein Beweis für die optische Reinheit unserer Verbin-dungen.

Die Tabelle 1 zeigt auszugsweise die aus den Versuchen erhaltenen kineti-schen Daten. k_3 und die substratspezifischen proteolytischen Koeffizienten C

TABELLE 1.   HYDROLYSE VON LYSIN- UND THIALYSINDERIVATEN DURCH PEPTIDASEN

Enzym	Substrat	pH	$k_3 \times 10^2$	$\dfrac{Lys}{Thialys}$	$\dfrac{C}{0{,}01\,M}$	$\dfrac{Lys}{Thialys}$
Carboxypeptidase B	Hip-Lys-OH	7,6	6,91	5,3	0,82	2,7
	Hip-Thialys-OH	7,6	1,31		0,30	
Trypsin	Hip-Lys-OMe	8,0	465	6,0	102	5,0
	Hip-Thialys-OMe	8,0	77,6		20,6	
	Hip-Lys-NH$_2$	8,0	5,08	9,4	1,06	8,1
	Hip-Thialys-NH$_2$	8,0	0,541		0,13	

Hip = hippuryl;   -Thialys- = —NH.CH.CO—

$$\overset{\displaystyle |}{\text{CH}_2.\text{S}.\text{CH}_2.\text{CH}_2.\text{NH}_2}$$

Erläuterungen: $k_3 = \dfrac{V_{max}}{e} \left[\dfrac{\text{Mol} \cdot \text{ml}}{\text{Liter} \cdot \text{min} \cdot \text{mg}}\right]$

$e = \dfrac{\text{mg N}}{\text{ml}}$ (für Trypsin); $e = \dfrac{\text{mg Enzym}}{\text{ml}}$ (für Carboxypeptidase B)

$C = \dfrac{K}{e}$ (für 0·01 M Substratlösung); $K = \dfrac{1}{\text{min}} \log \dfrac{100}{100 - \% \text{ Hydrolyse}}$

(hier für 0,01 M Substratlösung) sind angegeben, dazu die Relationen der Lysin- zu den Thialysinverbindungen.

In jedem Fall werden die Thialysinsubstrate langsamer hydrolysiert. Unsere Präparation der Carboxypeptidase B, die wir nach Literaturvor-schrift [3] aus Schweinepankreas hergestellt hatten, verlor schnell an Aktivi-tät, so daß hier nur die Relationen und nicht die Größe der kinetischen

Konstanten interessieren. Erwartungsgemäß hat Hippuryl-lysinmethylester einen hohen C-Wert, unseres Wissens existiert kein aktiveres Trypsinsubstrat (Hippuryl-argininester sollte aktiver sein).

Für die Peptidsynthese mit Thialysin sind eine Reihe von N^ε-monosubstituierten und unterschiedlich N^α,N^ε-disubstituierten Derivaten von Interesse. N^ε-Benzyloxycarbonyl-thialysin war durch Umsetzung von Benzyloxycarbonyl-β-bromäthylamin mit Cystein in wässrig-alkoholischer Lösung oder in flüssigem Ammoniak (nach Reduktion von Cystin mit Natrium) bereits erhalten worden (Lindley [4]), die weitere Reaktion mit Benzyloxycarbonyl-chlorid führte zur öligen N^α,N^ε-Dibenzyloxycarbonyl-Verbindung. Wir konnten diese Verbindung jetzt kristallin erhalten (Schmp. 80–82°). Die Einführung der Tosylgruppe gelang uns durch Reaktion von Tosyl-β-bromäthylamin (erhalten durch Umsetzung von Bromäthylamin-hydrobromid mit Tosyl-chlorid in Pyridin) oder Tosyl-β-jodäthylamin einmal in alkoholisch-wässriger Lösung bei pH 8–9 mit Cystein, zum anderen in flüssigem Ammoniak nach Reduktion von Cystin mit Natrium in etwa 80% Ausbeute.

Das kristalline N^ε-Tosyl-thialysin ließ sich mit Natrium in flüssigem Ammoniak detosylieren. Thialysin (als Monohydrochlorid isoliert) wurde in 73% Ausbeute erhalten. Mit Benzyloxycarbonyl-chlorid lieferte N^ε-Tosyl-thialysin die ölige N^α-Benzyloxycarbonyl-N^ε-Tosyl-Verbindung, die als Dicyclohexylamin-Salz kristallin erhalten wurde (siehe Schema 1).

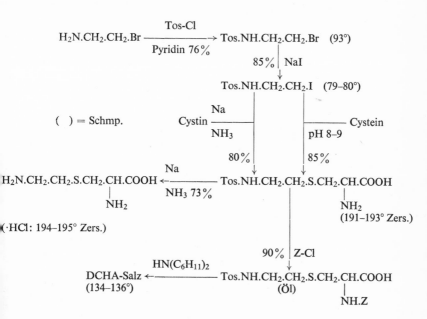

SCHEMA 1

Für Thialysin-monohydrochlorid, das wir nach drei verschiedenen Reaktionen erhalten haben (1. nach Cavallini [5] aus Cystein und Bromäthylamin (modifiziert), 2. nach Lindley [4] aus N^{ε}-Benzyloxycarbonyl-thialysin mit Bromwasserstoff in Eisessig, 3. wie oben beschrieben aus N^{ε}-Tosyl-thialysin), fanden wir übereinstimmend Linksdrehung. Unsere Präparate enthielten nach polarographischer Prüfung weniger als 0,1 % Cystin. Die Tabelle 2 vergleicht unsere Drehwerte mit denen der Literatur.

TABELLE 2.   OPTISCHE AKTIVITÄT VON THIALYSIN-MONOHYDROCHLORID
VERSCHIEDENER HERKUNFT

Thialys-HCl aus:	$[\alpha]_D$ gemessen	$[\alpha]_D$ Literatur
Cystein	$-5,3° \pm 0,2°$ ($c = 6$; 20°)	$+7,2°$ ($c = 1$; 25°) [5]
N^{ε}-Z-thialys	$-4,4° \pm 0,3°$ ($c = 4$; 22°)	$-4,4°$ ($c = 3$; 16°) [4]
N^{ε}-Tos-thialys	$-5,5° \pm 0,2°$ ($c = 6$; 20°)	—

Lösungsmittel: Wasser.

Versuche, die oben genannten Peptidasesubstrate über die N^{ε}-Tosylverbindung des Thialysins herzustellen, haben wir abgebrochen, da das Kupplungsprodukt aus dem kristallinen N^{ε}-Tosyl-thialysinmethylesterhydrochlorid und Hippursäure (Anhydridmethode) nicht kristallisierte. Auch die weitere Umsetzung mit Ammoniak in Methanol zum Amid und die Verseifung des Esters lieferten nur ölige Produkte.

Aus den Versuchen geht hervor, daß es bei der Peptidsynthese mit Thialysin nicht nötig sein wird, die Thioäthergruppe zu schützen, bei der Decarbobenzoxylierung und der Detosylierung von Thialysinderivaten beobachteten wir keine Störungen, wie sie etwa bei der Arbeit mit Methioninpeptiden auftreten.

Prinzipiell sollte es möglich sein, zur Herstellung von Thialysinpeptiden S-Benzyl-cysteinylpeptide einzusetzen. Entfernung des Benzylrestes und anschließende Kupplung mit Tosyl- oder Benzyloxycarbonyl-β-bromäthylamin oder geeigneten anderen N-substituierten Bromäthylaminen würde die Synthesemöglichkeiten von N^{ε}-geschützten Thialysinpeptiden erweitern.

Für die Synthese eines geschützten Tripeptidamides H-Pro-Thialys(N^{ε}-Tos)-Gly-NH_2 haben wir vorerst N^{α}-Benzyloxycarbonyl-N^{ε}-Tos-Thialys-Gly-NH_2 und N-Benzyloxycarbonyl-S-Benzyl-Cys-Gly-NH_2 hergestellt. Versuche, N-Benzyloxycarbonyl-S-Benzyl-cystein nach der Anhydridmethode und N^{α}-Benzyloxycarbonyl-N^{ε}-Tosyl-thialysin (als Öl oder als Dicyclohexylaminsalz) nach der Diimidmethode mit Glycinamid zu kuppeln, führten zu einer Reihe von Nebenprodukten, die schwer abtrennbar waren und die wir nicht näher untersucht haben. Wir haben deshalb mit Glycinester gekuppelt und anschließend das Amid hergestellt.

REFERENZEN

. H. Lindley, *Nature* **178**, 647 (1956).

. J. E. Folk, F. Tietze und J. A. Gladner, *Biochim. Biophysica Acta* **26**, 659 (1957).

. J. E. Folk, K. A. Pietz, W. R. Caroll und J. A. Gladner, *J. Biol. Chem.* **235**, 2272 (1960).

. H. Lindley, *Australian J. Chem.* **12**, 296 (1959).

. D. Cavallini, C. De Marco, B. Mondovi und G. F. Azzone, *Experientia* **11**, 61 (1955).

ALKALI INSTABILITY AS A COMPLICATING FACTOR IN WORK WITH 4-OXALYSINE

G. I. TESSER

Laboratory of Organic Chemistry, R.C. University, Nijmegen, Holland

WE previously [1] prepared DL-4-oxalysine dihydrochloride (I),

$$NH_2.CH_2.CH_2.O.CH_2.CH.CO.OH$$
$$\overset{|}{NH_2}$$

(I)

a lysine analogue, to compare the properties of this amino-acid with those of lysine in enzymatic reactions, such as tryptic hydrolysis. It was felt, however, that for unequivocal investigations, the use of optically pure enantiomers was desirable. So we tried to resolve the racemate [2]. The most promising way to obtain a good separation turned out to be through crystallization of the brucine salts of the N^α,N^ε-diphthaloyl derivative, because the introduction of the phthaloyl groups could be accomplished in a very mild way using carbethoxyphthalimide, and the salts obtained were well crystalline solids, differing widely in solubility from each other. After some recrystallizations from solvent mixtures containing isoamyl alcohol, positive- and negative-rotating N^α,N^ε-diphthaloyl-4-oxalysines were obtained in a pure form as diastereoisomeric brucine salts, one of which was colourless and apparently solvated with isoamyl alcohol, the other yellow and not solvated. After decomposition of these salts with dilute mineral acid, resolved diphthaloyl-4-oxalysine resulted with specific rotations of $+65\cdot5$ and $-65\cdot1°$ respectively.

The absolute configuration of the optical isomers was established using the method of the quasi-racemic compounds.

The melting curve of the binary system containing $(+)$ N^α,N^ε-diphthaloyl-4-oxalysine and N^α,N^ε-diphthaloyl-L-4-thialysine, showed a complicated course, whereas the system with $(-)$ N^α,N^ε-diphthaloyl-4-oxalysine and the same thialysine derivative gave a diagram with a normal eutectic point. So we concluded the former, positive-rotating 4-oxalysine derivative to have the D-form, the latter behaving like a compound of the L-series.

Difficulties, however, arose at the unmasking of the amino groups in the resolved 4-oxalysine derivative. Although it was felt that the substance

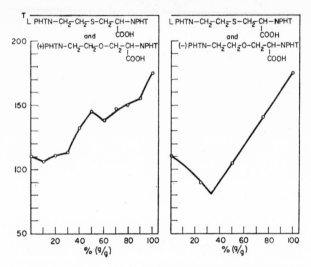

FIG. 1. Formation of a quasi-racemic compound after mixing (+) N^α,N^ε-di-phthaloyl-4-oxalysine and N^α,N^ε-diphthaloyl-L-4-thialysine.

might be alkali-labile because β-elimination might take place, DL-4-oxalysine could be benzyloxycarbonylated easily in a satisfactory yield (by treatment of the copper complex of the racemic amino-acid with benzyl chloroformate and alkali in the cold.) So we devised a mild method to remove both phthaloyl residues; it consisted of an opening of the imide ring by alkaline hydrolysis with exactly 2 equivalents half normal sodium hydroxide in the cold, followed by acid hydrolysis at 100° with N-hydrochloric acid. This method had appeared satisfactory for diphthaloyl-L-lysine from which L-lysine was obtained in 88 per cent yield and with racemic diphthaloyl-4-oxalysine which gave DL-4-oxalysine in a 55 per cent yield. After application of this procedure to diphthaloyl D-4-oxalysine fully racemic oxalysine was isolated as the sole product.

The racemization of this amino-acid under such mild conditions might be explained by assuming that even at pH 7–8 the following equilibrium was set up:

$$\underset{\overset{|}{R'.HN.CH}}{\overset{CH_2.OR}{}}\underset{\underset{O^-}{\diagdown}}{\overset{\diagup O}{C}} \rightleftharpoons \underset{\overset{|}{R'.HN.C^-}}{\overset{CH_2.OR}{}}\underset{\underset{O^-}{\diagdown}}{\overset{\diagup O}{C}} \;+\; H^+$$

As the steric stability of carbanions is not very great, racemization might have taken place by this mechanism. As the starting material was an acid, the indicated ionization is comparable with the second ionization in a dicarbxylic acid. This ionization is greatly suppressed by the first one, and decomposition by β-elimination, if any, will occur only to a limited extent. In the case of an ester the decomposition will inevitably be higher as its reaction velocity will depend on the concentration of carbanions.

We succeeded in obtaining optically active oxalysine dihydrochloride from diphthaloyl-D-4-oxalysine by hydrolysis with 6 N hydrochloric acid at 100° in a sealed tube. Using rotatory dispersion curves, the D-configuration could be established for this compound which confirmed the above mentioned result in which a quasi-racemate was formed (Fig. 2).

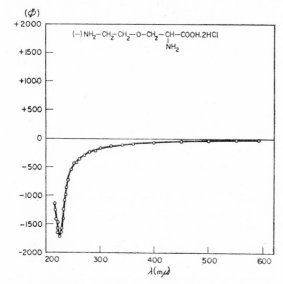

FIG. 2.   Negative Cotton effect in rotatory dispersion experiments with (−) 4-oxalysine.

From the alkali-lability of oxalysine derivatives one may conclude that the only way to introduce an optically pure 4-oxalysyl residue into a peptide chain, starting with optically pure 4-oxalysine derivatives, will be a coupling method which takes place in an acidic medium, for example the ethoxyacetylene method of Arens and collaborators.

Another approach towards the formation of optically pure dipeptides might be the resolution of the racemic amino-acid after conversion to diastereoisomeric dipeptides using a second optically pure amino-acid, followed by crystallization of the diastereoisomers. Applying this principle to our problem, we obtained two totally different substances after the reaction of optically pure phthaloyl-L-alanyl ethyl carbonate with racemic N^γ-benzyloxycarbonyl-4-oxalysine methyl ester. After dissolution of the oily reaction

13–2

product in ethyl alcohol, a crystalline fraction was obtained, comprising phthaloyl-L-alanyl-D-4-oxalysine methyl ester in a yield of 32 per cent, calculated on the amount of phthaloyl-L-alanine used. After purification of the mother liquor an oil was obtained which resisted crystallization for months and which in vacuum changed to a glassy mass. This last dipeptide was quickly hydrolysed by trypsin after decarbobenzoxylation, whereas the first mentioned crystalline diastereoisomer was completely inactive after the same treatment.

REFERENCES

1. G. I. TESSER and G. H. L. NEFKENS, *Rec. Trav. Chim.* **78,** 404 (1959).
2. G. I. TESSER, R. J. F. NIVARD and M. GRUBER, *Rec. Trav. Chim.*, in the press.

SYNTHESE VON PEPTIDDERIVATEN DER HYDRAZINOESSIGSÄURE

H. NIEDRICH

Institute für Medizin und Biologie der Deutschen Akademie der Wissenschaften,
Institut für Pharmakologie, Berlin-Buch

ZUR Einbeziehung von Hydrazinosäuren als Fremdbaustein in Peptide wurden wir u.a. durch die Entwicklungen auf dem Gebiet der Synthese von N-Hydroxyaminosäurederivaten und Peptoliden angeregt.

Die pharmakologische Aktivität der den Aminoxidasehemmern strukturverwandten Hydrazinosäurederivate läßt in Kombination mit Peptiden Modifikation der Wirksamkeit erwarten. Andererseits ist bei Ersatz bestimmter Aminosäurebausteine wirksamer Oligopeptide durch entsprechende α-Hydrazinosäuren die Synthese qualitativ neuartiger Peptidanaloger möglich. Diese lassen z.B. ein andersartiges Verhalten als natürliche Peptide oder deren Analoge gegenüber fermentativem Angriff erwarten.

Auf die Chemie der α-Hydrazinocarbonsäuren soll nicht näher eingegangen werden. Die Untersuchung ihrer chemischen Eigenschaften speziell unter den Bedingungen der Peptidsynthese wurde zunächst an der Hydrazinoessigsäure durchgeführt. Durch die Acylierbarkeit beider Stickstoffatome der Hydrazinosäure sind grundsätzlich zwei Bindungstypen bei der Synthese von Hydrazinopeptiden möglich, Peptide mit Hydrazidbindungen und N-Aminopeptide (—CO.NH.NH.CH$_2$— und —CO.N.CH$_2$—).

$$\underset{\text{NH}_2}{|}$$

Die im chemischen Verhalten der α-Hydrazinosäuren gegenüber den Aminosäuren auftretenden Unterschiede sind durchwegs auf die Acylierbarkeit des verbleibenden zweiten Stickstoffatoms zurückzuführen bzw. darauf, daß monoacylierte Hydrazinosäurederivate noch typische Hydrazinreaktionen wie z.B. die Hydrazinolyse von Estern, Reduktion alkalischer Kupfer- und Silbersalzlösungen zeigen und durch Hypobromid oxydierbar sind.

Mittels Dicyclohexylcarbodiimid wurde eine Reihe geschützter Hydrazinodipeptidester dargestellt.

Die in Abhängigkeit von der eingesetzten Benzyloxycarbonylaminosäure stark schwankenden Ausbeuten weisen auf Nebenreaktionen des α-Stickstoffs hin, wogegen die Hydrazinolyse von Glycincyanmethylester durch

$$R^2$$
$$|$$

TABELLE 1. $R^1.NH.CH.CO.NH.NH.CH_2.COR^3$

R^1	R^2 $|$ —NH.CH.CO—	R^3	DCCI Ausbeute (%)	
Z-	-glycyl-	—OC$_2$H$_5$	40,3	83,2†
Z-	-glycyl-	—OCH$_3$	33,2	74,5†
Z-	-L-valyl-	—OCH$_3$	72,1	
Z-	-L-leucyl-	—OCH$_3$	72,0	
Z-	-D,L-seryl-	—OC$_2$H$_5$	80,5	
Z-	-L-prolyl-	—OCH$_3$	47,7	
Z-	-L-phenylalanyl-	—OCH$_3$	63,6	
Z-	-ε-Z-L-lysyl-	—OCH$_3$	42,4	
Z-	-L-asparaginyl-	—OCH$_3$	38,2	
Z-	-glycyl-	—NH$_2$	94,5	
Z-	-glycyl-	—OH	56,9	
Z-	-L-valyl-	—OH	30,3	
Z-	-L-leucyl-	—NH$_2$	62,6	

† von $Z.NH.CH_2.CO.OCH_2.CN$ ausgehend.

Hydrazinoessigester wesentlich eindeutiger verläuft, wie die bessere Ausbeute zeigt.

Während mit Ammoniak in Methanol die Überführung in die Amide glatt vor sich geht, gelingt die Verseifung wegen der stark konkurrierenden intermolekularen Esterhydrazinolyse nur nach dem Verdünnungsprinzip.

Daß daran der freie α-Stickstoff die Schuld trägt, läßt sich wie folgt zeigen.

$$Z.NH.CH_2.CO.NH.NH.CH_2.COOC_2H_5$$

$$77,8\% \quad \begin{array}{l} + \text{ Z.chlorid/NaHCO}_3 \\ + \text{ NaOH} \end{array}$$

$$\downarrow$$

$$Z.NH.CH_2.CO.NH.N.CH_2.COOH$$
$$|$$
$$Z$$

$$+ \text{ DCCI } 65\% \quad + \text{ H}_2\text{N.CH}_2.\text{COOCH}_3$$

$$\downarrow$$

$$Z.NH.CH_2.CO.NH.N.CH_2.CO.NH.CH_2.COOCH_3$$
$$|$$
$$Z$$

Nach N^α-Carbobenzoxylierung verläuft die Verseifung mit guter Ausbeute. Nur an das zweifach geschützte Hydrazinopeptid lassen sich carboxylend-ständig weitere Aminosäurereste anfügen, wie an der Synthese von N^β-Benzyloxycarbonyl - glycyl - N^α - benzyloxycarbonyl - hydrazinoacetylglycinester gezeigt ist. Bisher ist eine Hydrazidbindung in den Hydrazinopeptiden formuliert worden. Ebensogut wäre eine *N*-Aminoamidbindung möglich. Der Beweis für die Hydrazidstruktur ergibt sich z.B. aus der Spaltung der N-N-Bindung von Benzyloxycarbonyl-valylhydrazinoessigsäure mittels Paladium/Wasserstoff, wobei Valinamid und Glycin entstehen. Den Beweis durch Synthese zeigt folgendes Formelschema.

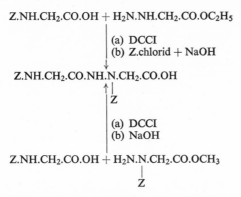

$$\text{Z.NH.CH}_2\text{.CO.OH} + \text{H}_2\text{N.NH.CH}_2\text{.CO.OC}_2\text{H}_5$$

(a) DCCI
(b) Z.chlorid + NaOH

$$\text{Z.NH.CH}_2\text{.CO.NH.N.CH}_2\text{.CO.OH}$$
$$\text{Z}$$

(a) DCCI
(b) NaOH

$$\text{Z.NH.CH}_2\text{.CO.OH} + \text{H}_2\text{N.N.CH}_2\text{.CO.OCH}_3$$
$$\text{Z}$$

Ausgehend von N^α-Benzyloxycarbonyl-hydrazinoessigsäure, deren Struktur durch die Ausbildung eines Benzalderivates bewiesen ist, gelangt man ebenfalls zur N^β-Benzyloxycarbonyl-glycyl-N^α-benzyloxycarbonyl-hydrazinoessigsäure. Die Identität beider Produkte ist durch die IR-Spektren belegt. Die Abspaltung der Benzyloxycarbonyl-Schutzgruppen gelingt mit Bromwasserstoff/Eisessig, während bei längerdauernder Hydrierung die N-N-Bindung teilweise gespalten wird.

Für das Anfügen weiterer Aminosäurereste an das Aminoende von Hydrazinopeptiden ergeben sich zwei Wege.

1. Man wählt Knüpfungsmethoden, die nur die Aminogruppe ($pK_b = 6,5$) acylieren und den schwach basischen α-Stickstoff ($pK_b = 11$) unacyliert hinterlassen.

2. Man führt am α-Stickstoff eine Schutzgruppe ein, die unter den Bedingungen der Benzyloxycarbonyl-Abspaltung von der Aminogruppe erhalten bleibt. Ähnlich ist es an Lysin-ε-Schutzgruppen schon verschiedenartig praktiziert worden.

Beide Wege wurden beschritten.

Nach der *p*-Nitrophenylester-Methode gelingt die selektive Acylierung der Aminogruppe, was die Carbodiimid-Methode nicht vermag. Als ein Beispiel ist die Synthese von Prolyl-leucyl-hydrazinoacetamid angeführt. Anfügen weiterer Aminosäuren an das Aminoende nach dieser Methode bereitete jedoch Schwierigkeiten.

Als Schutzgruppe für den α-Stickstoff wählten wir den Toluolsulfonylrest. Seine Einführung in die Benzyloxycarbonyl-aminoacylhydrazinoessigsäure-

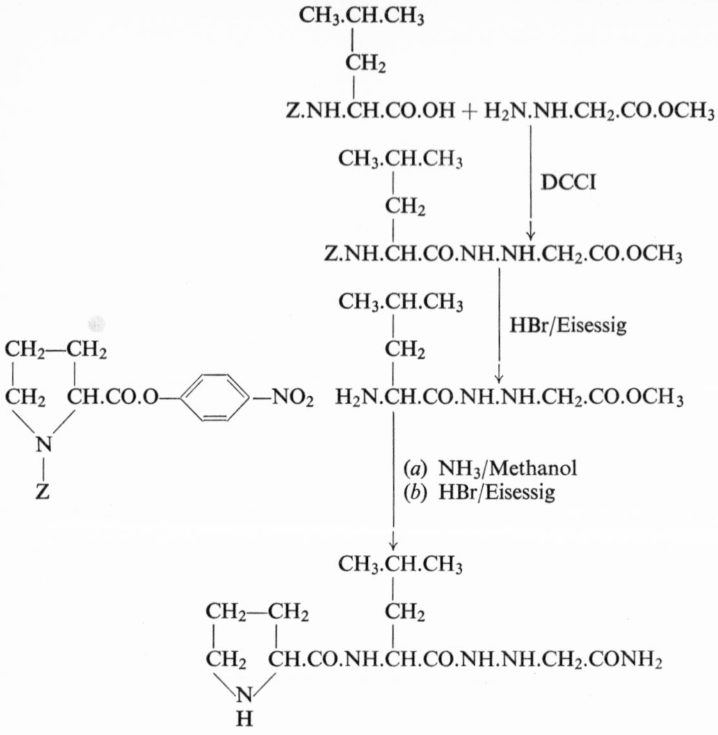

$$CH_3.CH.CH_3$$
$$|$$
$$CH_2$$
$$|$$
$$Z.NH.CH.CO.OH + H_2N.NH.CH_2.CO.OCH_3$$

$$CH_3.CH.CH_3$$
$$|$$
$$CH_2 \qquad \text{DCCI}$$
$$| \qquad \downarrow$$
$$Z.NH.CH.CO.NH.NH.CH_2.CO.OCH_3$$

$$CH_3.CH.CH_3$$
$$|$$
$$CH_2 \qquad \text{HBr/Eisessig}$$

$CH_2{-}CH_2$
$|$
$CH_2 \quad CH.CO.O{-}\langle\!\bigcirc\!\rangle{-}NO_2 \quad H_2N.CH.CO.NH.NH.CH_2.CO.OCH_3$
$|$
N
$|$
Z

(a) NH₃/Methanol
(b) HBr/Eisessig

$$CH_3.CH.CH_3$$
$$|$$
$CH_2{-}CH_2 \qquad CH_2$
$| \qquad | \qquad |$
$CH_2 \quad CH.CO.NH.CH.CO.NH.NH.CH_2.CONH_2$
$\diagdown N \diagup$
H

L-Prolyl-L-leucyl-hydrazinoacetamid

TABELLE 2. N^α-TOSYLIERUNG VON HYDRAZINOPEPTIDEN

X.NH.NH.CH₂.COY	$\xrightarrow[\text{in Pyridin}]{\text{Tos-Cl} + \text{NEt}_3}$	X.NH.N.CH₂.COY | Tos	
X	Y	Ausbeute (%)	Schmp.
1. Z-glycyl-	—NH₂	72,5	198–200°
2. Z-L-leucyl-	—NH₂	75,0	199–201°
3. Z-L-prolyl-L-leucyl-	—NH₂	65,4	171–172°
4. Z-glycyl-	—OC₂H₅	ca. 100	Nicht krist.
5. Z-L-leucyl-	—OCH₃	91	Nicht krist.
Aus 4 u. 5 durch Verseifung bzw. Hydrazinolyse			
6. Z-glycyl-	—OH	18,6	157–158°
7. Z-glycyl-	—NH.NH₂	93,8	154–156°
8. Z-L-leucyl-	—OH	14,5	142–144°

ester bzw. -amide gelingt in Pyridin in Gegenwart von Triäthylamin mit 1,2 Mol Tosylchlorid in optimaler Ausbeute. Aus den Estern sind dann die Hydrazide und die freien Säuren zugänglich, wie aus der Tabelle hervorgeht. Bei der Verseifung sind die hohen Ausbeuteverluste auffällig. Dabei entsteht im Falle der N^β-Benzyloxycarbonyl-glycyl-N^α-tosylhydrazinoessigsäure eine kristalline Verbindung, deren Konstitution noch nicht feststeht.

Bevor nun weitere Synthesen mit N^α-tosylierten Hydrazinopeptiden durchgeführt wurden, war zu untersuchen, ob der Tosylrest gegen Bromwasserstoff in Eisessig beständig ist und ob bei der endgültigen Entfernung aller Schutzgruppen mit Natrium in flüssigem Ammoniak die Hydrazidgruppierung irgendwelche Veränderungen erfährt. Diacylierte Hydrazinosäuren sind gegenüber monoacylierten durch Hypobromid nicht oxydierbar. Die Abspaltung des N^α-Tosylrestes läßt sich also durch Hypobromidtitration quantitativ erfassen.

In 4 N Bromwasserstoff/Eisessig wurden bei Zimmertemperatur nach 10 Min. 2,3% nach 20 Min. 3,5% und nach 40 Min. 7,2% Tosylabspaltung am N^β - Benzyloxycarbonyl - glycyl - N^α-tosyl - hydrazinoacetamid gefunden. N^β-Benzyloxycarbonyl-prolyl-leucyl-N^α-tosyl-hydrazinoacetamid zeigte nach 15 Min. keine Abspaltung der Tosylgruppe.

Die Behandlung von N^β-Benzyloxycarbonyl-leucyl-N^α-tosyl-hydrazinoacetamid mit Natrium in flüssigem Ammoniak ergab, daß eine reduktive Spaltung der N-N-Bindung nicht eintritt. Auch nach langdauernder Behandlung ist im Chromatogram kein Glycin nachzuweisen. Dagegen tritt bei Anwesenheit von Wasserspuren im Ammoniak sehr schnell eine Hydrolyse der Hydrazidbindung ein, was durch den chromatographischen Nachweis von Leucin zu erkennen ist.

Damit waren die Versuchsbedingungen soweit klargelegt.

$$\text{Z-Gly-Hya}(N^\alpha\text{-Tos})\text{NH}_2 \xrightarrow[\;84,5\%\;]{\text{H}_2/\text{Pd-C/HCl}} \text{Gly-Hya}(N^\alpha\text{-Tos})\text{NH}_2.\text{HCl}.\text{H}_2\text{O}$$

$$\xrightarrow[\;82,7\%\;]{\text{Z-Leu/DCCI}} \text{Z-Leu-Gly-Hya}(N^\alpha\text{-Tos})\text{NH}_2$$

$$\xrightarrow[\;97\%\;]{\text{H}_2/\text{Pd-C/DCCI}} \text{Leu-Gly-Hya}(N^\alpha\text{-Tos})\text{NH}_2.\text{HCl}$$

$$\xrightarrow[\;72,5\%\;]{\text{Z-Pro-ONP}} \text{Z-Pro-Leu-Gly-Hya}(N^\alpha\text{-Tos})\text{NH}_2$$

$$\xrightarrow{\text{HBr/Eisessig}} \text{Pro-Leu-Gly-Hya}(N^\alpha\text{-Tos})\text{NH}_2.\text{HBr}$$

$$-\text{Hya-} = -\text{NH.NH.CH}_2.\text{CO}- \qquad -\text{Hya}(N^\alpha\text{-Tos})\text{NH}_2 = -\text{NH.}\overset{\overset{\textstyle\text{Tos}}{|}}{\text{N}}.\text{CH}_2.\text{CO.NH}_2$$

Im Formelschema ist die Synthese der um Hydrazinoessigsäure verlängerten Oxytocinsequenz 7–9 dargestellt. Hier gelang auch die hydrierende Abspaltung des Benzyloxycarbonyl-Restes bei Zusatz eines Mols Chlorwasserstoff, was beim N^β-Benzyloxycarbonyl-leucyl-N^α-tosyl-hydrazinoacetamid und in anderen Fällen nicht glückte.

Die Einführung von Hydrazinosäuren in die Peptidsynthese erlaubt die Darstellung noch weiterer Verbindungstypen. Die Versuche zur Herstellung von Hydrazinopeptiden mit endständiger Hydrazinogruppe waren weniger erfolgreich.

N-geschützte Hydrazinoessigsäurederivate

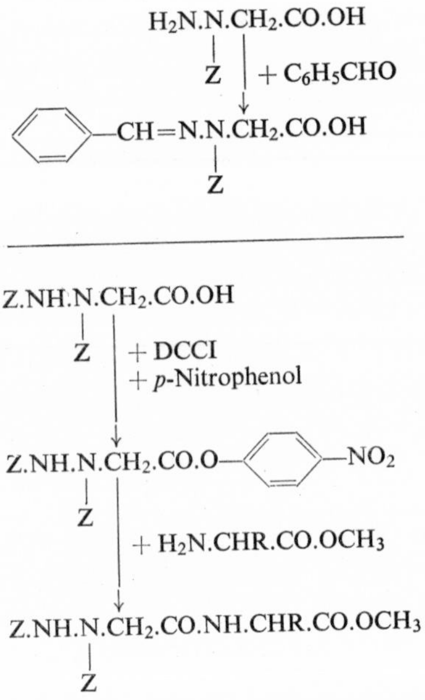

$H_2N.N.CH_2.CO.OH$
|
Z | $+ C_6H_5CHO$
↓

C_6H_5—$CH=N.N.CH_2.CO.OH$
|
Z

$Z.NH.N.CH_2.CO.OH$
|
Z | $+$ DCCI
   | $+ p$-Nitrophenol
↓

$Z.NH.N.CH_2.CO.O$—C_6H_4—NO_2
|
Z
   | $+ H_2N.CHR.CO.OCH_3$
↓

$Z.NH.N.CH_2.CO.NH.CHR.CO.OCH_3$
|
Z

$R = $ —H und —CH_2OH

Die Di-benzyloxycarbonyl-hydrazinoessigsäure mit Aminosäureestern umzusetzen, gelang lediglich in 2 Fällen und nur nach der Nitrophenylester-Methode. Sowohl die Abspaltung der Benzyloxycarbonyl-Schutzgruppen als auch die Verseifung von Di-benzyloxycarbonyl-hydrazinoacetyl-D,L-serin-und -glycinester führten zu undefinierbaren Produkten, so daß weitere Versuche in dieser Richtung zunächst unterlassen wurden.

Durch die Acylierbarkeit des α-Stickstoffes, die uns bisher nur als Schutzgruppen- und Nebenreaktionsproblem begegnete, ist ein weiterer Typ von Hydrazinopeptiden zugänglich.

Verzweigte Hydrazinopeptide
(*N*-Aminoacylamino-peptide)

$$Z.NH.CHR.CO.NH$$
$$|$$
$$Z.NH.CH_2.CO.OH \quad HN.CH_2.CO.OCH_3$$
$$| \quad \text{(a) DCCI}$$
$$\quad \text{(b) NaOH}$$
$$\quad \text{(c) HBr/Eisessig}$$
$$\downarrow$$
$$H_2N.CHR.CO.NH$$
$$|$$
$$H_2N.CH_2.CO.N.CH_2.CO.OH$$

Mittels Carbodiimid und nach anderen Methoden lassen sich geschützte Hydrazinopeptide mit freiem α-Stickstoff als Aminkomponente an Benzyloxycarbonyl-aminosäuren kondensieren.   Man gelangt so zu verzweigten Peptiden, die man auch als acylierte *N*-Aminopeptide ansprechen kann. Da jede Aminosäure einmal in der Kette und einmal in der Verzweigung vorliegen kann, existiert von jeder Kombination ein Isomerenpaar.

Durch Einführung verschiedener Schutzgruppen für beide Aminoenden ist die Verlängerung nur eines Zweiges möglich, was den Aufbau längerer verzweigter Peptidketten gestattet.

$$Tos.NH.CH_2.CO.NH.NH.CH_2.CO.OCH_3$$
$$|$$
$$+ DCCI \quad | \quad + Z.NH.CH_2.CO.OH$$
$$\downarrow$$
$$Z.NH.CH_2.CO.N.CH_2.CO.OCH_3$$
$$|$$
$$Tos.NH.CH_2.CO.NH$$
$$|$$
$$57\% \quad | \quad \text{(a) HBr/Eisessig}$$
$$\quad \text{(b) } Z.NH.CH_2.CO.OH + DCCI$$
$$\downarrow$$
$$Z.NH.CH_2.CO.NH.CH_2.CO.N.CH_2.CO.OCH_3$$
$$|$$
$$Tos.NH.CH_2.CO.NH$$

Durch Anwendung der Tosyl- und der Benzyloxycarbonyl-Schutzgruppe gelang die Herstellung des verzweigten Hydrazinotetrapeptides. N^α-Benzyloxycarbonyl-glycylglycyl-N^β-tosylglycyl-hydrazinoessigsäuremethylester.

Die an der Hydrazinoessigsäure studierten Reaktionsbedingungen zur Synthese von Hydrazinopeptiden verschiedenen Typs werden z.Zt. auf andere α-Hydrazinocarbonsäuren übertragen und zur Synthese von Peptidhormonanalogen angewandt.

SYNTHESIS OF DEPSIPEPTIDE ANALOGUES OF OPHTHALMIC ACID AND GLUTATHIONE

L. A. Shchukina and A. L. Jouse

Institute for Chemistry of Natural Products,
U.S.S.R. Academy of Sciences, Moscow, U.S.S.R.

An important aspect in the study of biologically active peptides is the structure–activity relationship and elucidation of the particular fragments of the molecule responsible for its activity. A closely related problem is the synthesis of peptide analogues of antagonistic action.

These problems are usually attacked by eliminating an amino-acid molecule from the peptides or replacing it with amino-acids possessing another configuration or other radicals. Usually such change leads to inactive compounds or to quite considerable loss in activity, although on rare occasions highly potent compounds have been obtained.

Another way of elucidating the significance of given structural elements in the molecule of a biologically active peptide might be not to vary the amino-acid radicals or the configuration, but retaining both, to substitute an ester bond for the amide bond; in other words, to replace one or more acids in the peptide chain by the corresponding hydroxy acids.

We have begun a series of studies in this direction by synthesis of the depsipeptide analogue of ophthalmic acid (I) [1–5, 8] to see whether this analogue, like ophthalmic acid itself, would be an antagonist of glutathione.

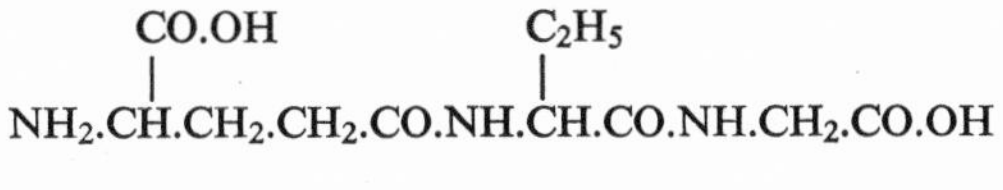

$$\begin{array}{ccc} CO.OH & & C_2H_5 \\ | & & | \\ NH_2.CH.CH_2.CH_2.CO.NH.CH.CO.NH.CH_2.CO.OH \end{array}$$

Fig. 1

The first objective was to replace the glycyl residue by a glycollic acid residue. The synthesis of this depsipeptide analogue of ophthalmic acid was achieved as follows.

189

SCHEME 1

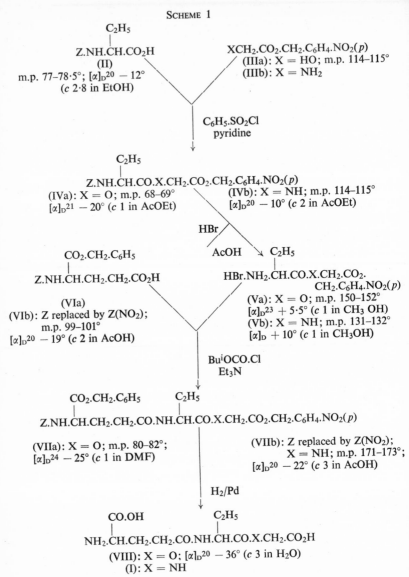

Benzyloxycarbonyl-L-α-aminobutyric acid (II) was condensed with *p*-nitro-benzyl glycollate (IIIa) by the mixed anhydride method using benzenesulphonyl chloride. On further treatment in the usual manner the crystalline condensation product (IVa) was obtained in 45 per cent yield. The hydro-bromide of (Va) was then isolated in 95 per cent yield by removal of the benzyloxycarbonyl group with hydrogen bromide in glacial acetic acid.

The hydrobromide (Va) was then condensed with α-benzyl *N*-benzyloxycarbonyl-L-glutamate (VI) by the mixed anhydride method (using isobutyl chloroformate). The yield of protected depsipeptide (VII) was 72 per cent.

Hydrogenation of the depsipeptide (VIIa) with the aid of palladium black in absolute alcohol in the presence of acetic acid led to the depsipeptide analogue of ophthalmic acid (VIII) with a yield of 96%. This substance isolated as a white (but not crystalline) solid had good analytical and chromatographic characteristics without further purification.

Inasmuch as both chemical [1] and enzymatic [5] routes to ophthalmic acid give yields not exceeding 20 per cent, we considered it feasible to attempt its synthesis by the above-described Scheme I.

This route, in which p-nitrobenzyl glycollate (IIIa) was replaced by p-nitrobenzyl glycinate (IIIb) and α-benzyl benzyloxycarbonyl-L-glutamate (VIa) by α-benzyl p-nitrobenzyloxycarbonyl-L-glutamate (VIb) led to pure ophthalmic acid with an over-all yield of 43 per cent (referred to L-α-aminobutyric acid). The next depsipeptide analogue attracting our attention was the analogue of glutathione also with glycine replaced by glycollic acid. The method of synthesis is outlined in Scheme 2.

Di-benzyloxycarbonyl-L-cystinyl dichloride (IX) [6] in tetrahydrofuran solution was condensed in the presence of pyridine with p-nitrobenzyl glycollate (III) to give the compound (X) in 40 per cent yield. On removal of the benzyloxycarbonyl-group with hydrogen bromide in glacial acetic acid the hydrobromide (XI) was isolated in 97 per cent yield.

Compound (XII) was synthesized in 82 per cent yield by condensing α-benzyl p-nitrobenzyloxycarbonyl-L-glutamate (VIb) with the hydrobromide (XI). This was performed by the mixed anhydride method using isobutyl chloroformate in the presence of triethylamine.

In order to obtain the depsipeptide analogue (XIII) of glutathione it was necessary to remove the numerous protecting groups and then reduce the —S—S— bond. We aimed to carry out this stage of the work by proceeding analogously to the method described by Berse, Boucher and Piche [7] in the synthesis of glutathione, namely, first hydrogenation over 10 per cent palladium on charcoal, which should have removed all the protecting groups, and then reduction of the —S—S— bond by hydrogenation over palladium black. But here we met with considerable difficulties, due evidently to the fact that partial reduction of the —S—S— bond takes place already in the initial stages of hydrogenation under the most varied conditions. This presumably leads to poisoning of the catalyst so that complete removal of the protecting groups could not be achieved. Such an assumption is supported by the fact that ophthalmic acid and its depsipeptide analogue were readily obtained by us on hydrogenation over palladium of the corresponding, similarly protected compounds. Work on the synthesis of the depsipeptide analogue of glutathione and other depsipeptide analogues of ophthalmic acid is being continued.

SCHEME 2

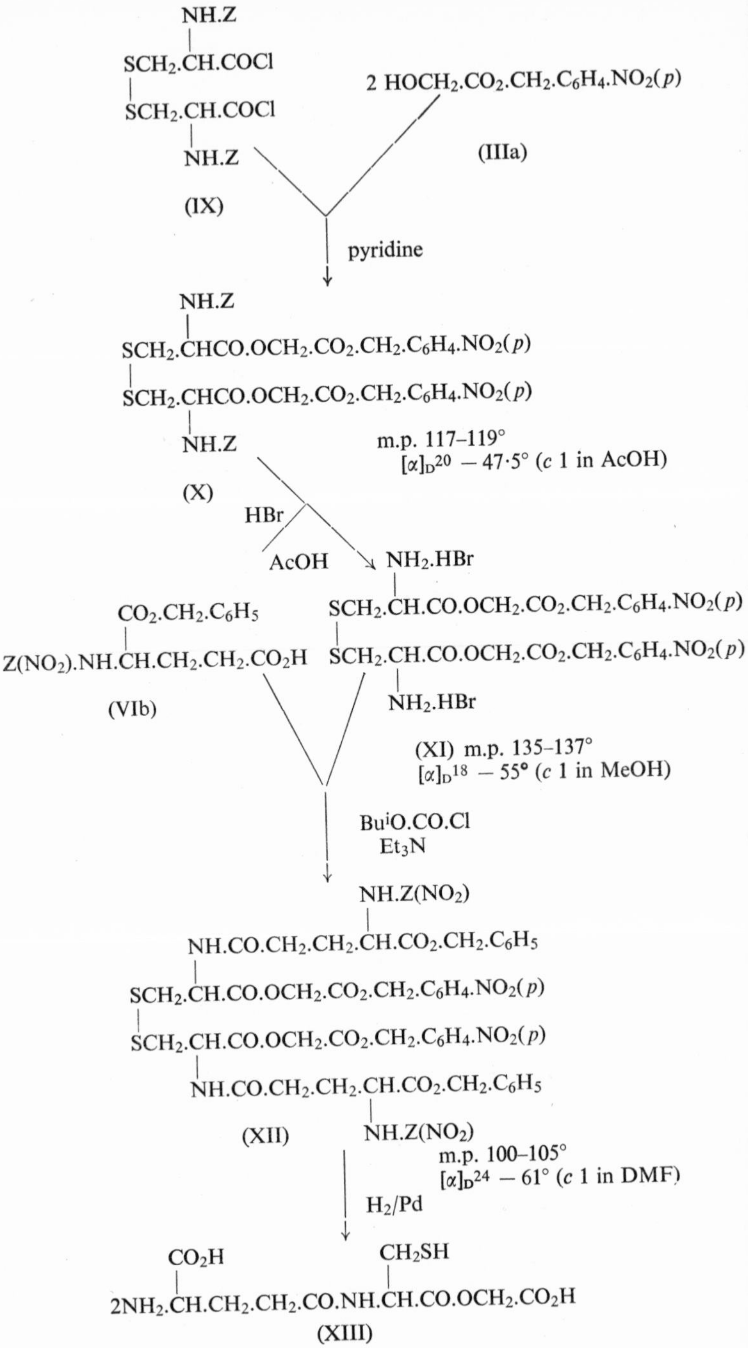

NH.Z
|
SCH$_2$.CH.COCl
|
SCH$_2$.CH.COCl
|
NH.Z

(IX)

2 HOCH$_2$.CO$_2$.CH$_2$.C$_6$H$_4$.NO$_2$(p)

(IIIa)

| pyridine

NH.Z
|
SCH$_2$.CHCO.OCH$_2$.CO$_2$.CH$_2$.C$_6$H$_4$.NO$_2$(p)
|
SCH$_2$.CHCO.OCH$_2$.CO$_2$.CH$_2$.C$_6$H$_4$.NO$_2$(p)
|
NH.Z

(X)

m.p. 117–119°
$[\alpha]_D^{20} - 47\cdot5°$ (c 1 in AcOH)

HBr

AcOH

NH$_2$.HBr
|
SCH$_2$.CH.CO.OCH$_2$.CO$_2$.CH$_2$.C$_6$H$_4$.NO$_2$(p)
|
SCH$_2$.CH.CO.OCH$_2$.CO$_2$.CH$_2$.C$_6$H$_4$.NO$_2$(p)
|
NH$_2$.HBr

CO$_2$.CH$_2$.C$_6$H$_5$
|
Z(NO$_2$).NH.CH.CH$_2$.CH$_2$.CO$_2$H

(VIb)

(XI) m.p. 135–137°
$[\alpha]_D^{18} - 55°$ (c 1 in MeOH)

Bu^{i}O.CO.Cl
Et$_3$N

NH.Z(NO$_2$)
|
NH.CO.CH$_2$.CH$_2$.CH.CO$_2$.CH$_2$.C$_6$H$_5$
|
SCH$_2$.CH.CO.OCH$_2$.CO$_2$.CH$_2$.C$_6$H$_4$.NO$_2$(p)
|
SCH$_2$.CH.CO.OCH$_2$.CO$_2$.CH$_2$.C$_6$H$_4$.NO$_2$(p)
|
NH.CO.CH$_2$.CH$_2$.CH.CO$_2$.CH$_2$.C$_6$H$_5$
|
NH.Z(NO$_2$)

(XII)

m.p. 100–105°
$[\alpha]_D^{24} - 61°$ (c 1 in DMF)

H$_2$/Pd

CO$_2$H   CH$_2$SH
| |
2NH$_2$.CH.CH$_2$.CH$_2$.CO.NH.CH.CO.OCH$_2$.CO$_2$H

(XIII)

REFERENCES

1. S. G. WALEY, *Biochem. J.* **68,** 189 (1958).
2. E. E. CLIFFE and S. G. WALEY, *Biochem. J.* **69,** 649 (1958).
3. E. E. CLIFFE and S. G. WALEY, *Biochem. J.* **73,** 25 (1959).
4. E. E. CLIFFE and S. G. WALEY, *Biochem. J.* **79,** 475 (1961).
5. E. E. CLIFFE and S. G. WALEY, *Biochem. J.* **79,** 669 (1961).
6. *Biochemical Preparations*, vol. 2, p. 74 (1952).
7. C. BERSE, R. BOUCHER and L. PICHE, *Can. J. Chem.* **37,** 1733 (1959).
8. E. TASCHNER, T. SOKOLOWSKA and D. BIRNAT, *Zhur. Vsesous. Khim. Obshchestva* im. D. T. MENDELEEVA **7,** 356 (1962), 4th European Peptide Symposium, Moscow, 1961.

ÜBER PEPTOLIDSYNTHESEN

UNTERSUCHUNGEN ZUM AUFBAU VON DI-, TRI-, UND TETRAPEPTOLIDEN

E. Schröder und K. Lübke

Aus dem Hauptlaboratorium der Schering AG, Berlin-West

Die von *Fusarien-* und *Streptomyces*-Arten gebildeten Verbindungen Enniatin A und B, Valinomycin, Amidomycin sowie das von dem Pilz *Pithomyces chartarum* produzierte Sporidesmolid I (Fig. 1) stellen eine Sondergruppe der "heterodet cyclischen heteromeren Peptide" dar. Für

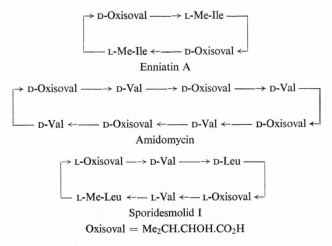

Enniatin A

Amidomycin

Sporidesmolid I

Oxisoval $= Me_2CH.CHOH.CO_2H$

FIG. 1

diese wurde von Russell [1] die Bezeichnung Peptolide vorgeschlagen, von Schemyakin [2] wurde der Typ dagegen in die Gruppe der Depsipeptide eingereiht, zu der außerdem noch *O*-Peptide und Peptidlactone gehören. Während *O*-Peptide und Peptidlactone homöomere Peptide darstellen, sind Peptolide heteromere Peptide. Wir schlagen daher vor, alle Verbindungen, die Peptid- und Esterbindung im Molekül enthalten entsprechend dem Vorschlag von Schemyakin, als "Depsipeptide" zu bezeichnen, diese sehr vielfältige Gruppe jedoch in die homöomeren *O*-Peptide und Peptidlactone und in die heteromeren Peptolide (Fig. 2) zu unterteilen.

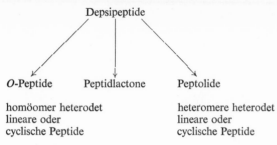

FIG. 2

Charakteristisch für die Peptolide ist also, daß die in allen Depsipeptiden vorhandene Esterbindung mit einer reinen Hydroxysäure gebildet wird und eine alternierende oder nicht alternierende Reihenfolge von Aminosäure und Hydroxysäure in cyclischer oder acyclischer Form möglich sein kann. Es ergibt sich somit eine eindeutige Abgrenzung zu den O-Peptiden des Serins und Threonins und zu der zweiten Untergruppe der " heterodet cyclischen heteromeren Peptide ", den Peptidlactonen, bei denen der Heterobestandteil außerhalb des heterodet cyclischen Ringes liegt und eine Esterbindung über eine β-Hydroxy-α-aminosäure erfolgt (z.B. Etamycin, Ostreogrycin, Actinomycine).

Bedingt durch das Vorhandensein von Esterbindungen zwischen Aminosäure und α-Hydroxysäuren (Peptolidbindung) ergeben sich gegenüber einer normalen Peptidsynthese besondere Probleme. Darüber hinaus sind bei der Synthese von Peptolid-Naturstoffen durch die Anwesenheit sterisch gehinderter Aminosäuren wie Leucin, Valin und N-Methylaminosäuren weitere Schwierigkeiten zu erwarten. Die Erfolge der Arbeitsgruppe um Schemyakin [3] haben gezeigt, daß die Synthese eines Peptolid-Naturstoffes durchaus im Bereich der präparativen Möglichkeiten liegt und, daß wie das Beispiel des Enniatin zeigt, diesen Synthesen eine große Bedeutung zur endgültigen Bestätigung der vorgeschlagenen Strukturformeln zukommt.

Um nun in präparativer Hinsicht eine möglichst große Variationsbreite zur Verfügung zu haben, erschien uns die Klärung prinzipieller Fragen der Peptolidsynthese erforderlich. Ausgehend von den Grundtypen Hydroxyacyl-Aminosäure (Ox-Am) Aminoacyl-Hydroxysäure (Am-Ox) wurden die Tripeptolid-Typen Ox-Am-Am, Am-Am-Ox und Am-Ox-Am eingehend untersucht, wobei der Typ Ox-Am-Am streng genommen nicht in die Depsipeptidgruppe gehört, da die charakteristische Esterbindung fehlt.

I. SYNTHESE DES TYPS
HYDROXYACYL-AMINOACYL-AMINOSÄURE (OX-AM-AM)

Der Aufbau ist prinzipiell nach zwei Wegen möglich: (a) aus Hydroxyacyl-Aminosäure und Aminosäure und (b) aus Hydroxysäure und Aminoacyl-aminosäure. Als geeignetes aktiviertes Hydroxysäurederivat wurde der Cyanmethylester, speziell L- und D-Hydroxyisovaleriansäure (Oxisoval)-cyanmethylester, verwendet. Dieses Verfahren hatte jedoch den Nachteil, daß infolge einer sehr langsamen Aminolyse mit Aminosäure- oder Peptid -methyl-, äthyl- oder benzylestern durch die erforderlichen langen Reaktionszeiten und erhöhten Temperaturen Diketopiperazine als Hauptprodukte entstanden. Nur bei den aminolytisch stabilen tert.-Butylestern war die Reaktion erfolgreich [4].

Bei Anwendung der Azid-Methode bestehen diese Nachteile nicht. Als Beispiel für diese Reaktion wurde ausgehend vom L- oder D-Hydroxyisovaleriansäurehydrazid (hergestellt aus dem entsprechenden Äthylestern und Hydrazinhydrat) auf verschiedenen Wegen und unter Verwendung verschiedener Carboxylschutzgruppen Ester der Sporidesmolsäure A bzw. deren optischer Antipode hergestellt. Die Synthese erfolgte sowohl durch stufenweisen Aufbau als auch durch Kupplung von Hydroxyisovaleriansäurehydrazid und Dipeptidester. Die Knüpfung der Peptidbindung zwischen Hydroxysäure und Aminosäure- oder Dipeptid -ester wurde nach dem von Honzl und Rudinger [5] modifizierten Azid-Verfahren mit tert.-Butylnitrit in absol. Tetrahydrofuran/Chlorwasserstoff durchgeführt. Eine Zusammenstellung dieser Synthesen zeigt das Reaktionsschema Fig. 3 und Fig. 4.

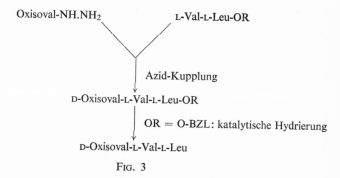

Oxisoval-NH.NH₂   L-Val-L-Leu-OR

Azid-Kupplung

D-Oxisoval-L-Val-L-Leu-OR

OR = O-BZL: katalytische Hydrierung

D-Oxisoval-L-Val-L-Leu

FIG. 3

Auch das Carbodiimid-Verfahren ist zur Synthese des Typs Hydroxyacyl-aminosäure geeignet. Gute Ergebnisse wurden entsprechend einer Publikation von Schwyzer und A. Tun-Kyi [6] mit Methanol als Lösungsmittel erzielt. Anhydrid- und Phosphorazo-Methode versagten [4], stärkere Aktivierungen, wie Säurechlorid waren wegen der freien Hydroxygruppe nicht möglich. Die weitere Umsetzung von Oxisoval-Val-R′ (Reaktionsschema, Fig. 4) gelang sowohl nach der Azid- als auch nach der Anhydrid-Methode. Schwierigkeiten wurden hier im Gegensatz zur Umsetzung mit nur der Hydroxysäure in keinem Fall beobachtet.

Hydroxyisovaleryl-Aminosäureester oder Hydroxyisovaleryl-dipeptidester, wobei als Aminosäuren L- und D-Valin sowie L- und D-Leucin und als Carb-

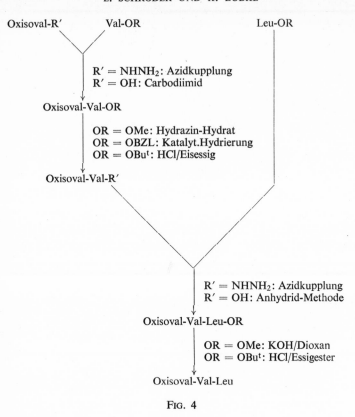

FIG. 4

oxylschutz Methyl-, tert.-Butyl- und Benzylester eingesetzt wurden, stellen gut kristallisierte Verbindungen dar, die mit 50–70%ig. Ausbeute in reiner Form anfallen [7].

Um das Azid-Verfahren auch in den Fällen anwenden zu können, wo die Derivate bereits eine Peptolidbindung enthalten, mußte ein geeigneter Weg zur Synthese von Hydraziden ausgearbeitet werden, da das übliche Verfahren, die Hydrazinolyse eines Esters infolge von Nebenreaktionen mit der Peptolidbindung nicht anwendbar war (vgl. Seite 173). Als sehr brauchbar erwiesen sich N'-geschützte Hydrazide, bevorzugt Benzyloxycarbonyl (Z)-, p-Nitrobenzyloxycarbonyl [Z(NO$_2$)]- und tert.-Butyloxycarbonyl(BOC)-hydrazide.

Die Darstellung von Hydroxyisovaleriansäure-2-[benzyloxycarbonyl]-hydrazid bzw. -2-[tert.-butyloxycarbonyl]-hydrazid gelang sowohl durch Reaktion von Hydroxyisovaleriansäurehydrazid mit Benzyloxycarbonyl-chlorid oder t-Butyloxycarbonyl-azid, als auch aus Hydroxyisovaleriansäure und Benzyloxycarbonyl-hydrazin bzw. t-Butyloxycarbonyl-hydrazin in Gegenwart von N,N'-Dicyclohexylcarbodiimid (Reaktionsschema Fig. 5).

Oxisoval
Oxisoval-NH.NH2
Oxisoval
BOC-NH.NH2 (DCCI)
BOC-N3
Z-Cl
Z-NH.NH2 (DCCI)
Oxisoval-NH.NH-BOC
DCCI: 65%; Azid: 75%
Oxisoval-NH.NH-Z
Säurechlorid: 75%; DCCI: 60%

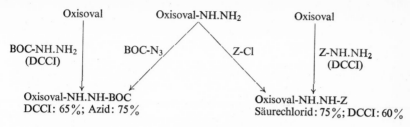

FIG. 5

Benzyloxycarbonyl-hydrazide und *p*-Nitrobenzyloxycarbonyl-hydrazide konnten auf einfache Weise durch Umsetzung von Chlorameisensäure-*p*-nitrophenylester mit Benzylalkohol bzw. *p*-Nitrobenzylalkohol in Chloroform/Pyridin bei 0° und anschliessende Hydrazinolyse erhalten werden [8] (Reaktionsschema Fig. 6). Benzyl-*p*-nitrophenylcarbonat konnte auch in glatter Reaktion aus Benzyloxycarbonyl-chlorid und *p*-Nitrophenol in Chloroform/Triäthylamin bei 0° gewonnen werden.

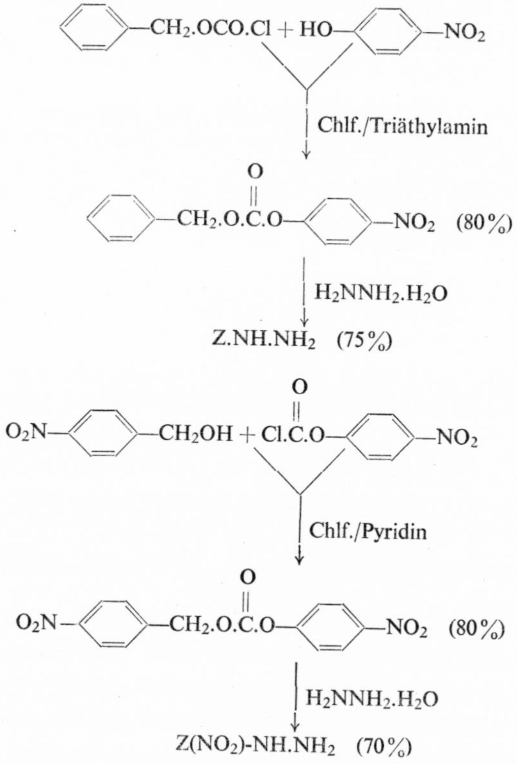

—CH2.OCO.Cl + HO—
—NO2
Chlf./Triäthylamin
O
—CH2.O.C.O—
—NO2 (80%)
H2NNH2.H2O
Z.NH.NH2 (75%)
O
O2N—
—CH2OH + Cl.C.O—
—NO2
Chlf./Pyridin
O
O2N—
—CH2.O.C.O—
—NO2 (80%)
H2NNH2.H2O
Z(NO2)-NH.NH2 (70%)

FIG. 6

II. SYNTHESE DES TYPS
AMINOACYL-AMINOACYL-HYDROXYSÄURE (AM-AM-OX)

Entscheidend für diesen Typ ist die Bildung der Esterbindung zwischen Aminosäure und Hydroxysäure. In der Literatur sind hierfür mehrere Möglichkeiten beschrieben worden: z.B. Kondensation nach dem Benzolsulfochlorid- [9], Phosgen- [10], Äthylkohlensäureanhydrid- [11], Oxazolin- [12], Carbonyldiimidazol-Verfahren [13] und die Reaktion über α-Diazocarbonsäureester [14]. Auf Grund unserer eigenen Erfahrungen geben wir der Kupplung mit Benzolsulfochlorid oder Carbonyldiimidazol den Vorzug. Dabei muß die Carboxylkomponente, also die N-geschützte Aminosäure, in einem mehr oder weniger großem Überschuß verwendet werden, da sich dieser nach der Reaktion im Gegensatz zur Hydroxylkomponente leicht durch Ausschütteln mit Alkali entfernen läßt. Es hat sich nun gezeigt, daß der Erfolg der Reaktion unabhängig, ob mit Benzolsulfochlorid oder Bisimidazolylcarbonyl gearbeitet wird, in hohem Maße von der Natur der Carboxylkomponente abhängig ist. So konnten bei der Umsetzung von Hydroxyisovaleriansäure-Benzylamid mit Benzyloxycarbonyl-Glycin 70–75% mit Benzyloxycarbonyl-Glycyl-Glycin dagegen nur 40% erhalten werden. Bei Verwendung von Benzyloxycarbonyl- bzw. t-Butyloxycarbonyl-Valin als

TABELLE 1

Z-Gly-D-Oxisoval-NH.BZL	CDI	70%
	Sulfochlorid	75%
Z-Gly-Gly-D-Oxisoval-NH.BZL	Sulfochlorid	40%
Z-D-Val-Gly-D-Oxisoval-NH.BZL	Sulfochlorid	20%
(60% D-Oxisoval-NH.BZL in Substanz zurückgewonnen)		
Z-Gly-D-Val-D-Oxisoval-NH.BZL	Sulfochlorid	0
	CDI	0
Z-D-Val-D-Val-D-Oxisoval-NH.BZL	Sulfochlorid	0
	CDI	0

aber:

X-D-Val-D-Oxisoval-NH.BZL
X: BOC bzw. Z; CDI; 80–90%
Verbindung enthält noch Hydroxylkomponente

$$\left| \begin{array}{l} X = BOC: HCl/EtOAc \\ X = Z: H_2/Pd \end{array} \right.$$
↓

D-Val-D-Oxisoval-NH.BZL.HCl
hygroskopisch, ca. 30–40% Ausbeute

$$\left| \begin{array}{l} + Z\text{-}D\text{-Val} \\ \text{Anhydrid-Methode} \end{array} \right.$$
↓

Z-D-Val-D-Val-D-Oxisoval-NH.BZL (60%)

CDI = Carbonyldiimidazol

Carboxylkomponente wurden 80–90% als Rohprodukt und mit Benzyloxy-carbonyl-Val-Gly werden nur 20% in kristalliner Form isoliert. Völlig negativ verlief die Reaktion mit Benzyloxycarbonyl-Gly-D-Val oder Benzyl-oxycarbonyl-D-Val-D-Val nach der Sulfochlorid- und Bisimidazolylcarbonyl-Methode (Tabelle 1). Durch einen stufenweisen Aufbau, ausgehend vom Hydroxyisovaleriansäure-benzylamid läßt sich jedoch auch Benzyloxycar-bonyl-D-Val-D-Val-Oxisoval-NH-BZL synthetisieren. Ähnlich sind auch die Verhältnisse bei Verwendung von *N*-geschützten Hydroxyisovaleriansäure-hydraziden als Hydroxylkomponente (Tabelle 2).

TABELLE 2

Z-Gly-D-Oxisoval-NH.NH-BOC† Öl	CDI	80%
BOC-Gly-D-Oxisoval-NH.NH-Z† EtOAc/PAe; amorph	Sulfochlorid CDI	70% 70%
Z-Gly-Gly-D-Oxisoval-NH.NH-BOC† Schaum	CDI 2+1	77%
BOC-Gly-Gly-D-Oxisoval-NH.NH-Z‡ krist.	CDI 2+1	60%
Z-D-Val-Gly-D-Oxisoval-NH.NH-Z‡ m.p. 152–156° (EtOAc/PAe), krist.	CDI 2+1	35%
Z-L-Val-Gly-D-Oxisoval-NH.NH-BOC Schaum	CDI 2+1	70%
BOC-D-Val-Gly-D-Oxisoval-NH.NH-Z‡ m.p. 168–170° (EtOAc/PAe), krist.	CDI 2+1	50%

CDI = Carbonyldiimidazol

† Verbindungen enthalten noch nachweisbare Mengen an Hydroxylkomponente.
‡ Verbindungen sind umkristallisierbar, Hydroxylkomponenten nicht mehr nachweisbar.

Durch die Wahl geeigneter, selektiv spaltbarer Amino- bzw. Hydrazid-Schutzgruppen besteht die Möglichkeit den Verbindungstyp Am-Am-Ox am Amino- oder Carboxylende weiter zu verlängern.

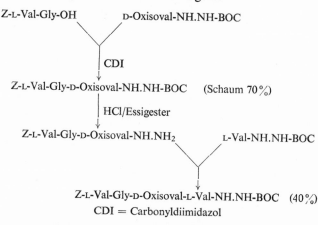

Z-L-Val-Gly-OH   D-Oxisoval-NH.NH-BOC

CDI

Z-L-Val-Gly-D-Oxisoval-NH.NH-BOC   (Schaum 70%)

HCl/Essigester

Z-L-Val-Gly-D-Oxisoval-NH.NH₂   L-Val-NH.NH-BOC

Z-L-Val-Gly-D-Oxisoval-L-Val-NH.NH-BOC   (40%)
CDI = Carbonyldiimidazol

FIG. 7

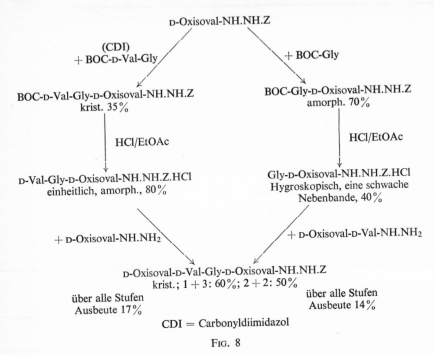

FIG. 8

Die Verbindungen: Z-L-Val-Gly-D-Oxisoval-L-Val-NH.NH-BOC   und
D-Oxisoval-D-Val-Gly-D-Oxisoval-NH.NH-Z

konnten auf diese Weise nach der Azid-Methode in 60 bzw. 40%ig. Ausbeute synthetisiert werden (Reaktionsschema Fig. 7 und Fig. 8), wobei die letztere Verbindung auch aus den Teilsequenzen 2+2 erhalten wurde.

III. SYNTHESE DES TYPS
AMINOACYL-HYDROXYACYL-AMINOSÄURE

Der Syntheseweg aus N-geschützter Aminosäure und Hydroxyacyl-Aminosäureester nach der Sulfochlorid- oder Carbonyldiimidazolyl Methode erwies sich als wenig vorteilhaft, da die Entfernung der Hydroxyl-komponente sehr erschwert ist. Eine Trennung ist nur dann möglich, wenn das Reaktionsprodukt gut kristallisierbar ist. Auf diese Weise gelang die Isolierung von

Z-(bzw. BOC-)Gly-D-Oxisoval-D-Val-D-Val-OBu^t (75%)

aus N-geschütztem Glycin und Hydroxysäurekomponente mittels Carbonyl-diimidazol bzw. Benzolsulfochlorid (Reaktionsschema Fig. 9).   Mit

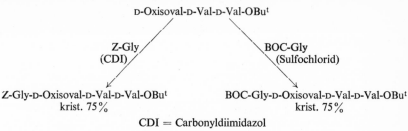

D-Oxisoval-D-Val-D-Val-OBu^t

Z-Gly (CDI)

BOC-Gly (Sulfochlorid)

Z-Gly-D-Oxisoval-D-Val-D-Val-OBu^t
krist. 75%

BOC-Gly-D-Oxisoval-D-Val-D-Val-OBu^t
krist. 75%

CDI = Carbonyldiimidazol

FIG. 9

sterisch gehinderten Aminosäuren, z.B. Z-Val-OH konnte auch hier (vgl. Seite 200) keine Umsetzung erzielt werden.

Weitaus günstiger und allgemein verwendbar für die Darstellung des Am-Ox-Am-Typs ist die Kupplung geeigneter aktivierter *N*-geschützter Aminoacyl-Hydroxysäurederivate mit Aminosäureestern. Mit der Darstellung von BOC-Am-Ox-OH durch katalytische Hydrierung des entsprechenden Benzylesters ist eine Anwendung der Methode der gemischten Anhydride möglich, die hier zu guten Ergebnissen führt.

Nicht ohne weiteres brauchbar ist die Azid-Methode, da eine Hydrazid-Bildung aus *N*-geschützten Am-Ox-ester zu Nebenreaktionen mit der Peptolidbindung führt. Selbst bei Verwendung des Cyanmethylesters verläuft die Hydrazinolyse nicht so schnell, daß eine Spaltung der Peptolid-bindung vermieden wird (Reaktionsschema Fig. 10).

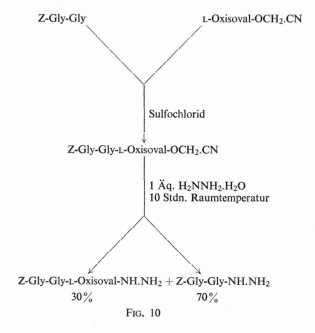

Z-Gly-Gly

L-Oxisoval-OCH$_2$.CN

Sulfochlorid

Z-Gly-Gly-L-Oxisoval-OCH$_2$.CN

1 Äq. H$_2$NNH$_2$.H$_2$O
10 Stdn. Raumtemperatur

Z-Gly-Gly-L-Oxisoval-NH.NH$_2$ + Z-Gly-Gly-NH.NH$_2$
30%   70%

FIG. 10

Die Azid-Methode läßt sich jedoch anwenden, wenn die Einführung der Hydrazidgruppe wieder in Form eines N'-geschützten Hydrazids vor der Knüpfung der Peptolidbindung erfolgt. Das bereits erwähnte Hydroxyisovaleriansäure-NH.NH-Z (bzw. NH.NH-BOC und NH.NH-Z(NO$_2$)) läßt sich dann in üblicher Weise mit N-geschützten Aminosäuren mit Benzolsulfochlorid oder mit Carbonyldiimidazol umsetzen. Allerdings ist auch hier die Herstellung von reinen Verbindungen schwierig, da sich die Hydroxylkomponente nicht entfernen läßt und die Verbindungen oft eine geringe Neigung zur Kristallisation zeigen. In diesem Fall können nach Abspaltung der Hydrazid-Schutzgruppe durch eine Verteilung in Essigester/Wasser über wenige Stufen jedoch elektrophoretisch einheitliche Substanzen erhalten werden. Über eine Weiterkupplung eines N-geschützten Aminoacylhydroxyisovaleriansäure-hydrazids unterrichtet das Reaktionsschema Fig. 11.

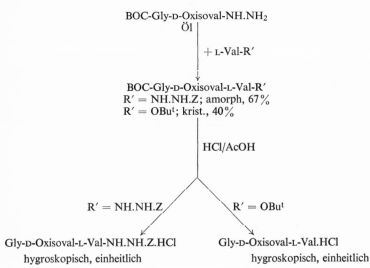

FIG. 11

Durch selektive Abspaltung der Butyloxycarbonyl-Gruppe aus dem mit 67%ig. Ausbeute erhaltenen BOC-Gly-D-Oxisoval-L-Val-NH.NH-Z liegt ein zur Weiterkupplung geeignetes Derivat vor. Gleichzeitige Abspaltung von Butyloxycarbonyl- und tert.-Butylestergruppe liefert ein freies elektrophoretisch einheitliches Tripeptolid. Ein weiteres Beispiel ist im Reaktionsschema Fig. 12 aufgeführt. Das synthetisierte BOC-Gly-D-Oxisoval-Gly-Gly-OBZL ist mit der vom Carboxylende durch stufenweisen Aufbau erhaltenen Verbindung identisch.

Wie aus dem Geschilderten ersichtlich ist, bestehen also auch auf dem Peptolid-Gebiet durch geeignete Schutzgruppenkombinationen und Kupplungsmethoden eine vielfältige Variation von Synthesemöglichkeiten. Diese

Tatsache kann jedoch nicht darüber hinweg täuschen, daß der Aufbau selbst kurzkettiger Peptolide, bedingt durch eine schwierige oder manchmal gar nicht mögliche Reinigung von Zwischenstufen und erschwerte Kristallisation, im Vergleich zur Peptidsynthese unendlich mühsamer ist.

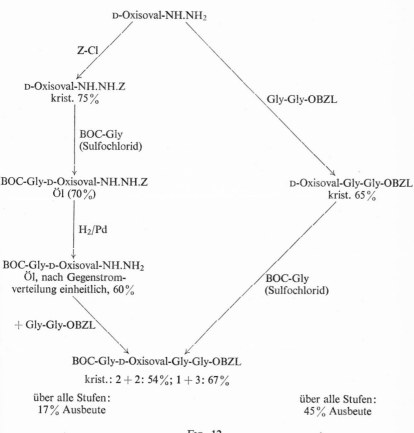

FIG. 12

REFERENZEN

1. D. W. RUSSELL und M. E. BROWN, *Biochim. Biophys. Acta* **38**, 382 (1960).
2. M. M. SCHEMYAKIN, *Angew. Chem.* **72**, 342 (1960).
3. M. M. SCHEMYAKIN, Yu. A. OVCHINNIKOV, A. A. KIRYUSHKIN und V. T. IVANOW, *Tetrahedron Letters* 301 (1962).
4. E. SCHRÖDER und K. LÜBKE, *Liebig's Ann. Chem.* **655**, 211 (1962).
5. J. HONZL und J. RUDINGER, *Coll. Czechoslov. Chem. Commun.* **26**, 2333 (1961).
6. R. SCHWYZER und Aung TUN-KYI, *Helv. Chim. Acta* **45**, 859 (1962).
7. K. LÜBKE und E. SCHRÖDER, *Liebig's Ann. Chem.*: im Druck.
8. L. A. CARPINO, *J. Amer. Chem. Soc.* **79**, 98 (1957).
9. J. H. BREWSTER und C. J. CIOTTI, Jr., *J. Amer. Chem. Soc.* **77**, 6214 (1955).

10. M. Brenner, J. P. Zimmermann, P. Quitt, W. Schneider und A. Hartmann, *Helv Chim. Acta* **40**, 604 (1957).
11. M. M. Botwinik, S. M. Awajewa, L. M. Kokscharowa und W. A. Oladkina *Zhur. Obshchei. Khim.* **30**, 3887 (1960).
12. M. M. Botwinik, B. I. Otoslawskaja und L. L. Iwanow, *Zhur. Obshchei. Khim* **31**, 42 (1961).
13. H. A. Staab, W. Rohr und A. Mannschreck, *Angew. Chem.* **73**, 143 (1961).
14. H. Gibian und K. Lübke, *Liebig's Ann. Chem.* **644**, 130 (1961); R. Schwyzer und P. Carrion, *Helv. Chim. Acta* **43**, 2101 (1960).

SYNTHESIS OF CYCLIC DEPSIPEPTIDES

Yu. A. Ovchinnikov, V. T. Ivanov, A. A. Kiryushkin and
M. M. Shemyakin

Institute for Chemistry of Natural Products,
U.S.S.R. Academy of Sciences, Moscow, U.S.S.R.

In recent years peptide chemists have shown considerable interest in abnormal peptides such as depsipeptides, glycopeptides, etc. A general method for the preparation of optically active linear depsipeptides had been developed in our laboratory [1] and was reported to the previous European Peptide Symposium in Moscow by M. M. Shemyakin. These studies have now been extended to cyclic members of this class, inasmuch as all naturally occurring depsipeptides known so far possess a ring structure. In this connection we turned to the synthesis of naturally-occurring depsipeptides and their analogues, choosing as the first objective antibiotics of the enniatin group.

In 1947 Pl. A. Plattner and collaborators [2] isolated from the mycelium of a number of *Fusarium* strains two new antibiotics, enniatin A and enniatin B, possessing high *in vitro* activity against various mycobacteria (Table 1).

Based on their acid and alkaline degradation products the antibiotics were assigned the cyclotetradepsipeptide structures I and II, respectively, built up of D-α-hydroxyisovaleryl and N-methyl-L-isoleucyl (or N-methyl-L-valyl) units [3].

$$(CH_3)_2CH \qquad\qquad R$$
$$\diagdown \qquad\qquad |$$
$$\diagup CO.CH.O.CO.CH\diagdown$$
$$H_3C.N\diagup \qquad\qquad \diagdown N.CH_3$$
$$\diagdown CH.CO.O.CH.CO\diagup$$
$$| \qquad\qquad \diagdown$$
$$R' \qquad\qquad CH(CH_3)_2$$

(I) $R = R' = CH(CH_3)CH_2CH_3$
(II) $R = R' = CH(CH_3)_2$
(III) $R = R' = CH_2CH(CH_3)_2$
(IV) $R = CH(CH_3)CH_2CH_3$, $R' = CH(CH_3)_2$
(V) $R = CH(CH_3)CH_2CH_3$, $R' = CH_2CH(CH_3)_2$
(VI) $R = CH(CH_3)_2$, $R' = CH_2CH(CH_3)_2$

The Swiss workers also discovered the antibiotic enniatin C (III) and furthermore arrived at the conclusion that there may exist enniatins containing two different N-methylamino-acids in the molecule [4], which, by analogy, could be ascribed formulae (IV), (V) or (VI).

TABLE 1

Antibiotic	Molecular formula	M.p.°	$[\alpha]_D^{20}$ in $CHCl_3$
Enniatin A	$C_{24}H_{42}N_2O_6$	121–122°	$-92°, c\ 1\cdot0$
Enniatin B	$C_{22}H_{38}N_2O_6$	173–175	$-108, c\ 0\cdot6$

In the same year of 1947 in England A. H. Cook and coworkers isolated five closely related antibiotics, lateritiin I, lateritiin II, avenacein, sambucinin and fructigenin [5] (Table 2).

TABLE 2

Antibiotic	Molecular formula	M.p.°	$[\alpha]_D^{20}$ $c\ 1$ in EtOH
Lateritiin I	$C_{26}H_{46}N_2O_7$	121–122°	$-95\cdot6°$
Lateritiin II	$C_{26}H_{46}N_2O_7$	125	-92
Avenacein	$C_{25}H_{44}N_2O_7$	139	-101
Sambucinin	$C_{24}H_{42}N_2O_7$	86–87	-83
Fructigenin	$C_{26}H_{44-46}N_2O_7$	129	-103

Lateritiin I was at that time found to be identical with enniatin A. Later, however, Cook and coworkers [6] showed that on degradation of lateritiin I the same compounds were formed as in the case of enniatin B (but not enniatin A).

The divergence in the above results showed that formulae (I) and (II) proposed by the Swiss chemists for enniatins A and B cannot be considered as strictly established. In view of this our synthesis of cyclotetradepsipeptides (I)–(VI), carried out according to Scheme 1, could be of certain interest.

Condensation of *p*-nitrobenzyloxycarbonyl-*N*-methyl-L-isoleucine (VII), *p*-nitrobenzyloxycarbonyl-*N*-methyl-L-valine (VIII) or *p*-nitrobenzyloxycarbonyl-*N*-methyl-L-leucine (IX) with tert.-butyl D-α-hydroxyisovalerate (X) by the mixed anhydride method afforded the corresponding diesters (XI), (XII) and (XIII) in 75–80 per cent yields. Refluxing benzene solutions of the latter in the presence of toluene-*p*-sulfonic acid gave rise to the *p*-nitrobenzyloxycarbonyl acids (XIV), (XV) and (XVI). On the other hand hydrolysis of the *p*-nitrobenzyloxycarbonyl esters (XI), (XII) and (XIII) gave the corresponding amino-esters (XVII), (XVIII) and (XIX) in 70–75 per cent yields. The fragments (XIV–XVI) and (XVII–XIX) were then joined together by an amide bond, affording the tetradepsipeptides (XX–XXV) in 90–95 per cent yields.

Simultaneous removal of the *C*- and *N*-protective groups from the depsipeptides (XX–XXV) gave 70 per cent yields of the corresponding hydrobromides (XXVI–XXXI). Ring closure of the latter was accomplished by the acid chloride method: on reaction of XXVI–XXXI with thionyl chloride the corresponding acid chlorides were formed, cyclization of which in benzene solution in the presence of triethylamine (dilution to 2 mmole/l.) led to the cyclotetradepsipeptides (I–VI) in yields reaching 70–75 per cent. The constants of these compounds are presented in Table 3.

TABLE 3

Comp.	Molecular formula	M.p.°	$[\alpha]_D^{20}$ in CHCl$_3$	Molecular weight (Cryosc. in benzene)
I	$C_{24}H_{42}O_6N_2$ (454·6)	215–216°	+ 13·5°, c 0·8	461
II	$C_{22}H_{38}O_6N_2$ (426·5)	228–229	+ 4·8°, c 0·9	424†, 417‡, 460§
III	$C_{24}H_{42}O_6N_2$ (454·6)	156–157	+ 35°, c 1·0	441
IV	$C_{23}H_{40}O_6N_2$ (440·6)	206–207	+ 9°, c 0·8	439
V	$C_{24}H_{42}O_6N_2$ (454·6)	164–165	+ 24°, c 0·9	449
VI	$C_{23}H_{42}O_6N_2$ (440·6)	164–165	+ 22°, c 0·8	430

† The same value was obtained mass spectroscopically.
‡ Isothermal distillation in acetone.
§ Thermoelectrically in butyl acetate.

The structure of the cyclodepsipeptides (I–VI) was established as follows. Analytical and molecular weight data were in conformity with the respective formulas. On acid hydrolysis of the cyclodepsipeptides (I–III) D-α-hydroxy-isovaleric acid (XXXII), N-methyl-L-isoleucine (XXXIII), N-methyl-L-valine (XXXIV) or N-methyl-L-leucine (XXXV), respectively (Scheme 2), were isolated in high yield. Saponification of compounds (I–III) and subsequent treatment of the products with diazomethane gave the corresponding methyl esters (XXXVI), (XXXVII) and (XXXVIII). These were also obtained by a counter-synthesis using the acid chloride method (with O-benzyloxycarbonyl-D-α-hydroxyisovaleric acid (XXXIX) and the methyl ester hydrochlorides of the corresponding N-methylamino-acids (XL), (XLI) and (XLII) as starting materials), followed by hydrogenolysis of the benzyloxycarbonyl esters (XLIII), (XLIV) and (XLV). The compounds (XXXVI) and (XXXVII) (in the case of XXXVII also the respective amide and hydrazide) were found to be identical with the previously described degradation products of enniatins A and B [3, 7].

SCHEME 1

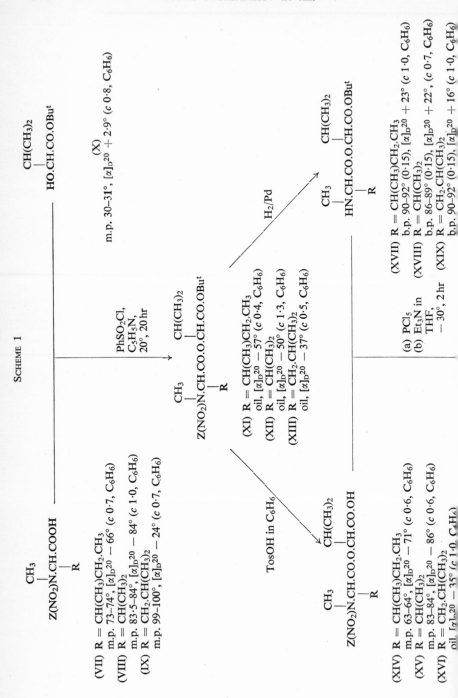

CH₃
|
Z(NO₂)N.CH.COOH
|
R

(VII) R = CH(CH₃)CH₂.CH₃
m.p. 73–74°, [α]_D^20 −66° (c 0·7, C₆H₆)
(VIII) R = CH(CH₃)₂
m.p. 83·5–84°, [α]_D^20 −84° (c 1·0, C₆H₆)
(IX) R = CH₂.CH(CH₃)₂
m.p. 99–100°, [α]_D^20 −24° (c 0·7, C₆H₆)

CH(CH₃)₂
|
HO.CH.CO.OBuᵗ
                (X)
m.p. 30–31°, [α]_D^20 +2·9° (c 0·8, C₆H₆)

PhSO₂Cl,
C₅H₅N,
20°, 20 hr
→

CH(CH₃)₂
|
CH₃   CH.CO.O.CH.CO.OBuᵗ
|
Z(NO₂)N.CH.CO.O.CH.CO.OBuᵗ
|
R

(XI) R = CH(CH₃)CH₂.CH₃
oil, [α]_D^20 −57° (c 0·4, C₆H₆)
(XII) R = CH(CH₃)₂
oil, [α]_D^20 −50° (c 1·3, C₆H₆)
(XIII) R = CH₂.CH(CH₃)₂
oil, [α]_D^20 −37° (c 0·5, C₆H₆)

H₂/Pd

CH(CH₃)₂
|
CH₃ |
|
HN.CH.CO.O.CH.CO.OBuᵗ
|
R

(XVII) R = CH(CH₃)CH₂.CH₃
b.p. 90–92° (0·15), [α]_D^20 + 23° (c 1·0, C₆H₆)
(XVIII) R = CH(CH₃)₂
b.p. 86–89° (0·15), [α]_D^20 + 22° (c 0·7, C₆H₆)
(XIX) R = CH₂.CH(CH₃)₂
b.p. 90–92° (0·15), [α]_D^20 + 16° (c 1·0, C₆H₆)

TosOH in C₆H₆

(a) PCl₅
(b) Et₃N in
THF,
−30°, 2 hr

CH(CH₃)₂
|
CH₃ |
|
Z(NO₂)N.CH.CO.O.CH.CO.OH
|
R

(XIV) R = CH(CH₃)CH₂.CH₃
m.p. 63–64°, [α]_D^20 −71° (c 0·6, C₆H₆)
(XV) R = CH(CH₃)₂
m.p. 83–84°, [α]_D^20 −86° (c 0·6, C₆H₆)
(XVI) R = CH₂.CH(CH₃)₂
oil, [α]_D^20 −35° (c 1·0, C₆H₆)

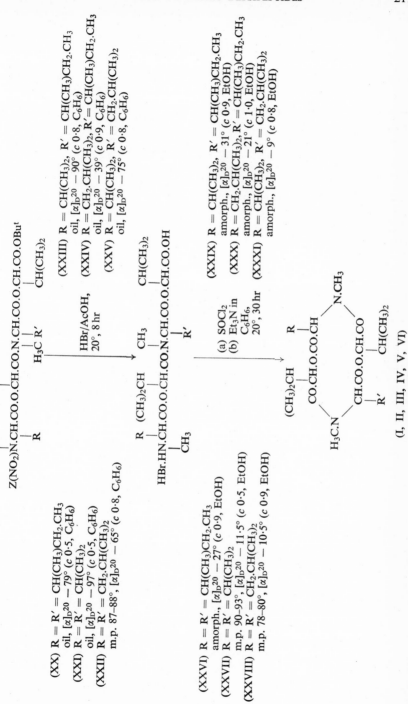

(XX) R = R' = CH(CH₃)CH₂.CH₃
oil, [α]_D²⁰ −79° (c 0·5, C₆H₆)
(XXI) R = R' = CH(CH₃)₂
oil, [α]_D²⁰ −97° (c 0·5, C₆H₆)
(XXII) R = R' = CH₂.CH(CH₃)₂
m.p. 87–88°, [α]_D²⁰ −65° (c 0·8, C₆H₆)

(XXVI) R = R' = CH(CH₃)CH₂.CH₃
amorph., [α]_D²⁰ −27° (c 0·9, EtOH)
(XXVII) R = R' = CH(CH₃)₂
m.p. 90–93°, [α]_D²⁰ −11·5° (c 0·5, EtOH)
(XXVIII) R = R' = CH₂.CH(CH₃)₂
m.p. 78–80°, [α]_D²⁰ −10·5° (c 0·9, EtOH)

(XXIII) R = CH(CH₃)₂, R' = CH(CH₃)CH₂.CH₃
oil, [α]_D²⁰ −90° (c 0·8, C₆H₆)
(XXIV) R = CH₂.CH(CH₃)₂, R = CH(CH₃)CH₂.CH₃
oil, [α]_D²⁰ −39° (c 0·9, C₆H₆)
(XXV) R = CH(CH₃)₂, R' = CH₂.CH(CH₃)₂
oil, [α]_D²⁰ −75° (c 0·8, C₆H₆)

(XXIX) R = CH(CH₃)₂, R' = CH(CH₃)CH₂.CH₃
amorph., [α]_D²⁰ −31° (c 0·9, EtOH)
(XXX) R = CH₂.CH(CH₃)₂, R' = CH(CH₃)CH₂.CH₃
amorph., [α]_D²⁰ −21° (c 1·0, EtOH)
(XXXI) R = CH(CH₃)₂, R' = CH₂.CH(CH₃)₂
amorph., [α]_D²⁰ −9° (c 0·8, EtOH)

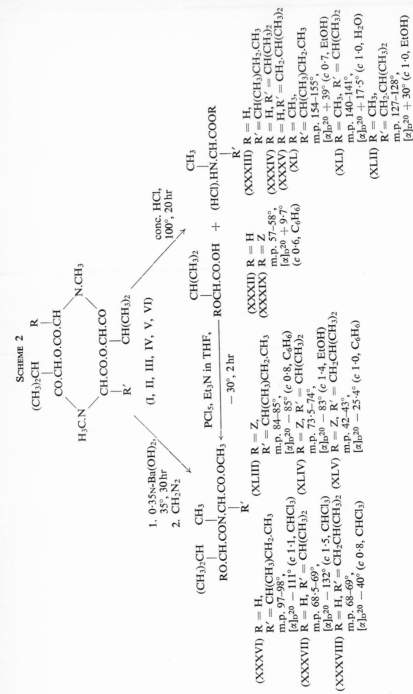

The cyclotetradepsipeptides (I–VI) differ considerably from all the antibiotics of the enniatin group described by Plattner and Cook, both in physical properties and to a certain extent in their chemical behaviour (for instance, greater resistance towards acid and alkaline hydrolysis). Furthermore, all the compounds we have synthesized manifest no activity against *Mycobacterium phlei* at concentrations up to 100 γ/ml, whereas enniatins A and B are active at concentrations 1–3 γ/ml. Prof. Plattner, who kindly made a direct comparison between compound II and enniatin B, also showed them to be different, although with very similar IR and NMR spectra.

It thus follows that not one of the formulas (I–VI) represents the antibiotics of the enniatin group and the problem of their structure must be still considered to be unresolved.

I shall now dwell very briefly on some of the first results obtained in our laboratory by Vinogradova, Feigina and Aldanova concerning the structure of the depsipeptide antibiotics valinomycin and amidomycin (Table 4).

Valinomycin was isolated in 1955 by Brockmann's group and was assigned a cyclo-octadepsipeptide structure from studies of the degradation products. Of the two possible formulas (XLVI) and (XLVII), preference was given to the former [8]. The antibiotic amidomycin was isolated in 1957 by Canadian investigators [9] and was assigned the structure (XLVIII).

(XLVI) (L*-L-D-D-L-L-D-D), R=R″=CH₃, R′=R‴=CH(CH₃)₂
(XLVII) (L*-L-L-L-D-D-D-D), R=R′=CH₃, R″=R‴=CH(CH₃)₂
(XLVIII) (all D), R=R′=R″=R‴=CH(CH₃)₂

As part of our program concerning the cyclic depsipeptides we undertook the synthesis of cyclodepsipeptides (XLVI) and (XLVIII). The corresponding linear octadepsipeptides (XLIX, L, LI) had been prepared earlier [10].

TABLE 4

Antibiotic	Molecular formula	M.p.°	$[\alpha]_D^{20}$
Valinomycin	$C_{36}H_{60}O_{12}N_4$	190°	$+31°$ $(c\ 1{\cdot}6,\ C_6H_6)$
Amidomycin	$C_{40}H_{68}O_{12}N_4$	192	$+19{\cdot}2°$ $(c\ 1{\cdot}2,\ \text{EtOH})$

Removal of the protective groups led to the open octadepsipeptides (LII) and (LIII), of which cyclization by the chloride method gave the respective cyclo-depsipeptides (XLVI) and (XLVIII) in low yield (5–10 per cent) (Scheme 3). Curiously enough, the same cyclo-octadepsipeptides (XLVI) and (XLVIII) also form (alongside the cyclotetradepsipeptides) on cyclization of the corresponding open tetradepsipeptides. This phenomenon is at present being investigated in further detail.

The structures of the resultant compounds (XLVI) and (XLVIII) were established in the same way as that of the enniatin cyclodepsipeptides. Analytical data and molecular weight determinations (isothermal distillation and thermoelectrical methods) gave values corresponding to the respective formulae. On alkaline hydrolysis of XLVI and XLVIII the corresponding hydroxyacids (LIV) and (LV) were isolated, identical with those obtained on counter-synthesis by the azide method, issuing from L-lactic acid (LVI) or D-α-hydroxyisovaleric acid (XXXII) and L- or D-valine.

Compounds (XLVI) and (XLVIII) possess greatly different properties from those of the corresponding antibiotics (Table 5). In the case of cyclo-

TABLE 5

Comp.	Molecular formula	M.p.°	$[\alpha]_D^{20}$	Molecular weight
XLVI	$C_{36}H_{60}O_{12}N_4$ (740·8)	218–219°	$-6°$ $(c\ 1{\cdot}0,\ C_6H_6)$	748†, 773‡
XLVIII	$C_{40}H_{68}O_{12}N_4$ (797)	234–236	$+131°$ $(c\ 0{\cdot}75,\ \text{CHCl}_3)$	795†, 767‡

† Isothermal distillation in acetone.
‡ Thermoelectrical method.

depsipeptide (XLVI) this was shown by direct comparison with a sample of valinomycin kindly placed at our disposal by Prof. Brockmann (mixed m.p., chromatographic behaviour, etc.).

Compounds (XLVI) and (XLVIII) display no activity against *Mycobacterium tuberculosis* and *Candida albicans*, respectively, at concentrations up to 200 γ/ml, whereas the specimen of valinomycin was active under the conditions prevailing in our tests at concentrations of 35 γ/ml.

SCHEME 3

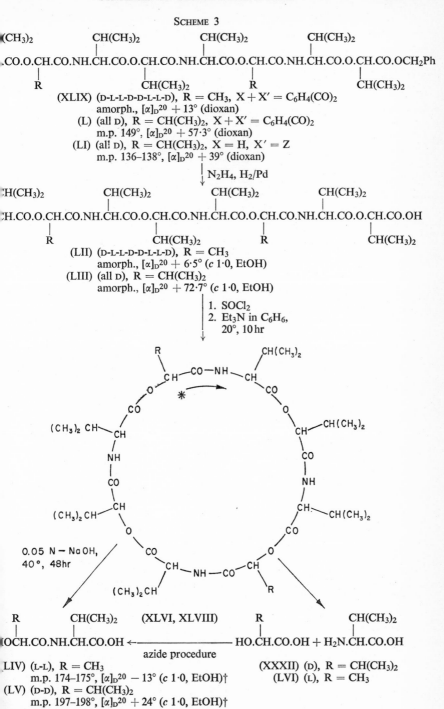

(CH₃)₂   CH(CH₃)₂   CH(CH₃)₂   CH(CH₃)₂
  | | | |
.CO.O.CH.CO.NH.CH.CO.O.CH.CO.NH.CH.CO.O.CH.CO.NH.CH.CO.O.CH.CO.OCH₂Ph
  | | | |
  R   CH(CH₃)₂   R   CH(CH₃)₂

(XLIX) (D-L-L-D-D-L-L-D), R = CH₃, X + X′ = C₆H₄(CO)₂
amorph., [α]$_D^{20}$ + 13° (dioxan)
(L) (all D), R = CH(CH₃)₂, X + X′ = C₆H₄(CO)₂
m.p. 149°, [α]$_D^{20}$ + 57·3° (dioxan)
(LI) (all D), R = CH(CH₃)₂, X = H, X′ = Z
m.p. 136–138°, [α]$_D^{20}$ + 39° (dioxan)

N₂H₄, H₂/Pd

H(CH₃)₂   CH(CH₃)₂   CH(CH₃)₂   CH(CH₃)₂
  | | | |
H.CO.O.CH.CO.NH.CH.CO.O.CH.CO.NH.CH.CO.O.CH.CO.NH.CH.CO.O.CH.CO.OH
  | | | |
  R   CH(CH₃)₂   R   CH(CH₃)₂

(LII) (D-L-L-D-D-L-L-D), R = CH₃
amorph., [α]$_D^{20}$ + 6·5° (c 1·0, EtOH)
(LIII) (all D), R = CH(CH₃)₂
amorph., [α]$_D^{20}$ + 72·7° (c 1·0, EtOH)

1. SOCl₂
2. Et₃N in C₆H₆,
   20°, 10 hr

0.05 N — NaOH,
40°, 48hr

(XLVI, XLVIII)

azide procedure

R   CH(CH₃)₂   R   CH(CH₃)₂
  | | | |
OCH.CO.NH.CH.CO.OH ←———————————— HO.CH.CO.OH + H₂N.CH.CO.OH

(LIV) (L-L), R = CH₃
m.p. 174–175°, [α]$_D^{20}$ − 13° (c 1·0, EtOH)†
(LV) (D-D), R = CH(CH₃)₂
m.p. 197–198°, [α]$_D^{20}$ + 24° (c 1·0, EtOH)†

(XXXII) (D), R = CH(CH₃)₂
(LVI) (L), R = CH₃

† Dicyclohexylammonium salt

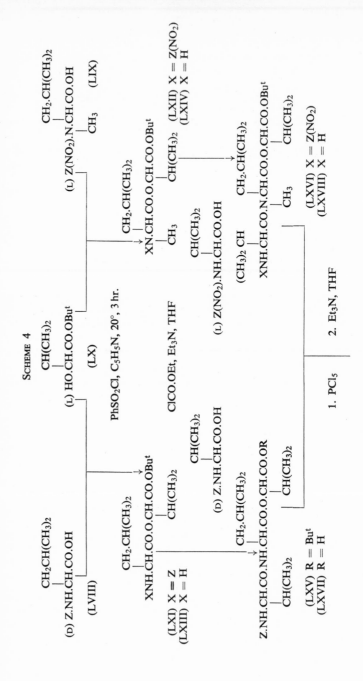

Scheme 4

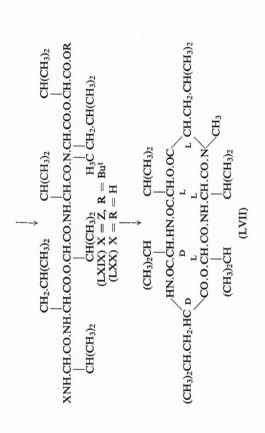

From all the above said it follows that formula (XLVIII) does not correspond to amidomycin and that at least one of the formulae proposed for
valinomycin, namely (XLVI), has not received confirmation.

Hence not one of the cyclodepsipeptide structures proposed for this group
of antibiotics has withstood synthetic test. Naturally this calls for precaution
in the assignment of such structures to newly discovered naturally occurring
compounds. However, since the compounds synthesized yield on degradation the same, highly characteristic products as the natural antibiotics, one
may suppose that the latter differ in structure from the cyclodepsipeptides
only by some minor details. Work on the elucidation of the structure of
these unique antibiotics is being continued.†

When we had discovered that the cyclodepsipeptide structure had been
incorrectly assigned to a number of antibiotics, the question arose whether
in general cyclodepsipeptides occur as such in nature and whether such
structures assigned to other natural compounds actually did correspond to
the facts. Therefore we undertook the synthesis of a number of other cyclodepsipeptides, in particular of sporidesmolide I, isolated in 1960 from among
the metabolites of the fungus *Sporidesmium bakeri* [11].

We synthesized the cyclohexadepsipeptide (LVII) corresponding to the
structure proposed for sporidesmolide I as follows (Scheme 4). Condensation
of benzyloxycarbonyl-D-leucine (LVIII) or of *p*-nitrobenzyloxycarbonyl-*N*-
methyl-L-leucine (LIX) with tert.-butyl L-α-hydroxyisovalerate (LX) by the
mixed anhydride method gave the corresponding tert.-butyl esters of benzyl-
oxycarbonyl-D-leucyl- or *p*-nitrobenzyloxycarbonyl-*N*-methyl-L-leucyl-L-α-
hydroxyisovaleric acids (LXI) or (LXII). Hydrogenolysis of (LXI) and
(LXII) yielded the respective amino-esters (LXIII) and (LXIV), which on
reaction with benzyloxycarbonyl-D-valine or *p*-nitrobenzyloxycarbonyl-L-
valine afforded the tridepsipeptides (LXV) and (LXVI), respectively.
Removal of the tert.-butyl protective group from (LXV) gave the acid
(LXVII); on the other hand, hydrogenolysis of (LXVI) led to the amino-
ester (LXVIII). The fragments (LXVII) and (LXVIII) were then joined by an
amide bond with the aid of the chloride method to give the protected hexa-
depsipeptide (LXIX); this was converted to the hydrobromide of D-valyl-D-
leucyl-L-α-hydroxyisovaleryl-L-valyl-*N*-methyl-L-leucyl-L-α-hydroxyisovaleric
acid (LXX), which was then cyclized by the chloride method to the cyclodepsipeptide (LVII).

We were very happy to find that the properties of the resultant compound
purified only chromatographically were identical with those of sporidesmolide I. It had the following constants: m.p. 255–257°, $[\alpha]_D^{20}$ −210°

---

† We have recently synthesized two cyclopolymer homologues of compound (II)—
the corresponding cyclo-hexa- and cyclo-octadepsipeptide. Of these the first was found
to be identical with enniatin B and the second to possess antibiotic activity commensurate
with the first.

(c 0·5, $CHCl_3$) which were the same as those reported in the literature for a number of specimens of sporidesmolide I [12].

Hence, synthesis of this metabolite completely confirmed the validity of the formula proposed for it by Russell. Now we can answer with certainty the questions posed above as to the existence in nature of cyclodepsipeptides.

Although we entertain no doubt that we have in our hands the true synthetic counterpart of sporidesmolide I, we naturally consider it necessary to make a direct comparison of our product with the natural substance. In the very near future we intend to send a specimen of our compound to Russell and hope to obtain from him a sample of his product, so that by our combined efforts we could put the "finishing touches" to this problem. The experimental details of this synthesis will appear either in *Tetrahedron Letters* or in a Soviet journal.†

REFERENCES

1. M. M. SHEMYAKIN, *Angew. Chem.* **71**, 741 (1959); **72**, 342 (1960); *Uspekhi Khimii* (*SSSR*), **31**, 269 (1962).
2. E. GÄUMANN, S. ROTH, L. ETTLINGER, Pl. A. PLATTNER, U. NAGER, *Experientia*, **3**, 202 (1947); Pl. A. PLATTNER, U. NAGER, *Experientia*, **3**, 325 (1947); Pl. A. PLATTNER, U. NAGER, A. BOLLER, *Helv. Chim. Acta* **31**, 594 (1948).
3. Pl. A. PLATTNER and U. NAGER, *Helv. Chim. Acta* **31**, 665, 2192 (1948).
4. Pl. A. PLATTNER and U. NAGER, *Helv. Chim. Acta* **31**, 2203 (1948).
5. A. H. COOK, S. F. COX, T. H. FARMER and M. S. LACEY, *Nature* **160**, 31 (1947).
6. A. H. COOK, S. F. COX and T. H. FARMER, *Nature* **162**, 61 (1948); *J. Chem. Soc.* **1949**, 1022.
7. G. E. HALL, *Chem. and Ind.* 1272 (1960).
8. H. BROCKMANN and G. SCHMIDT-KASTNER, *Chem. Ber.* **88**, 57 (1955); H. BROCKMANN and H. GEEREN, *Liebig's Ann. Chem.* **603**, 216 (1957).
9. W. A. TABER and L. C. VINING, *Bacteriol. Proc.* (Soc. Am. Bacteriologists) 70 (1957); *Can. J. Microbiol.* **3**, 953 (1957); L. C. VINING and W. A. TABER, *Can. J. Chem.* **35**, 1109 (1957).
10. M. M. SHEMYAKIN, E. I. VINOGRADOVA, M. Yu. FEIGINA, N. A. ALDANOVA, V. A. OLADKINA and L. A. SHCHUKINA, *Doklady Akad. Nauk, S.S.S.R.* **140**, 387 (1961).
11. D. W. RUSSELL, *Biochem. Biophys. Acta* **45**, 411 (1960).
12. D. W. RUSSELL, R. L. SYNGE, A. TAYLOR and E. P. WHITE, *J. Chem. Soc.* **1962**, 554.

† Recently we have established the identity of synthetic and natural compounds by their direct comparison (*Izv. Akad. Nauk SSSR, Otd. Khim. Nauk* 1699 (1962)).

TAUTOMERISM OF
HYDROXYACYLCYCLOPEPTIDES

V. K. Antonov, A. M. Shkrob and M. M. Shemyakin

Institute for Chemistry of Natural Products,
U.S.S.R. Academy of Sciences, Moscow, U.S.S.R.

At the Basel Peptide Symposium two years ago we discussed the possibility of isomeric or tautomeric conversions of ergot alkaloids of peptide type [1, 2].

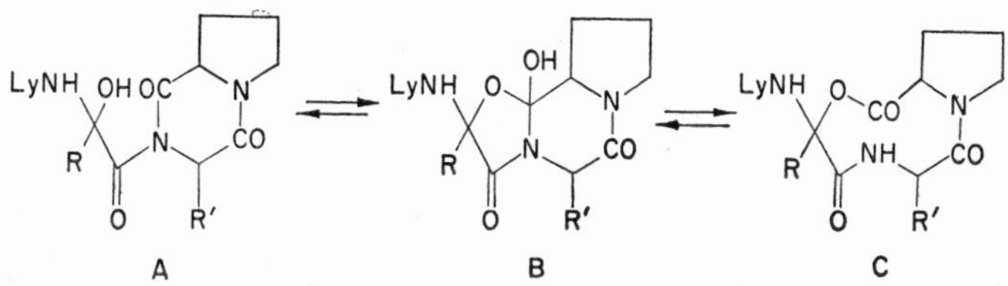

Ly = Lysergyl

The same idea lay at the basis of the brilliant synthesis of ergotamine and its analogues by Hofmann *et al.* [3, 4]. Hofmann's data and our own findings left no doubt as to the correctness of Stoll's cyclol formula for ergotamine. The problems of cyclolization, however, have a much more general character, extending far beyond the domains of ergot alkaloid synthesis. We are now engaged in investigating the cyclolization reaction occurring on intramolecular addition to the amide group of such nucleophilic residues as, for example, OH or NH_2.

X = O, NH

Cyclol structures can form also in other ways, such as transannular amide-amide or amide-ester reaction in cyclic peptides or depsipeptides. We are also exploring the possibility of reactions of the type B ⇄ C but, these studies not being completed, we shall not dwell upon them here.

It should be noted that cyclol formation is the underlying principle of Wrinch's hypothesis of peptide structure [5] which has, however, received no experimental verification. But even in cases when the existence of cyclol intermediates is more firmly based, as in the $N \rightleftarrows O$, $N \rightleftarrows S$ or $N \rightleftarrows N$ migrations of the acyl residue [6, 7] or in the Brenner rearrangement [8], owing to their instability they have never been isolated.

We assumed the stability of cyclol to be dependent not only upon the steric specificities of the molecule, as for instance in ergotamine, but also upon the electrophilicity of the amide carbonyl. Clearly a decrease in electron density at the amide carbon in such activated amides as N-acylamides, should in itself facilitate the formation of relatively stable cyclols. We, therefore, deemed it possible to find the unusual structure of the peptide moiety of ergotamine in much simpler compounds.

Quite obviously the " gist " of the problem lies in the unequivocal detection of the cyclol structures, such as by means of concrete spectral assignments. Regrettably, these were not reported in the communications by Hofmann et al.

The objects of our study were N-hydroxyacyldiketopiperazines and N-hydroxyacyllactams. The corresponding O-benzyl derivatives were synthesized by acylation of diketopiperazines and lactams with benzyloxyacyl chlorides in boiling benzene or toluene. The infrared spectra of the resulting compounds exhibited absorption bands in the region $1710-1740 \mathrm{cm}^{-1}$, characteristic of the —CO.NCO— group [9, 10]. Compounds I, II and V moreover possessed a band in the $1690 \mathrm{cm}^{-1}$ region corresponding to the glycyl or leucyl carbonyl in the diketopiperazine moiety of the molecule.

(I) R = CH$_2$Ph,
   R′ = CH$_2$.CHMe$_2$
(II) R = CH$_2$.Ph, R′ = H
(III) R = H,
   R′ = CH$_2$.CHMe$_2$
(IV) R = H, R′ = H

(V) R = CH$_2$.Ph
(VI) R = H

(VII) R = CH$_2$.Ph
(VIII) R = H

(IX) R = CH$_2$.Ph,
   n = 1
(X) R = CH$_2$.Ph,
   n = 2
(XI) R = CH$_3$, n = 1
(XII) R = H, n = 1
(XIII) R = H, n = 2

(XIV) R = C
(XV) R = H

(XVI) R=H,
   R′=CH$_2$.CHMe$_2$
(XVII) R=H, R′=H
(XVIII) R=CH$_3$, R′=H

(XIX)

(XX)

(XXI) R=H, n = 1
(XXII) R=H, n = 2
(XXIII) R=CH$_3$, n = 1

(XXI

Hydrogenolysis of these compounds in tetrahydrofuran solution in the presence of palladium-black leads to the corresponding hydroxy derivatives, of which many were found to transform into cyclols. Since the cyclization reaction was studied in greatest detail with compounds IV and XII, we shall first describe these studies and then touch upon the reactions of the other compounds of this type.

N-Glycollylprolylglycyldiketopiperazine (IV) was obtained in the form of viscous oil and characterized by its conversion into α-naphthylurethane (XXV). When kept for 10–15 days in tetrahydrofuran or dioxan solution IV converted to the cyclol XVII, isolated in the crystalline form. The structure of the latter was proved by transformation into the methyl derivative (XVIII). On acid hydrolysis of XVIII only glycollic acid but no sarcosine or methoxy-acetic acid is detected, demonstrating its cyclol structure. In the infrared spectra of both XVII and XVIII a band appears in the region $1675 \, \text{cm}^{-1}$ instead of the $1695 \, \text{cm}^{-1}$ band displayed by IV and XXV. This shift in frequency of the glycyl carbonyl, evidently due to deformation of the six-membered ring, was found to be a very convenient indicator of cyclization in N-glycollyldiketopiperazines. The frequency of the oxazolidinone carbonyl [11] was found to coincide with that of the —CO.NCO— group.

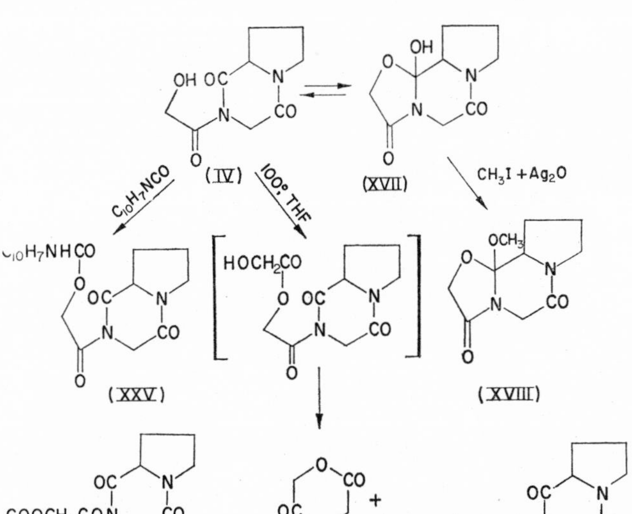

On dissolving XVII in tetrahydrofuran or dioxan it is partially converted into IV, the reaction being accelerated by traces of water. This reaction is reversible and the spectral pictures during the transitions IV → XVII and XVII → IV with time become more and more similar to each other (see

Fig. 1). Complete identity is impeded by the occurrence of side reactions. Thus the high concentration of the open form in fresh solutions of IV permits intermolecular acylation to take place, leading to the formation of a glycollide (XXVII) and possibly of some polymer (XXVIII). However, we could not observe the ester band of the polymer at $1760\,\text{cm}^{-1}$ where it is displayed in the case of N-acetoxyacetylglycylprolyldiketopiperazine (XXVI).

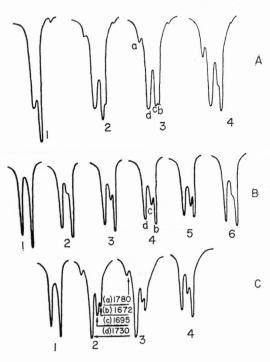

FIG. 1.   Carbonyl region of the infrared spectra of IV and XVII in THF A: 1. Solution of IV following hydrogenolysis; 2, 3 and 4. After 5, 10 and 15 days (20°); B: 1. Fresh solution of XVII; 2, 3, 4 and 5. After 30, 60, 90 and 120 min (35°); 6. Control (240 min at 20°); C: 1. Fresh solution of XVII; 2. After heating to 100° (15 min); 3. After cooling and keeping for 12 hr at 35°; 4. Control (12 hr at 35°).

Another observation is worthy of mention. The specific rotation of solutions of IV was found to diminish gradually at a rate commensurable with that of the spectral changes. The crystalline cyclol XVII isolated was found to be devoid of optical activity (measurements made in the range of 290–600 mμ). On hydrolysis with 20 per cent hydrochloric acid the hydrolysate was also found to be optically inactive, i.e. racemic proline is formed. We are at present engaged in a study of the mechanism of the racemization.

In all the above cases cyclolization is associated with the disappearance of the chromophore —CO.NCO—. Indeed, establishment of the equilibrium
|
IV ⇄ XVII on dissolution of XVII in dioxan is accompanied by an appreciable increase in absorption at $\lambda_{max} = 215\,m\mu$ (Table 1). Therefore, when it

TABLE 1. ULTRAVIOLET SPECTRA OF DIOXAN SOLUTIONS†

Compound	$\lambda_{max}^{init.}$	$\varepsilon^{init.}$	$\lambda_{max}^{fin.}$	$\varepsilon^{fin.}$	Time of observ. (hr)
II	214·5	11,500			
V	213	10,800			
VI	216	7500	214	5650	24
VII	215	13,700			
VIII	< 214	1700 (214 mμ)			
IX	216	11,300			
X	214	11,100			
XI	220·5	9500			
XIII (XXXII?)	< 214	750 (214 mμ)			
XIV	215	15,800			
XV	220	7240			
XVII	214	3280	215	4210	24
XVIII	220	1150			
XXI	221	300	222	1600	2
XXIII	220	160			
XXVI	219	7000			
N-Acetylpyrrolidone	215	10,700			
N-Acetylpiperidone	217·5	8500			
N-Acetylcaprolactam	218·5	9350			

† Spectra were obtained with the aid of Zeiss VSU-1 or Hitachi EPS-2 spectrophotometers at cell thickness 0·5–1 cm, and are given only for the 220 mμ region.

was found that fresh solutions of the crystalline compound obtained on hydrogenolysis of IX possess negligible absorption in comparison with N-acetylpiperidone [10] we assigned the cyclol structure (XXI) to the former. This was confirmed by comparison of the methyl derivatives (XXIII) and (XI). Further, we found that in dioxan solutions of (XXI) absorption at $\lambda_{max} = 222\,m\mu$ rapidly increases from 300 to 1600. Equilibrium value was reached approximately within an hour. This bears witness to tautomeric equilibration also in the present case.

Further evidence for the presence of the open form (XII) in solution of XXI is to be found in the isolation of 1-(α-naphthyl)-oxazolidine-2,5-dione (XXX) on reaction with α-naphthyl isocyanate [12] or of methyl N-methoxyacetyl-4-aminovalerate (XXIX) on reaction with methyl iodide in the presence of silver oxide. As in the case of XVII, heating of solutions of (XXI) leads to the formation of some glycollide.

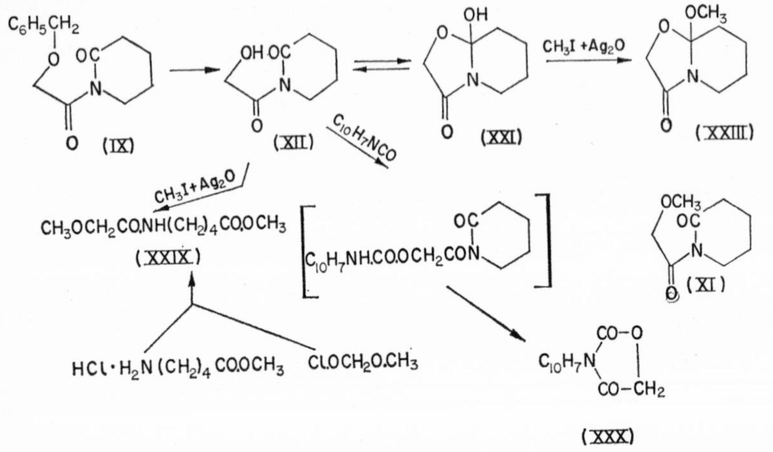

Following this, we began a study of the dependence of cyclol formation upon steric and electronic factors. A comparison of the infrared spectra of ergotamine, of its analogue (XXXI) [4] (the synthesis of which was reproduced in our laboratory by K. P. Butin), and of the leucine derivative XVI

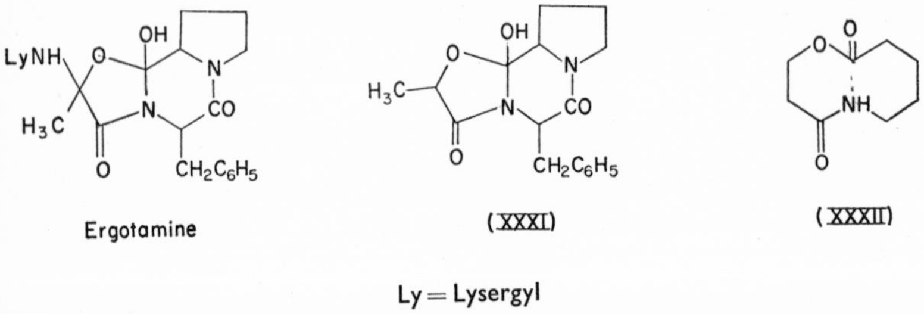

Ergotamine   (XXXI)   (XXXII)

Ly = Lysergyl

with that of XVII, showed that all these compounds possessed a cyclol structure (Table 2). However, their solutions showed no signs of tautomeric conversion. Nevertheless, prolonged heating of the tetrahydrofuran solution of XXXI at 100° leads to the appearance of a weak band at 1780 cm^{-1}, evidently belonging to the lactolide, which can arise only from the open form.

In the crystalline state N-glycollylsarcosylglycyldiketopiperazine (VI) exists in the open form, but in solution partial cyclization to XIX is manifested by a weakening of the absorption at $\lambda_{max} = 215$ mμ and the appearance of a band at 1676 cm^{-1}. The ultraviolet spectra of solutions of N-glycollyl-caprolactam (VIII) and N-glycollylpyrrolidone (XV) show that with these

TABLE 2. CONSTANTS AND INFRARED DATA

Compound	M.p.°	B.p.°	$[\alpha]_D$ c 1 (THF)	Carbonyl absorption bands (0·5% THF solution, cm⁻¹)
Ergotamine				1736, 1669
I	112°		+ 103	1720, 1680
II	150		− 43·6	1725, 1694
IV	Oil		− 53·6	1730, 1695
V	133			1723, 1693
VI	120			1730, 1693
VII	− 20	164–165° 0·1 mm		1705
VIII	Oil			1719
IX	41			1708
X	Oil	156–158 0·05 mm		1698
XI	28			1708
XIII (XXXII?)	110			1745, 1689 (1545) (nujol: 1720, 1657 1645)
XIV	108			1738, 1711
XV	69			1745, 1700
XVI	117			1730, 1662
XVII	148		0 ± 1°	1730, 1672
XVIII	173			1737, 1678
XXI	97			1719
XXIII	Oil	45–48 0·02 mm		1728
XXV	220 dec.			1745, 1725, 1695
XXVI	111·5		− 22·0	1760, 1728, 1693
XXIX	+ 2			(mull: 1745, 1678 (1545))
XXX	143			1825, 1760
XXXI	175		− 22·1	1732, 1664

compounds no noticeable formation of the cyclol forms (XX) and (XXIV) takes place. As for the product obtained by hydrogenolysis of X, however the infrared and ultraviolet spectra showed that it was not the expected XIII. We are at present investigating the question of whether it is a cyclol (XXII) or has a macrocyclic structure (XXXII).†

Among the N-glycollyllactams we have investigated, cyclolization was revealed only in the case of piperidone derivative (XII). It seems to us that this may be placed in analogy with the dependence of hemiacetal formation upon the size of the ring [13]. One can see from the Table 3 that among normal ring compounds such tendency is maximum in cyclohexanone.

One may assume that in the case of macrocyclic N-glycollyllactams the

† Our recent investigations showed that the formation of XXXII took place indeed. Moreover, we found the same transformations to occur with N-glycollyl- and N-β-hydroxy-propionyl-lactams (diketopiperazines) if the resulting rings are more than ninemembered.

tendency towards cyclolization approaches that of the acyclic systems, the study of which we are at present carrying out.†

TABLE 3.   DISSOCIATION CONSTANTS OF HEMIACETALS
OF CYCLIC KETONES [13]

Size of ring	5	6	7	8
$K_{25°}$	15·3	2·1	53·5	268

Hence we were able to show that the tendency to form cyclols is not a specific attribute of ergot alkaloids and can be observed in even the simplest of such molecules. At the same time the stability of the cyclols is greatly dependent upon their structure.

We should like to say in conclusion that in recent years cyclolization has been advanced by various authors to explain the unusual properties of such compounds as bacitracin A [14], lycomarasmin [15] or aspartylserine peptides, the latter evidently forming part of the active centres of esterases [16]. We hope that further elaboration of the conditions of formation and of the chemistry of stable cyclols will aid in the solution of these as well as the more general problems of intramolecular interaction in peptides.

ACKNOWLEDGMENT

Infrared spectra were performed by L. B. Senyavina (of the Institute's Physico-Chemical Laboratory under the direction of Dr Yu. N. Sheinker).

REFERENCES

1. V. K. ANTONOV, G. A. RAVDEL and M. M. SHEMYAKIN, Chimia 14, 374 (1960).
2. G. A. RAVDEL, N. A. KRIT, L. A. SHCHUKINA and M. M. SHEMYAKIN, Doklady. Akad. Nauk SSSR 137, 1377 (1961).
3. A. HOFMANN, A. J. FREY and H. OTT, Experientia 17, 206 (1961).
4. A. HOFMANN, A. J. FREY, H. OTT and J. RUTSCHMANN, 4th Europ. Symp. on Peptides, Moscow, 1961, Zhur. Vsesoyuz. Khim. Obshchestva im. D. I. Mendeleeva 7, 468 (1962).
5. D. WRINCH, Chemical Aspects of the Structure of Small Peptides, Munksgaard, Copenhagen, 1960.
6. L. COHEN and B. WITKOP, Angew. Chem. 73, 253 (1961).
7. A. B. SILAEV, G. S. KATRUKHA and N. A. KUZ'MINA, Zhur. Obshchei Khim. 31, 3111 (1961).
8. H. BRENNER, CIBA Foundation Symposium on Amino Acids and Peptides with Antimetabolic Activity, London, 1958, p. 157.
9. H. K. HALL and R. ZBINDEN, J. Amer. Chem. Soc. 80, 6428 (1958).
10. C. M. LEE and W. D. KUMLER, J. Amer. Chem. Soc. 84, 565 (1962).
11. K. EICHENBERGER, E. GANZ and J. DRUEY, Helv. Chim. Acta 38, 284 (1955).
12. J. W. CLARK-LEWIS, Chem. Rev. 58, 91 (1958)
13. O. H. WHEELER, J. Amer. Chem. Soc. 79, 4191 (1957).
14. D. WRINCH, Nature, 179, 536 (1957).
15. P. LIECHTI, Doctoral Thesis, Zürich, 1958.
16. S. BERNHARD, J. Cellular Comp. Physiol. 54, Suppl. 1, 252 (1959).

† Now, we succeeded to observe transformations similar to that of the type A → C in the acyclic series, for instance, the isomerization of N-glycollyl-N-methylacetamide into acetoxyacetyl-N-methylamide.

A SYNTHETIC CYCLOL TRIPEPTIDE

D. S. JONES, G. W. KENNER and R. C. SHEPPARD

The Robert Robinson Laboratories, University of Liverpool, England

THE oxazolone (I), m.p. 82–85°, of α-methylalanyl-α-methylalanyl-α-methyl-alanine was obtained by hydrogenolysis of the benzyloxycarbonyl derivative. Solutions of this oxazolone in ethyl acetate gradually deposited a crystalline compound (79 per cent), which was freed from contaminant polymer by recrystallization from ethanol/ether. The product does not melt below 300°, but it sublimes completely with loss of water. The imidazolone structure (III) is assigned to the sublimate, m.p. 255° (sealed tube), on the basis of mass spectrometry (M.W. 237) and infrared spectrometry (ν_{max} 1730, 1670, 1640 cm^{-1}, no amide II band). Accordingly the initial product (ν_{max} 1685, 1632 cm^{-1}) must be the cyclol (II). Inspection of molecular models shows that this can be formed by a concerted electronic shift, breaking the oxazolone ring while two new bonds are formed, and subsequent prototropy.

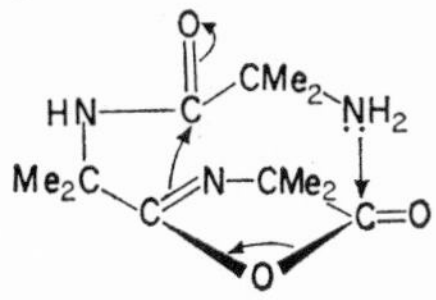

I

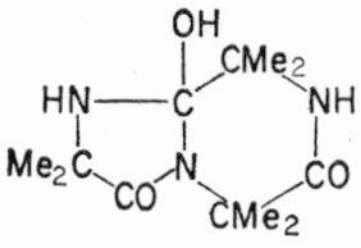

II

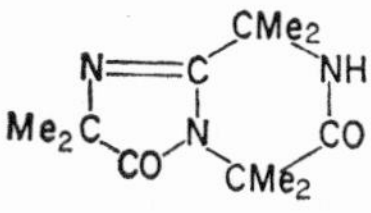

III

PROPERTIES OF MODEL COMPOUNDS RELATED TO GLYCOPEPTIDES

V. A. Derevitskaya, L. M. Likhosherstov and N. K. Kochetkov

Institute for Chemistry of Natural Products,
U.S.S.R. Academy of Sciences, Moscow, U.S.S.R.

At the previous Symposium we reported the synthesis of glycopeptide models, O-aminoacylglucose derivatives from amino-acids and simple di- and tripeptides.

Investigation of the stability of the ester bond of these model compounds may help to improve the methods for the isolation of natural glycopeptides, and their structural analysis. O-aminoacyl derivatives readily undergo solvolysis in water and methanol, due to the lability of the ester bond. We have undertaken a more detailed investigation of the effect of the nature of the aminoacyl residue on the stability of the ester bond. Therefore we examined the hydrolysis of O-aminoacylglucose derivatives of glycine, alanine, valine, norleucine, β-alanine and ε-aminocaproic acid. The stability of 6-O-diglycyl- and 6-O-triglycyl-glucose was also studied in order to elucidate the influence of a peptide chain ; 6-O-(N-benzyloxycarbonylglycyl)-glucose lacking a free amino group was taken as a standard substance. The stability was determined in buffer solutions in the range of pH from 1·2 to 8·0. The The O-aminoacyl derivatives used in the experiment were not isolated in a pure state but obtained in appropriate buffer solutions by quantitative hydrogenolysis of the N-benzyloxycarbonyl compounds. The temperature of the reaction mixture was maintained at 37° and aliquots were periodically subjected to paper electrophoresis at 40–45 V/cm for 10–15 min. The spots were developed by means of silver nitrate spray and evaluated densitometrically or by visual comparison with a series of standards. The stability was calculated in terms of half-lives. Most of our stubstances in 0·01 M concentration undergo decay independently of the pH-value, at different rates according to the common scheme of ester bond hydrolysis. We could not detect any N-glycoside formation, intramolecular aminolysis of the ester bond, or acid hydrolysis of peptide bonds in the case of 6-O-diglycylglucose and 6-O-triglycylglucose. The only exception is in the former case, when intramolecular aminolysis of the ester bond results in the formation of diketopiperazine in the range of pH from 8·0 to 6·0; glycylglycine is produced only in negligible amount. The dependence of half-lives of the aminoacyl-derivatives on the pH of the medium at 37° for 0·01 M solutions is plotted in the following figures (Fig. 1).

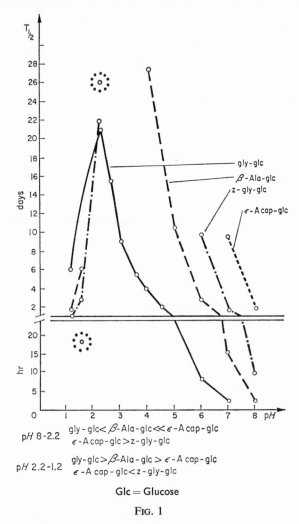

pH 8-2.2   gly - glc < β-Ala-glc ≪ ε -A cap - glc
            ε -A cap - glc > z - gly - glc

pH 2.2 -1.2   gly-glc > β-Ala - glc > ε -A cap - glc
               ε -A cap - glc < z - gly - glc

Glc = Glucose

Fig. 1

All the compounds tested exhibit distinct stability maxima in the range of pH between 4·5 and 2·2. It is likely that the hydrolysis in the range of pH 8–4 is due to nucleophilic catalysis, and in the range of pH 2·2–1·2 to electrophilic catalysis. In the nucleophilic catalysis region, the presence of the free amino group near the ester bond greatly promotes the hydrolysis, as can be seen by comparison of the curve for 6-O-benzyloxycarbonylglycyl-glucose with that for the same compound with the free α-amino group. The stability of compounds increases when the amino group is removed from the ester bond environment (Fig. 1) so 6-*O*-β-alanylglucose is much more stable than 6-*O*-glycylglucose, and 6-*O*-ε-aminocaproyl-glucose is even more

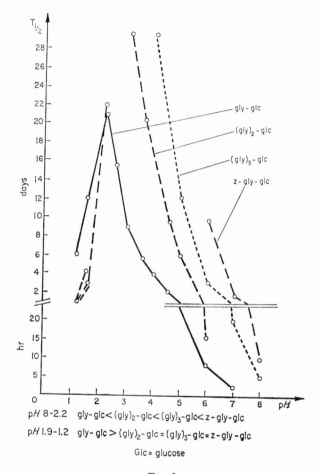

Fig. 2

stable than the benzyloxycarbonyl-derivative, evidently owing to the influence of the α-amide group.

The stability of the ester bonds of peptide derivatives increases in the following sequence (Fig. 2): 6-*O*-glycyl- < 6-*O*-diglycyl- < 6-*O*-triglycyl-glucose. The free amino group effect is large even in the case of triglycyl-glucose, which is less stable than 6-*O*-benzyloxycarbonylglycyl-glucose. The structure of the aminoacyl residue causes a marked effect on the stability of the ester bond (Fig. 3). The stability of the compounds tested increases in the sequence:

6-*O*-alanyl- < 6-*O*-glycyl- < 6-*O*-norleucyl- < 6-*O*-valyl-glucose (Fig. 3)

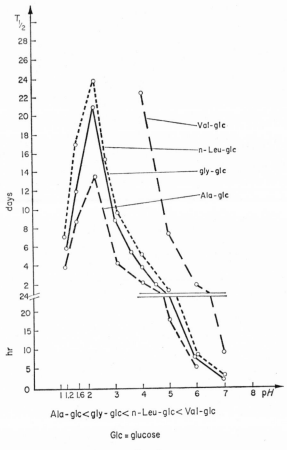

Ala-glc < gly-glc < n-Leu-glc < Val-glc

Glc = glucose

Fig. 3

The lower stability of 6-*O*-alanylglucose compared with 6-*O*-glycylglucose must be due to the inductive effect caused by the methyl group. The stabilizing effect in case of the norleucyl residue can be explained by steric hindrance. Such steric hindrance plays the most important role in the case of 6-*O*-valyl-glucose.

In the electrophilic catalysis region the free amino group causes an opposite, stabilizing effect. This can be deduced from the fact that 6-*O*-benzyloxy-carbonylglycyl-glucose is less stable than 6-*O*-glycylglucose (Fig. 1). The nearer the free amino group lies to the ester bond, the greater is the stability of the compound. The stability decreases in the sequence 6-*O*-glycyl- > 6-*O*-β-alanyl- > 6-*O*-ε-aminocaproyl-glucose.

The α-amide group has a stabilizing effect, 6-*O*-ε-aminocaproyl-glucose being less stable than 6-*O*-benzyloxycarbonylglycyl-glucose. A similar regularity is observed in case of peptide derivatives (Fig. 2).

The structure of the aminoacyl residue in the acid region causes as well a marked effect on the ester bond stability. The sequence of increasing stability in this case is the same as for nucleophilic catalysis (Fig. 3).

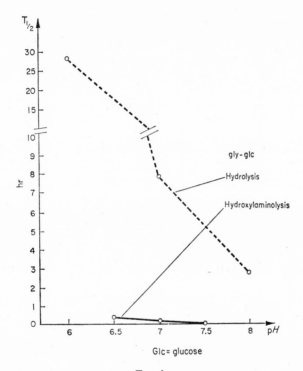

Fig. 4

The steric effect in the hydrolysis of 6-*O*-norleucylglucose and 6-*O*-valylglucose becomes still greater, so that the half-life of the latter is more than 30 days.

As one can see from the figures, all the compounds tested exhibit stability maxima in the region of pH from 4·5 to 2·2; for α- and β-amino-acids the maximum lies at pH 2·2–2·6; for 6-*O*-aminocaproyl-glucose at 4·5. Such deviations must be due to mixed nucleophilic and electrophilic hydrolysis near these maxima, the situation of the optimum point being dependent on the sensitivity of the substance to one or the other type of catalysis.

We investigated also the stability of O-aminoacyl compounds in presence of hydroxylamine. Half-lives of these compounds as functions of pH at a 50-fold excess of hydroxylamine at 20° are represented in the following

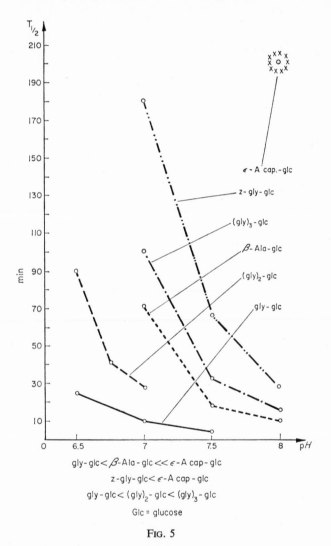

gly-glc $<$ β-Ala-glc $<<$ ϵ-A cap-glc

z-gly-glc $<$ ϵ-A cap-glc

gly-glc $<$ (gly)$_2$-glc $<$ (gly)$_3$-glc

Glc = glucose

FIG. 5

figures. The cleavage by hydroxylamine proceeds much faster than does hydrolysis (Fig. 4). The reaction follows, however, all the regularities noted for nucleophilic hydrolysis: the stability increases when the amino group is removed further away from the ester bond in sequence: 6-O-glycyl- $<$ 6-O-β-alanyl- $<$ 6-O-ϵ-aminocaproyl-glucose (Fig. 5); the first is less stable than is 6-*O*-ε-aminocaproyl-glucose, as a result of the action of the α-amide group.   A similar increase of stability occurs on lengthening the peptide chain, in the sequence: 6-*O*-glycyl- < 6-*O*-diglycyl- < 6-*O*-triglycyl-glucose (Fig. 5).   The rate of ester bond cleavage increases at higher concentrations of hydroxylamine.

It may be noted here that the data of the present work concerning the stability of model compounds, and particularly the results of hydroxylaminolysis, are proving helpful in our structural analysis of blood group Substance A glycopeptides.

DARSTELLUNG DER
GLYKOSYLESTER VON AMINOSÄUREN

L. Kisfaludy und M. Löw

Gedeon Richter Factory, Budapest, Hungary

Nach der Synthese der O-Glykosyl-Derivate des Tyrosins und der aus diesen zugänglichen O-Glucosyl-Tyrosin- und Tyrosyl-Peptide setzten wir uns das Ziel, die Glykosylester der Aminosäuren darzustellen. Bei der Reaktion einer geschützten Aminosäure mit Acetobromglucose in Gegenwart von Silbercarbonat und Lauge konnte kein einheitliches Produkt isoliert werden. Bei der Reaktion des Silbersalzes des Leücins mit Acetobromglucose in benzolischem Medium erhielten wir eine bei 173° schmelzende kristalline Substanz. Obzwar die Ergebnisse der Elementaranalyse des Produktes mit den für den erwarteten Ester berechneten Werten übereinstimmten, konnte aus den Eigenschaften des Produktes, der negativen Ninhydrinreaktion, der Löslichkeitsverhältnisse usw. darauf geschlossen werden, daß sich auch eine Sekundärreaktion abgespielt hat. Diese letztere konnte auf Grund des IR-Spektrums als $O \rightarrow N$ Acylwanderung identifiziert werden, die wahrscheinlich nach folgendem Schema vor sich geht:

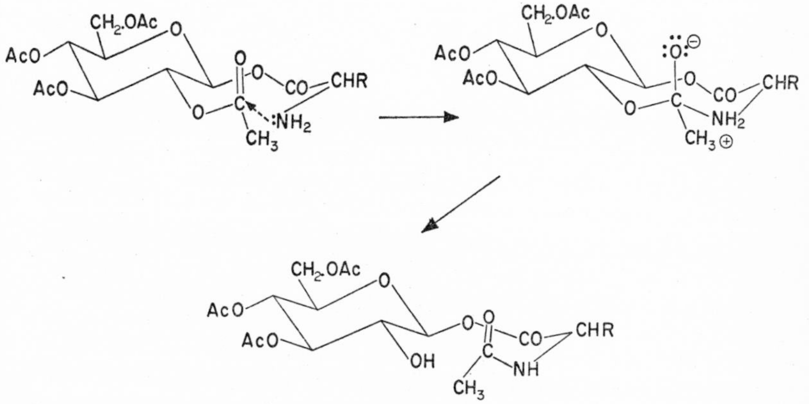

Ein positives Ergebnis brachten jene Versuche, in denen wir das Silber-Salz der geschützten Aminosäure mit Acetobromglucose bzw. die geschützte Aminosäure mit 2,3,4,6-Tetraacetylglucose in Gegenwart von Dicyclohexylcarbodiimid reagieren ließen. Die acetylierten Glykosylester der geschützten Aminosäuren können im ersteren Falle mit 50% im letzteren mit mehr als 60% betragenden Ausbeuten erhalten werden. Mit der letzteren Methode wurden zahlreiche Aminosäure-Glucosylester hergestellt, von denen das Glycin- und Alanin-Derivat kristallinisch erhalten werden konnte. Eine bessere Kristallisationsbereitschaft zeigen die acetylierten Cellobiosylester. Die Untersuchung des kristallinen Produktes führte zum Ergebnis, daß mit eisessigsaurer Bromwasserstoffsäure beide Schutzgruppen abgespalten werden können, so läßt sich z.B. Glycin-Bromhydrat aus Benzyloxycarbonyl-Glycin-tetraacetyl-glykosyl-ester mit 90%iger und Acetobromglucose mit *ca.* 50%iger Ausbeute erhalten. Auf Grund der IR-Spektren der Produkte kann angenommen werden, daß das Wasserstoffatom der CO-NH-Gruppe im Glycin-Derivat in einer intermolekularen Wasserstoffbrückenbindung teilnimmt.

DISCUSSION ON ABNORMAL PEPTIDES

M. ROTHE:

Unter verschiedenen untersuchten *N*-Aminoacyl-lactamen reagiert *N*-Glycol-capro-lactams analog unter Addition der NH_2-Gruppe an die Lactam-carbonylgruppe, unter sofertiger Wasserabspaltung zum 1,2-Pentamethylen-imidazolon-(5).

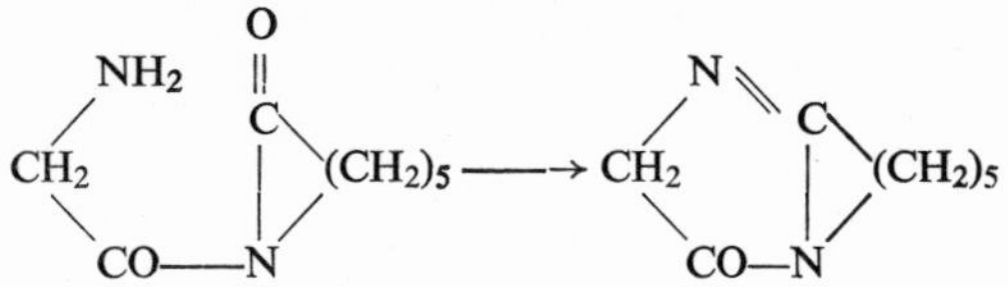

$$
\begin{array}{c}
NH_2 \\ \diagdown \\ CH_2 \quad C \diagdown \\ \diagdown \quad CO\!-\!N
\end{array}
\;(CH_2)_5 \longrightarrow
\begin{array}{c}
N \diagdown \\ CH_2 \quad C \diagdown \\ \diagdown \quad CO\!-\!N
\end{array}
\;(CH_2)_5
$$

SECTION IV

CHEMICAL AND PHYSICAL PROPERTIES OF PEPTIDES

DIELECTRIC INCREMENTS AND
CONFORMATIONS OF SOME SIMPLE PEPTIDES
IN AQUEOUS SOLUTION

P. M. HARDY, G. W. KENNER and R. C. SHEPPARD

The Robert Robinson Laboratories, University of Liverpool, England

CONFORMATIONS of peptide chains in proteins and synthetic polypeptides have been derived theoretically by applying two principles [1]. The first is that resonance of the amide groups between structures (I) and (II) stabilizes planar conformations of them and that *trans*-conformations are preferred to *cis*. Secondly, only structures containing the maximum number of hydrogen bonds need be considered. Some attention has also been paid [2] to possible preferences for particular angles of rotation about the single bonds between the amide groups and the tetrahedral carbon atoms within the chain (termed hereafter $N-C_\alpha$ and $C_\alpha-CO$ bonds; cf. III). This paper deals with conformations of non-helical oligopeptides dissolved in water and similar solvents, which minimize influences of hydrogen-bonding on conformations. In these circumstances, any restriction of rotation about the $N-C_\alpha$ or $C_\alpha-CO$ bonds should be more apparent.

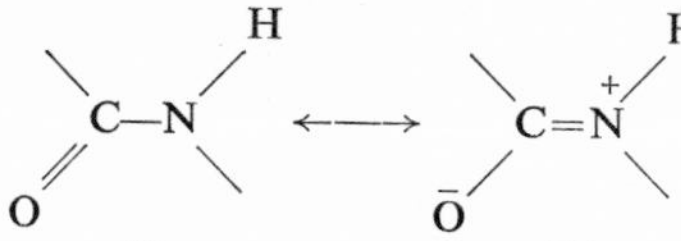

(I)   (II)

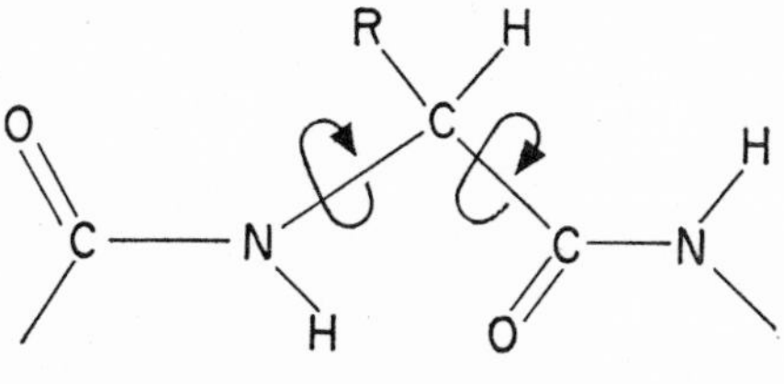

(III)

Restriction of rotation is less easy to define for $N-C_\alpha$ and $C_\alpha-CO$ bonds in peptides than for bonds between two tetrahedral carbon atoms. Barriers to rotation between trigonal and tetrahedral carbon atoms in olefins and carbonyl compounds have been the subject of thermodynamic and spectroscopic investigations [2b, 3], which show that a substituent on the tetra-hedral atom preferably eclipses the substituent doubly bound to the trigonal atom.   This initially surprising conclusion can perhaps be qualitatively understood by considering the double bond as a pair of bent single bonds [4], when it is seen that the preferred conformation corresponds to the familiar staggered orientation of two tetrahedral atoms [5].   The chief difficulty in applying this simple concept to C_α—CO bonds of peptides is that resonance between structures (I) and (II) imparts double-bond character to both sides of the trigonal carbon atom.   In nitromethane, which has equivalent meso-meric structures, the barrier to rotation is only 0·006 kcal [6], but acetic acid (0·48 kcal [7]) is more analogous to a peptide and barriers above 1 kcal are recorded for acetyl halides etc. [3b].   Turning to N—C_α bonds, it might be thought that partial double-bond character in the link to the carbonyl group would result in this substituent being eclipsed, but the contrary assumption that the hydrogen atom is eclipsed has been made [2b].   To sum up, the situation concerning rotation around C_α—CO and N—C_α bonds is confused, and we suspect that many chemists have assumed that the barriers would be too low to have conformational consequences.

The dielectric increments of peptides [8] provide evidence for the actual existence of preferred conformations of the type just discussed.   Dipolar ions generally increase the dielectric constant of water when they are dissolved in it, and in dilute solutions the increase is proportional to the concentration of solute.   Their dielectric increment specifies the increase in dielectric con-stant calculated for a molar solution, assuming " dilute " properties; our measurements were made in the region up to 0·04 M.   The dielectric increment is related to the dipole moment, and thus it can provide information about the length, and hence the conformations, of flexible molecules.   We have already reported that the dielectric increment of glycyl-L-leucylglycyl-L-leucylglycine is considerably lower than that of the L-L isomer [9].   Values for five more diastereoisomeric pairs are given in Table 1.   The dielectric increments of di-, tri-, and penta-glycine are 70, 114, and 202 respectively, and thus the D-L or L-D isomers may perhaps be regarded as abnormal.

In any consideration of relations between dielectric increments and con-formations, the first question is how many conformations have major roles. The large differences between the increments of diastereoisomers dispose of the supposition [8, 10] based on the proportionality of increment to num-ber of residues in oligopeptides of glycine, that there is a random distribution of conformations.   In the following discussion, going to the other extreme, we assume that, except where residues of glycine are involved, one conforma-tion is dominant and that the conformations of two diastereoisomers are governed by the same rules.   (It is conceivable that we are merely observing the effects of direct interaction of the two side-chains, but it is difficult to see why they should influence each other when so widely separated.)   This is

TABLE 1. DIELECTRIC INCREMENTS OF PEPTIDES IN
AQUEOUS SOLUTION AT 30·5°

Structure	Dielectric increments of diastereoisomers	
	L-L	D-L or L-D
Leucylleucine	83	40
Leucyltyrosine	90	45
Glycylleucylleucine	112	55
Leucylleucylglycine	113	81·5
Glycylleucylleucylglycylglycine	204	130
Glycylleucylglycylleucylglycine	207†	

† This value differs from that previously recorded [9] (186) by much more than the variations in the present measurements with this compound (± 1·5 per cent), but we are unable to account for the discrepancy. The recorded value (169) for the diastereoisomer must likewise be regarded with reserve until another sample has been examined.

a working hypothesis to be tested by the consistency of deductions from it, but it is given some support by examination of molecular models. This reveals considerable variations between the dipole moments of conformational isomers, and consequently it would be surprising if the mean values corresponding to mixtures of a few conformational isomers showed considerable dissimilarities between pairs of diastereoisomers. Dr A. D. Buckingham has drawn our attention to the desirability of testing the hypothesis by making measurements at different temperatures, and we intend to do this.

The relation between dipole moment and dielectric increment has been studied several times [8, 11], and probably the most satisfactory treatment is that of Buckingham [12], who derived dipole moments for glycine and β-alanine in good agreement with their molecular dimensions. The main difficulty in applying this theory to peptides is that the shape of the molecule has to be incorporated in the calculation. This information can be obtained from separate determinations at very high frequencies via calculation of relaxation times [13], but we have relied on the simple data, employing calculation by successive approximation and feeding back the shape corresponding to the dipole moment until constancy was reached [14]. We regard these calculations with some reserve and the deduced dipole moments are probably not absolutely significant, because some of the corresponding separations of charges are too small to be simulated with Dreiding molecular models. Moreover, the separation does not increase with chain length to a superficially reasonable extent. However, the calculations are useful in confirming that the average separation of charges in a D-L-diastereoisomer is distinctly less than in the L-L. The following charge separations (Å) were calculated for the di- and tri-peptides; leucylleucine, 4·3 and 6·3; glycylleucylleucine, 4·1 and 6·2; leucylleucylglycine, 4·8 and 6·2.

Ideally the dominant conformations of peptides could be deduced from the average charge separations by equating them to chain lengths, provided that sufficient examples had been studied and that, in each case, one conformer is so dominant that contributions from the others can be neglected. In the present work, we have been less ambitious and our attention has been confined to peptides containing only two asymmetric carbon atoms. The pentapeptides display a large difference in increment, concordant with the difference in yields from cyclizations, but it is difficult to make any conformational deductions because the residues of glycine, which are not subject to so much stereochemical control, are responsible for too many uncertainties. On the other hand, in the dipeptides the amide group is not in a typical environment. The carboxylate group may be sufficiently equivalent to an amide substituent for the C_α—CO bond to be equivalent to one in a chain, but the same cannot be said of the N—C_α bond because the ammonium substituent cannot be equated for even these purposes to an amide without further justification. For these reasons we selected glycylleucylleucine as the theoretically simplest case for initial analysis; in it, the three bonds depicted in (IV) by lines may be regarded as typical of a polypeptide. Dreiding models of the two diastereoisomers were arranged in thirty-six ways, which were derived from the following considerations.

$$\overset{+}{N}H_3.CH_2.CO.NH\text{----}CH(R)\text{----}CO.NH\text{----}CH(R)\overline{C}O_2$$

IV.

V.

VI.

VII.

VIII.

IX.

X.

Apparently the only closely relevant investigation of rotational barriers is a study of N-methylchloroacetamide [15]. In the solid state and in polar solutions the preferred conformation is that depicted in (V), while (VI) predominates in the vapour and in non-polar solutions. Even these results cannot be carried directly over to peptides and therefore, bearing in mind the arguments put forward at the beginning of this paper, we have considered the six arrangements of the C_α—CO bonds summarized by (VII) or (VIII) with (x = R, H, or NH). "Perpendicular" forms, similar to (VI), are probably sufficiently near to (VII) and (VIII) to be covered in these approximate calculations. Likewise we have considered six arrangements of the

N—C_α bonds, which are summarized in (IX) and (X) with ($x = $ R, N, or CO). Measurements were made with Dreiding models fitted with collars to restrict rotation in the chain. The carboxylate end group was treated like an amide group, the measurement being taken from the point midway between the two oxygen atoms. Except in two columns (VII and VIII, $x = $ NH), there are two positions for the glycyl residue because R = H; this C_α—CO bond was placed so as to bisect the angle between these two positions.

TABLE 2. MEASURED DISTANCES (Å) BETWEEN CHARGES IN 36 CONFORMATIONS OF THE DIASTEREOISOMERIC GLYCYLLEUCYLLEUCINES

C_α—CO / N—C_α		VII						VIII					
		$x = $ H		$x = $ R		$x = $ NH		$x = $ H		$x = $ R		$x = $ NH	
		LL	LD	LL	LD	LL	LD	LL	LD	LL	LD	LL	LD
	$x = $												
IX	H	5·3	7·3	7·7	5·6	9·9	9·3	9·4	7·6	9·1	10·0	5·7	5·5
	R	7·7	5·7	5·3	7·2	9·9	9·3	9·0	10·0	9·5	7·7	5·8	5·4
	CO	7·7	7·6	7·7	7·7	6·1	6·2	6·3	6·4	6·3	6·3	7·6	7·8
X	H	8·2	6·4	6·6	8·0	8·0	7·1	6·8	8·3	8·5	6·0	7·2	7·0
	R	6·5	8·0	8·2	6·5	8·0	7·1	8·4	6·0	6·8	8·3	7·1	7·1
	CO	6·1	6·1	6·1	6·0	10·3	10·3	9·6	9·6	9·6	9·7	4·7	4·7

Table 2 records the charge separations measured on Dreiding models of these thirty-six conformations of each diastereoisomer of glycylleucylleucine. Some of the thirty-six conformations of a diastereoisomer must have identical charge separations but they have all been considered individually in order to check the accuracy of the measurements; the discrepancies are no more than 0·2 Å. Sixteen arrangements of this tripeptide, including all those with (IX, $x = $ CO) or (X, $x = $ CO), have identical or closely similar (< 0.4 Å) charge separations in the diastereoisomers and eight, including that of the α-helix, viz. (VII, $x = $ H) with (X, $x = $ R), lead to a smaller charge separation in the L-L isomer. Some of these twenty-four arrangements may contribute to the entire assembly of conformations but only to a minor extent. We are left with twelve arrangements as possible major contributors to the actual mixture. Of these twelve, the four based on (VII, $x = $ NH) are eliminated by the results with leucylleucylglycine, leucylleucine and leucyltyrosine because in these instances diastereoisomers would be indistinguishable. The remaining arrangements, which are picked out in heavy type in Table 2, are (1) (VII, $x = $ H) with (X, $x = $ H); (2) (VII, $x = $ R) with (X, $x = $ R); (3) (VII, $x = $ H) with (IX, $x = $ R); (4) (VII, $x = $ R) with (IX, $x = $ H); (5) (VIII, $x = $ H) with (IX, $x = $ H); (6) (VIII, $x = $ R) with (IX, $x = $ R); (7) (VIII, $x = $ H) with (X, $x = $ R); (8) (VIII, $x = $ R) with (X, $x = $ H). Examination of peptides containing several asymmetric carbon atoms would help to distinguish between these possibilities but it should be noted that there are pairs, viz. (1) and (2), (3) and (4), (5) and (6), (7) and (8), which have identical dipole moments not only in this instance but in all peptides, and they cannot in principle be differentiated by this method. Molecular models of these eight arrangements are instructive. There is severe repulsion between the alkyl substituent and the N–H hydrogen atom next along the chain in (VIII, $x = R$) (i.e. (6) and (8)). In (VIII, $x = H$) (i.e. (5) and (7)) the hydrogen atom on the asymmetric carbon atom and the N–H hydrogen atom just mentioned are separated by $2 \cdot 1$ Å; this repulsion would not be large enough to prevent the arrangement if other circumstances were favourable. In (IX, $x = R$) (i.e. (3) and (6)) the alkyl group and the carbonyl preceding it in the chain are separated by $2 \cdot 2$ Å, perhaps a permissible amount. Arrangements (1) and (2) incorporate a hydrogen bond in a seven-membered ring and they correspond to the 2_7 helix [16]. Although intramolecular hydrogen bonds are unlikely to play an important role in favouring conformations in aqueous media there is no obvious reason why they should be excluded. Arrangement (4) is apparently without appreciable repulsions but it cannot be selected on that score alone because some of the effects mentioned are probably small.

Independent evidence of conformational selection in peptides is provided by studies of cyclization. We have already reported [9] that the p-nitrophenyl thiolester of glycyl-L-leucylglycyl-D-leucylglycine gives the cyclic peptide in 57 per cent yield, whereas only 41% was obtained from the L-L isomer. We have now found an even greater difference (39 per cent compared with 12 per cent) in the same direction for the isomers of glycylleucylleucylglycylglycine, and, rather remarkably, identical results from cyclizations of the free pentapeptides with dicyclohexylcarbodi-imide in aqueous methanol [17]. We interpret these results as indicating smaller average distances between the ends of the L-D or D-L chains than in the L-L or D-D isomers. Some observations on the dissociation constants [18] and proton magnetic resonance spectra [19] of the diastereoisomeric leucyltyrosines are also indicative of a more compact arrangement in the D-L isomer.

REFERENCES

1. L. PAULING, R. B. COREY and H. R. BRANSON, *Proc. Nat. Acad. Sci. U.S.* **37**, 205 (1951).
2a. L. PAULING and R. B. COREY, *Proc. Nat. Acad. Sci. U.S.* **37**, 729 (1951).
2b. S. MIZUSHIMA and R. SHIMANOUCHI, *Advances in Enzymol.* **23**, 1 (1961).
3a. W. G. DAUBEN and K. S. PITZER, *Steric Effects in Organic Chemistry* (edited by M. S. Newman), pp. 58–59. John Wiley, New York (1956).
3b. E. B. WILSON, *Advances in Chem. Phy.* **2**, 367 (1959).
3c. R. J. ABRAHAM and J. A. POPLE, *Mol. Phys.* **3**, 609 (1960).
4. J. A. POPLE, *Quart. Revs. (London)* **11**, 273 (1957).
5. L. PAULING, *Proc. Nat. Acad. Sci. U.S.* **44**, 211 (1958).

6. E. TANNENBAUM, R. J. MYERS and W. D. GWINN, *J. Chem. Phys.* **25**, 42 (1956).
7. W. J. TABOR, *J. Chem. Phys.* **27**, 974 (1957).
8. E. J. COHN and J. T. EDSALL, *Proteins, Amino Acids and Peptides*, pp. 152–154. Reinhold, New York (1943).
9. G. W. KENNER, P. J. THOMSON and J. M. TURNER, *J. Chem. Soc.* **1958**, 4148.
10. W. P. CONNER, R. P. CLARKE and C. P. SMYTH, *J. Amer. Chem. Soc.* **64**, 1379 (1942).
11a. J. C. KIRKWOOD, ref. 8, p. 294.
11b. J. L. ONCLEY, ref. 8, p. 546.
12. A. D. BUCKINGHAM, *Australian J. Chem.* **6**, 323 (1953).
13. W. P. CONNER and C. P. SMYTH, *J. Amer. Chem. Soc.* **64**, 1870 (1942).
14. P. M. HARDY, Ph.D. Thesis, Liverpool (1961).
15. S. MIZUSHIMA, T. SHIMANOUCHI, I. ICHISHIMA, T. MIYAZAWA, I. NAKAGAWA and T. ARAKI, *J. Amer. Chem. Soc.* **78**, 2038 (1956).
16. C. H. BAMFORD, A. ELLIOTT and W. E. HANBY, *Synthesic Polypeptides*, pp. 119–121, Academic Press, New York (1956).
17. T. WIELAND and K. W. OHLY, *Liebig's Ann. Chem.* **605**, 179 (1957).
18a. E. ELLENBOGEN, *J. Amer. Chem. Soc.* **78**, 369 (1956).
18b. N. C. LI, G. W. MILLER, N. SOLONY and B. T. GILLIS, *ibid.* **82**, 3737 (1960).
19. F. A. BOVEY and G. V. D. TIERS *J. Amer. Chem. Soc.* **81**, 2870 (1959).

NON-ENZYMATIC CLEAVAGE OF PEPTIDE CHAINS AT THE CYSTEINE AND SERINE RESIDUES†

A. Patchornik and M. Sokolovsky

Department of Biophysics, The Weizmann Institute of Science, Rehovoth, Israel

THE specific cleavage of peptide chains at a chosen amino-acid residue is of great importance, e.g. in the determination of amino-acid sequences in proteins. Enzymatic methods are available, which achieve this task to a certain degree. Some of these are highly selective—involving one or two amino-acid residues—others are less selective, splitting bonds adjacent to a larger number of amino-acid residues.

Recently, chemical methods have been developed which enable one to cleave a peptide chain at specific bonds. Thus, bonds involving the residues of tryptophan, tyrosine, methionine, histidine or aspartic acid can be cleaved specifically with varying yields. The literature dealing with this type of reaction has been reviewed by Witkop [1].

In the present paper we describe the chemical cleavage of peptides at cysteine or serine residues, by the conversion of these two amino-acid residues into dehydroalanine residues and the subsequent scission of the dehydropeptide formed. The cleavage reaction proceeds in three stages: (a) conversion of the amino-acid residue into a derivative that possesses a good " leaving group " on the β-carbon suitable for a subsequent β-elimination reaction; (b) formation of a dehydroalanine peptide; (c) cleavage of the dehydropeptide. These steps are summarized in the following scheme:

Step a

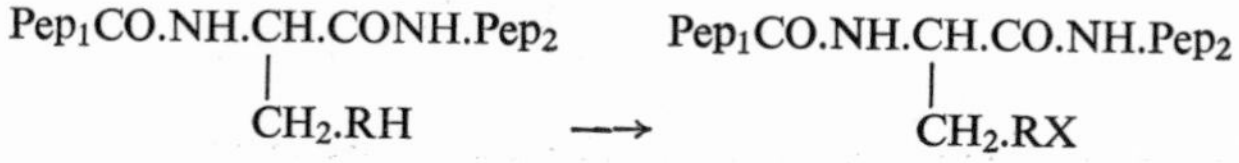

$$\underset{\displaystyle CH_2.RH}{Pep_1CO.NH.\overset{|}{C}H.CONH.Pep_2} \qquad \underset{\displaystyle CH_2.RX}{Pep_1CO.NH.\overset{|}{C}H.CO.NH.Pep_2}$$

$$\longrightarrow$$

Step b

$$\overset{\displaystyle BASE}{\underset{}{\longrightarrow}} \underset{\displaystyle CH_2}{Pep_1CO.NH.\overset{\|}{C}.CO.NH.Pep_2} + RX^- + H^+$$

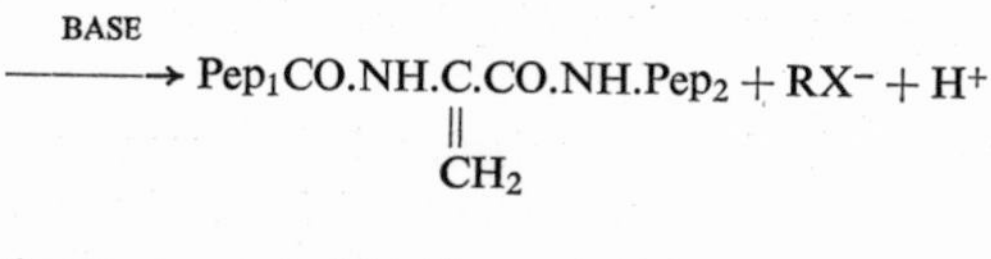

† This investigation was supported by Grants A-3171 and A-5098 of National Institutes of Health, United States Public Service.

Step c

$$\longrightarrow Pep_1CO.NH_2 + Y\ CO.CO.NH.Pep_2$$

RH = —OH; —SH.

RX = —O-Tosyl; —O.P=(OR)$_2$; —S—⟨C$_6$H$_3$(NO$_2$)$_2$⟩—NO$_2$; —$\overset{+}{S}Me_2$

Pep = Peptide chain
Y = —CH$_3$ (hydrolytic cleavage)
   —CH$_2$ OH (oxidative cleavage)

    The groups used for the β-elimination reaction in cysteine peptides are the thiodinitrophenyl group [2] or the dialkylsulfonium group [3]. The leaving groups for the conversion of serine residues into dehydroalanine residues are the O-diphenylphosphate [4] [5] or the O-toluene-p-sulfonyl group [5].

    The second step, the β-elimination, is brought about by a mild base in aqueous or non-aqueous solutions. Examples are shown in Table 1.

TABLE 1.   CONVERSION OF CYSTEINE AND SERINE RESIDUES
INTO DEHYDROALANINE

Compounds	Elimination condition	Dehydroalanine derivative isolated (%)
Z-Cys-Gly-OEt [6] | (CH$_3$)$_2$Br$^-$	Sodium hydrogen carbonate 2 hr room temperature	75
Z(NO$_2$)-Gly-Cys-OMe [6] | DNP	0·01 N-sodium methoxide 5 min, room temperature	80
Z-Ser-OEt [4] \ O.P(OC$_6$H$_5$)$_2$ ‖ O	0·1 N-sodium hydroxide [5] 30 min, room temperature	60
Z–Ser-Gly-OEt [7]† | Tos	Diethylamine [5] 3–4 hr, room temperature	52

† Dr. I. Photaki kindly supplied us with a sample of this compound.

    In the third step the resulting dehydropeptide is cleaved either hydrolytically or oxidatively [8].

    The hydrolytic fission of dehydroalanine derivatives was originally carried out by heating the compounds in water at pH 7 [3]. Hydrolysis, is, however, considerably faster at a lower pH. Thus, a 96 per cent yield of cleavage was obtained with benzyloxycarbonyldehydroalanylglycine after boiling for 1 hr at pH 2·2, whereas a reaction time of 12 hr was necessary at pH 7. The products of the hydrolysis in this case were benzyl carbamate and pyruvoylglycine. Hydrolysis under these mild conditions of peptides containing dehydroalanine leads to the formation of a peptide amide and an N-substituted amide of pyruvic acid.

Pep$_1$CO.NH.CCO.NHPep$_2$ Pep$_1$CO.NH$_2$ + CH$_3$CO.CO.NHPep$_2$

$\|$ $\xrightarrow{\text{H}_2\text{O}}$

CH$_2$

Analogously, benzyloxycarbonyldehydroalanine yielded benzyl carbamate and pyruvic acid, and benzyloxycarbonylglycyldehydroalanine yielded benzyloxycarbonylglycylamide and pyruvic acid. In both cases cleavage yields were almost quantitative.

Dehydroalanine residues react readily with oxidizing reagents such as bromine [8] or performic acid in acidic solutions. One mole of the oxidizing reagent is consumed. On treatment of the oxidation products with alkali, a peptide amide and an N-substituted amide of hydroxypyruvic acid are formed in high yields (Table 2).

Pep$_1$CO.NH.C.CO.NHPep$_2$ 1. HCO$_3$H or Br$_2$ at pH < 6

$\|$ $\xrightarrow{\hspace{2cm}}$

$\|$ 2. OH$^-$

CH$_2$ Pep$_1$CO.NH$_2$ + HOCH$_2$.CO.CO.NHPep$_2$

TABLE 2. THE OXIDATIVE CLEAVAGE OF DEHYDROALANYL COMPOUNDS

Dehydroalanyl compound	Cleavage product	Oxidative cleavage (%)	
		With bromine	With performic acid
Z(NO$_2$)-Gly-Dhal [9]	Z(NO$_2$)-Gly-NH$_2$	94	96
Z(NO$_2$)-Gly-Dhal-OMe [9]	Z(NO$_2$)-Gly-NH$_2$	92	94
Glu(Dhal-Gly) [6]	Glu(NH$_2$)	89	—
Z-Dhal-Gly [9]	Z-NH$_2$	85	91

Dhal = Dehydroalanyl residue

The pyruvoyl as well as the hydroxypyruvoyl groups can be removed by treatment with hydrogen peroxide in alkali [10] with the generation of a new terminal amino group.

XCH$_2$.CO.CO.NHPep$_2$ $\begin{array}{c} 1.\ \text{H}_2\text{O}_2.\text{OH}^- \\ \xrightarrow{\hspace{1.5cm}} \\ 2.\ \text{H}^+ \end{array}$ XCH$_2$.CO.OH + CO$_2$ + NH$_2$.Pep$_2$

X = H; OH

The yield of the unmasking of the amino group is generally 50–60 per cent as shown in Table 3.

TABLE 3. YIELDS OF LIBERATED AMIDES AND AMINO-ACIDS IN THE
CLEAVAGE OF VARIOUS PEPTIDES OF CYSTEINE AND SERINE

Compound	Amide (%)	Amino-acid released (%)
Z-Ser-OMe [7] | Tos	Z-NH$_2$, 90	
Z-Ser-Gly-OEt [7] | Tos		Glycine, 52
Z-Cys-Gly-OEt [6] | (CH$_3$)$_2$ Br$^-$		Glycine, 56
Z-Gly-Cys-OMe [6] | (CH$_3$)$_2$ Br$^-$	Z-Gly-NH$_2$, 90	
Glu(Cys-Gly) | DNP	Glutamine, 89	Glycine, 56
Z(NO$_2$)-Gly-Cys-OMe [6] | DNP	Z(NO$_2$)-Gly-NH$_2$, 94	
Z(NO$_2$)-Gly-Cys-Gly [6] | DNP		Glycine, 58
Oxytocin		Proline, 75 Tyrosine, 40

As higher molecular weight model compounds for the above cleavage reactions oxytocin and phosvitin were used, the former for the cleavage at cysteine residues and the latter for cleavage at serine residues.

A micromole quantity of the oxytocin was reduced by thioglycollic

Cys-Tyr-Ile-Glu(NH$_2$)-Asp(NH$_2$)-Cys-Pro-Leu-Gly-NH$_2$

acid at pH 8·5, and treated with excess of fluorodinitrobenzene to form the dinitrophenyl derivative of reduced oxytocin. The modified oxytocin was treated with alcoholic 0·1 N-sodium hydroxide and the elimination of the thiodinitrophenolate ion was followed spectrophotometrically [11] (75 per cent yield). The reaction mixture was oxidized with performic acid and then with alkaline hydrogen peroxide. Two new amino terminal groups, identified as tyrosine (40 per cent dinitrophenyltyrosine) and free proline (75 per cent yield as determined by digestion with proline imino peptidase) [12], were formed during the course of these reactions.

In the case of phosvitin it could be demonstrated that the appearance of inorganic phosphate on treatment with 0·25 M-alkali is accompanied by the formation of an equivalent amount of dehydroalanine residues which yielded, on acid hydrolysis, one mole of pyruvic acid and one mole of primary amide per mole of phosphate liberated. Alternatively, the formation of dehydroalanine residues was followed quantitatively by oxidation with bromine or performic acid. Further oxidation with hydrogen peroxide at high pH cleaved phosvitin into a number of fragments. On a " fingerprint " [13] 9 ninhydrin positive spots could be distinguished.

The almost specific reaction of fluorodinitrobenzene with the thiol group of cysteine at low pH values [6, 14], together with the high yields of elimination of the thiodinitrophenolate ion and the high yield of cleavage of the dehydroalanine formed, seems to make this new method a promising one for the fragmentation of proteins at the cysteine residue. In the case of serine, a good general method for the selective substitution of the serine oxygen in higher peptides is still lacking.

REFERENCES

1. B. WITKOP, *Advances in Protein Chemistry*, vol. **16**, pp. 221–321. Academic Press 1961.
2. A preliminary report: M. SOKOLOVSKY, M. WILCHEK and A. PATCHORNIK, *Proc. 30th Meeting of the Israel Chemical Society*, **11A**, 79 (1962).
3. Preliminary report: A. PATCHORNIK, M. SOKOLOVSKY and T. SADEH, *Proc. 5th Internat. Congr. Biochem., Moscow*, p. 11 (1961).
4. G. RILEY, J. H. TURNBULL and W. WILSON, *J. Chem. Soc.* **1957**, 1373.
5. L. I. PHOTAKI, University of Athens, personal communication.
6. M. SOKOLOVSKY, T. SADEH and A. PATCHORNIK, in preparation.
7. L. I. PHOTAKI, University of Athens, personal communication.
8. A. PATCHORNIK and M. SOKOLOVSKY, *Bull. Research Council Israel* **11A**, 80 (1962).
9. A. PATCHORNIK and M. SOKOLOVSKY, in preparation.
10. W. H. MCGREGOR and F. H. CARPENTER, *Biochemistry* **1**, 53 (1962).
11. A. PATCHORNIK and M. SOKOLOVSKY, *Bull. Research Council Israel* **11A**, 226 (1962).
12. S. SARID, A. BERGER and E. KATCHALSKI, *J. Biol. Chem.* **234**, 1740 (1959).
13. A. M. KATZ, W. J. DREYER and C. B. ANFINSEN, *J. Biol. Chem.* **234**, 2897 (1959).
14. H. ZAHN, K. TRAUMANN, *Z. Naturforsch* **9B**, 518 (1954); H. P. BURCHFIELD, *Nature* **181**, 49 (1958).

SECTION V
NOMENCLATURE

REPORT OF THE
COMMITTEE ON NOMENCLATURE

Introduced by G. T. YOUNG

The Dyson Perrins Laboratory, Oxford, England

I AM indeed sorry that the Chairman of this Committee, Professor R. Schwyzer, has been unable to be with us at this meeting; he has asked me to present the Report in his absence, and since the recommendations have been circulated beforehand I can do this quite briefly.

The Committee members have held discussions amongst themselves and with their colleagues over a period of two years. To the extent that questions of logic and consistency are involved, there has been no difficulty in reaching agreement; when matters of taste and personal preference arise, it is useless to expect unanimity, and here we have compromised. In trying to devise a system which will meet our ever-growing requirements, we have borne in mind two important considerations: (a) that we should, as far as possible, be consistent with the Tentative Rules published by the International Union of Pure and Applied Chemistry; (b) that we should always be aware of the danger of making our papers unintelligible to the non-specialist. We hope that our recommendations will be thought to steer a reasonable course between these often contrary considerations. Without question, many will feel that their own alternative abbreviations are much to be preferred; we are only too well aware of the difficulty of choice, but the desirability of uniformity is so great that we hope members will not be unwilling to sacrifice some of their preferences in order to achieve it.

The fundamental principle of the system is simply that the abbreviations for the amino-acids, standing by themselves, should represent the free amino-acid, but the introduction of a hyphen *before* the symbol indicates substitution for a hydrogen of the amino group; *after* the symbol, substitution in place of the hydroxyl of the carboxyl group; and *above* or *below* the symbol, substitution in the side-chain, as defined in each case. The logic of this system requires revision of the common abbreviation for cysteine, CySH, which we recommend should become Cys.

The only other comment which I would make concerns the use of the abbreviation " Bz " for benzyl. This has long been used in general organic chemistry to denote benzoyl, and it does seem unfortunate that it should have a different meaning in peptide chemistry. We shall all find difficulty in accustoming ourselves to a new symbol, but I feel it is an effort we should make in the interest of clarity. The Report follows.

ABBREVIATIONS FOR AMINO-ACIDS AND POLYPEPTIDES

At the 3rd European Peptide Symposium at Basle in September 1960, a Committee was appointed to make recommendations on abbreviations commonly required in papers concerned with peptide synthesis. Since that time, the International Union of Pure and Applied Chemistry has published "Tentative Rules for Abbreviations and Symbols for Chemical Names of Special Interest in Biological Chemistry" (Appendix B to Information Bulletin No. 12). In our Report we have felt compelled to diverge from these Tentative Rules in three cases: in the symbols for cysteine (and therefore for "half-cystine") (Sections 1 (b) and 2 (c) below), for isoleucine (Section 1 (b) below) and in the formulation of ionized structures (Section 3 (a) below). Otherwise, our recommendations represent extensions within the framework envisaged by the Tentative Rules.

1. *Abbreviations for Amino-acids*

(a) *General.* It is fundamental to the system we recommend that the lettered abbreviations (Ala, Arg, etc.) standing by themselves represent the free amino-acid, and *not* its residue: i.e. Gly denotes $NH_2.CH_2.CO_2H$. This is the usage envisaged in the "Comment" in Section 2.1 of the Tentative Rules.

(b) *Common amino-acids.* We support the use of the abbreviations listed in Section 2.1 of the Tentative Rules, with the important exceptions of those for cysteine and "half-cystine", and isoleucine. For reasons elaborated below (Section 2 (c)), we strongly recommend the use of Cys for cysteine, in place of CySH. Since isoleucine is so widely distributed, we feel there is a good case for changing to a three-letter symbol, Ile, to facilitate the tabular comparison of analogues. We choose Ile and not iLe because in the name isoleucine "iso" is not used with its usual meaning, and it is therefore not a prefix but part of the trivial name. The frequency with which hydroxylysine and hydroxyproline occur is perhaps insufficient to justify a change from current practice, and of the alternatives offered in the Tentative Rules we recommend Hylys and Hypro.

alanine	Ala	histidine	His
arginine	Arg	hydroxylysine	Hylys
aspartic acid	Asp	hydroxyproline	Hypro
cysteine	Cys	isoleucine	Ile
glutamic acid	Glu	leucine	Leu
glycine	Gly	lysine	Lys

methionine	Met	serine	Ser
ornithine	Orn	threonine	Thr
phenylalanine	Phe	tryptophan	Try
proline	Pro	tyrosine	Tyr
sarcosine	Sar	valine	Val

(c) *Abbreviations for less common amino-acids.* The Tentative Rules left these for discussion, and we make the following proposals:

(i) *Allo-amino-acids:* prefix *a* (italicized).
allo-isoleucine *a*Ile
allo-hydroxylysine *a*Hylys
allo-hydroxyproline *a*Hypro

(ii) " *Nor* " *amino-acids.* " Nor " (e.g. in norvaline) is not used in its accepted sense (denoting a lower homologue) but to turn the trivial name of a branched chain compound to that of a straight chain compound. The situation is comparable to that of " iso " in isoleucine and, as in that case, " nor " should be included in the abbreviation without special emphasis:

norvaline   Nva
norleucine   Nle

(iii) *Higher unbranched amino-acids.* We suggest the following general rules for guidance in forming abbreviations:

The functional prefix " amino " should be included in the symbol as the letter A, " diamino " as Da.

The trivial name of the parent acid should be abbreviated to leave between two and four letters, as convenient and necessary for clarity. The word " acid " (" acidum ", suffix " -säure ", etc.) should be omitted from the symbol as carrying no significant information.

Unless otherwise indicated (see paragraph below), single amino groups are in the α position, two amino groups in the α,ω (monocarboxylic acids) or α,α' positions (dicarboxylic acids).

The location of amino groups in positions other than α is shown by the appropriate Greek letter prefix.

Examples:
α-aminobutyric acid	Abut
α-aminoadipic acid	Aad
α-aminopimelic acid	Apim
α,γ-diaminobutyric acid	Dab
α,β-diaminopropionic acid	Dapro
α,α'-diaminopimelic acid	Dapim
β-alanine	β-Ala
ε-aminocaproic acid	ε-Acap
β-aminoadipic	β-Aad

2. *Amino-acid Residues*

The three-letter symbols standing by themselves represent amino-acids and therefore should not be used without modification to represent their *residues*. We recommend the following modifications:

(a) *Lack of hydrogen on the α-amino group* (the α-amino group is always understood to be on the left-hand side of the symbol).

$-HNCH_2.CO.OH$ –Gly

$-HN\overset{CH_3}{\overset{|}{C}}H.CO.OH$ –Ala

$>NCH_2.CO.OH$ >Gly or ⊥Gly

$>N\overset{CH_3}{\overset{|}{C}}H.CO.OH$ >Ala or ⊥Ala

(b) *Lack of hydroxyl on the α-carboxyl group* (the α-carboxyl group is always understood to be on the right-hand side of the symbol).

$H_2NCH_2.CO—$ Gly—

$H_2N\overset{CH_3}{\overset{|}{C}}H.CO—$ Ala—

(c) *Lack of hydrogen on amino, imino, guanidino, hydroxyl and thiol functions in the side chain.*

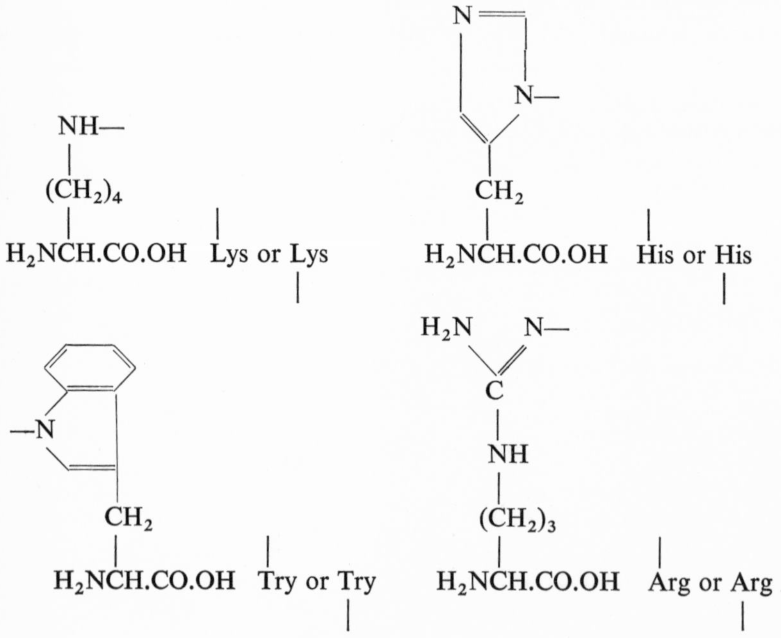
NH—
(CH2)4
H2NCH.CO.OH
Lys or Lys
N
N—
CH2
H2NCH.CO.OH
His or His
—N
CH2
H2NCH.CO.OH
Try or Try
H2N
N—
C
NH
(CH2)3
H2NCH.CO.OH
Arg or Arg

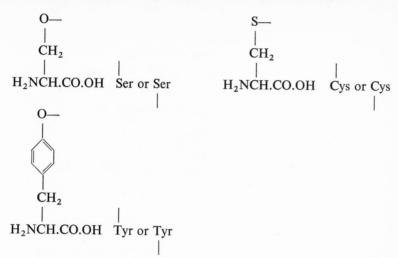

It is now clear why the anomalous treatment which has grown up in the case of cysteine cannot be incorporated into a logical system of this kind; if the letters SH in the common symbol for cysteine, CySH, represent the thiol group, then Cy must represent $NH_2.CH.CO_2H$, and by analogy serine should

$$CH_2—$$

be SerOH. It is, in our view, essential for the development of a logical system for portraying substituted amino-acids and peptides, that cysteine should be brought into line by making Cys represent $NH_2.CH.CO_2H$;

$$CH_2.SH$$

" half-cystine " is then Cys or Cys, as shown above, and cystine becomes

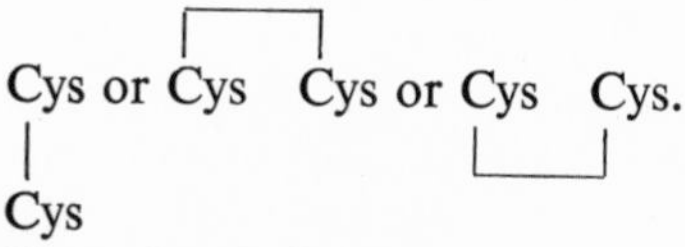

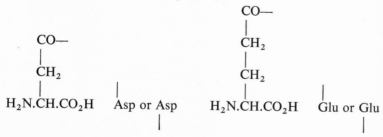

Cys or Cys Cys or Cys Cys. This is an important divergence from the Cys

Tentative Rules.

(d) *Lack of hydroxyl on carboxyl groups in the side chain.*

3. *Substituted Amino-acids*

(a) *Substitution in the α-amino and α-carboxyl groups.* The following examples will make the usage clear:

N-acetylglycine	Ac-Gly
glycine ethyl ester	Gly-OEt
isoglutamine	Glu-NH$_2$
N-methyl-leucine	Me-Leu

$$\text{N-ethylmethylglycine} \qquad \underset{\text{Et}}{\overset{\text{Me}}{\diagdown}}\!\!\!\diagup\text{Gly} \text{ or } \text{Et}\overset{\text{Me}}{\underset{}{-\!\!\!\perp}}\text{Gly}$$

In the last example, if a linear presentation is required, one substituent could be placed immediately before the symbol for the amino-acid, e.g. Et-MeGly.

Clearly, NH$_2$.CH$_2$.CO$_2$H can be represented by H-Gly-OH; analogously, $^+$NH$_3$.CH$_2$.CO$_2$$^-$ would be $^+$H$_2$-Gly-O$^-$. The representations $^+$H-Gly-Val-Thr-OH, $^+$Gly-Val-Thr and Gly-Val-Thr$^-$ in Section 2.6 of the Tentative Rules are inconsistent with this system.

(b) *Substitution in the side chain.* Side chain substituents may be portrayed above or below the amino-acid symbol, or by placing the symbol for the substituent *in brackets* immediately after the amino-acid symbol, as in the following examples:

$$
\begin{array}{l}
\phantom{\text{glutamine}}\quad \text{NH}_2 \\
\phantom{\text{glutamine}}\quad | \\
\text{glutamine}\quad \text{Glu or Glu or Glu(NH}_2) \\
\phantom{\text{glutamine}}\quad | \\
\phantom{\text{glutamine}}\quad \text{NH}_2
\end{array}
$$

(Contrast isoglutamine, Glu-NH$_2$)

$$
\begin{array}{l}
\phantom{\text{β-methyl aspartate}}\quad \text{OMe} \\
\phantom{\text{β-methyl aspartate}}\quad | \\
\text{β-methyl aspartate}\quad \text{Asp, Asp, or Asp(OMe)} \\
\phantom{\text{β-methyl aspartate}}\quad | \\
\phantom{\text{β-methyl aspartate}}\quad \text{OMe}
\end{array}
$$

$$
\begin{array}{l}
\phantom{\text{ε-acetyl-lysine}}\quad \text{Ac} \\
\phantom{\text{ε-acetyl-lysine}}\quad | \\
\text{ε-acetyl-lysine}\quad \text{Lys or Lys or Lys(Ac)} \\
\phantom{\text{ε-acetyl-lysine}}\quad | \\
\phantom{\text{ε-acetyl-lysine}}\quad \text{Ac}
\end{array}
$$

$$
\begin{array}{l}
\phantom{\text{O-acetylserine}}\quad \text{Ac} \\
\phantom{\text{O-acetylserine}}\quad | \\
\text{O-acetylserine}\quad \text{Ser or Ser or Ser(Ac)} \\
\phantom{\text{O-acetylserine}}\quad | \\
\phantom{\text{O-acetylserine}}\quad \text{Ac}
\end{array}
$$

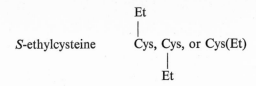

S-ethylcysteine   Cys, Cys, or Cys(Et)

4. *Polypeptides*

(a) Polypeptides are of course substituted amino-acids and may be dealt with logically as indicated in Section 3:
e.g.

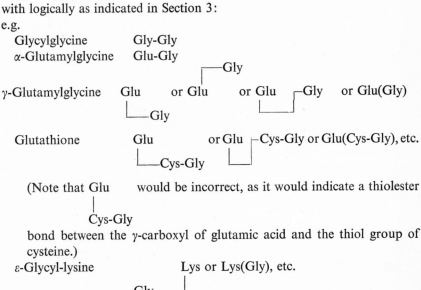

Glycylglycine   Gly-Gly

α-Glutamylglycine   Glu-Gly

γ-Glutamylglycine   Glu ... or Glu ┌─Gly ... or Glu ... or Glu ┌─Gly or Glu(Gly)
                                      └─Gly

Glutathione   Glu ... or Glu ┌─Cys-Gly or Glu(Cys-Gly), etc.
                     └─Cys-Gly

(Note that Glu
              |
              Cys-Gly
would be incorrect, as it would indicate a thiolester bond between the γ-carboxyl of glutamic acid and the thiol group of cysteine.)

ε-Glycyl-lysine   Lys or Lys(Gly), etc.
                Gly─┘

(b) *Peptides substituted at* N^α. If disubstitution of the α-amino group is to be indicated by ⟩Gly or ⊥Gly (Section 3(a) above), then N^α-substituted peptides could be formulated as shown:

Glycylsarcosine   Me⟩Gly, or Gly─Me─Gly, or Gly-MeGly
                 Gly

(c) *Cyclic polypeptides: Homodetic cyclic polypeptides.* Three alternative methods are envisaged:

(i) The sequence is formulated in the usual way, but placed in brackets and preceded by (italic) *cyclo*: e.g.

Gramicidin-S   *cyclo*-(Val-Orn-Leu-D-Phe-Pro-Val-Orn-Leu-D-Phe-Pro-) (where the configuration is L unless otherwise stated).

(ii) The terminal residues (written on one line) are joined by a lengthened bond: e.g.

┌─Val-Orn-Leu-D-Phe-Pro-Val-Orn-Leu-D-Phe-Pro─┐
└──┘

(iii) The residues are written on more than one line, in which case the -CO-NH- direction *must* be indicated by arrows, thus:

$$\rightarrow \text{Val} \rightarrow \text{Orn} \rightarrow \text{Leu} \rightarrow \text{D-Phe} \rightarrow \text{Pro} \rightharpoondown$$
$$\llcorner \text{Pro} \leftarrow \text{D-Phe} \leftarrow \text{Leu} \leftarrow \text{Orn} \leftarrow \text{Val} \leftarrow\lrcorner$$

Heterodetic cyclic polypeptides. These follow logically from the formulation of substituted amino-acids: e.g.

Oxytocin Cys-Tyr-Ile-Asp(NH$_2$)-Glu(NH$_2$)-Cys-Pro-Leu-Gly-NH$_2$

or   Cys-Tyr-Ile-Asp(NH$_2$)-Glu(NH$_2$)-Cys-Pro-Leu-Gly-NH$_2$

5. *Abbreviations for Substituents*

The accepted symbols of general organic chemistry should be used as far as possible, but there is a need for symbols for many other substituents frequently used in this field, and in some cases the common abbreviations are still too bulky to enable a formulation to be read easily. The Committee urges that the use of " Bz " for benzyl, although now common, should be strongly discouraged, since this symbol has long been used for the benzoyl group. In view of this confusion, we recommend that whenever the symbol " Bz " is used in papers in this field it should be defined, until the new practice is well established. In many cases it is most difficult to decide which of the several symbols already in use to recommend, but we feel that the over-riding importance of consistency makes it necessary for a decision to be made now. Although we are fully aware of the merits of alternative symbols and the disadvantage of some of those below, we recommend the adoption of the following. The difficult choice of Z for benzyloxycarbonyl in preference to longer-established symbols such as C_{BZO} is based on (a) the fact that the latter is an abbreviation of a name (carbobenzoxy) which is now inconsistent with accepted nomenclature, and (b) Z is briefer and allows substituted benzyloxycarbonyl groups to be formulated in a reasonably short space. Capital letters are used in order to avoid the possibility of confusion with the symbols for amino-acid residues.

(a) *N-Protecting groups of the urethane type.*

benzyloxycarbonyl	Z-
p-nitrobenzyloxycarbonyl	Z(NO$_2$)-
p-bromobenzyloxycarbonyl	Z(Br)-
p-methoxybenzyloxycarbonyl	Z(OMe)-
p-methoxyphenylazo- benzyloxycarbonyl-	MZ-

p-phenylazobenzyloxycarbonyl	PZ-
t-butyloxycarbonyl-	BOC-
cyclopentyloxycarbonyl-	POC-

(b) *Other protecting groups.*

acetyl	Ac
benzoyl	Bz
tosyl	Tos
trifluoroacetyl	TFA
phthalyl	PHT
benzyl	BZL
trityl	TRI
tetrahydropyranyl	THP
dinitrophenyl	DNP
benzylthiomethyl	BTM

(c) *Carboxyl-protecting groups.*

methyl ester (OCH_3)	OMe
ethyl ester	OEt
tertiary butyl ester	OBu^t

(or as customary in the Journal concerned)

benzyl ester	OBZL
p-nitrobenzyl ester	ONB
p-nitrophenyl ester	ONP
phenyl thiolester	SPh
p-nitrophenyl thiolester	SNP
cyanomethyl ester	$OCH_2.CN$

Note: In these abbreviations the O and S are respectively the oxygen and sulphur atoms in the group; e.g. the p-nitrophenyl ester of glycine is Gly-ONP, etc.

R. SCHWYZER (Chairman)
J. RUDINGER
E. WÜNSCH
G. T. YOUNG